CW00420998

FOLK TRADITION
AND FOLK MEDICINE
IN SCOTLAND

FOLK TRADITION AND FOLK MEDICINE IN SCOTLAND

The Writings of David Rorie

Edited by
DAVID BUCHAN

CANONGATE ACADEMIC

First published in 1994 by Canongate Academic, an
imprint of Canongate Press Ltd, 14 Frederick Street,
Edinburgh EH2 2HB,
Scotland

ISBN 1 898410 01 1

Published with the aid of a grant from the David Rorie
Society.

The publisher also gratefully acknowledges subsidy of the
Scottish Arts Council for publication of this book.

British Library Cataloguing-in-Publication Data
A catalogue record for this book is available on request
from the British Library.

Typeset by The Electronic Book Factory Ltd, Fife, Scotland

Printed and bound by Bookcraft Ltd, Midsomer Norton

ACKNOWLEDGMENTS

Permission to reprint material has been willingly granted by the Folklore Society, the Buchan Club, the *Scots Magazine*, and the *British Medical Journal*. Invaluable aid in the research for the book has been accorded, in Aberdeen, by the staffs of the University Archives, the Public Library Local Collections Section, and the Medical Library, Foresterhill, and, in St John's, by Ms Linda Barnett, Health Sciences Library, and Dr Diane Goldstein. Working with old friends on this project has proved a particular pleasure and I proffer my special thanks to Mrs Jean Leith, Mrs Prue King, Dr Colin Milton, General Editor of the David Rorie Society, and, above all, to the indefatigable Secretary-Treasurer of the Society, Dr Ian Olson. Let me also record my appreciation of the sterling good sense of John Tuckwell of Canongate Academic.

The cover illustration, a detail from David Wilkie's 'Pitlessie Fair', is reproduced by kind permission of the National Galleries of Scotland. The photograph of David Rorie on page x is reproduced by kind permission of Aberdeen Central Library.

CONTENTS

FOUR. THE LIGHTER SIDE OF TRADITION

David Rorie, on active service during the First World War
(Photo: *Aberdeen Central Library*).

Introduction

David Rorie was a man of many talents: doctor, poet, performer, editor, songwriter, colonel, afterdinner speaker, belleslettrist, committee-man, and folklorist. Though born in Edinburgh, in 1867, he had a long-standing association with the Northeast of Scotland, his parents' natal place and his home both in boyhood and from 1905 till his death in 1946. During his lifetime he achieved a popular reputation in Scotland as a poet, a status he reductively characterised for himself as 'a gangrel's stance on the lower slopes of Helicon'.[1] This reputation, however, has tended to overshadow and obscure the extent and significance of his work as a folklorist.

Rorie's father, a bank manager, was transferred by the Bank of Scotland from Edinburgh to Aberdeen, where the young Rorie went to the Aberdeen Collegiate School and, at the age of fifteen, to the University of Aberdeen to spend the 1882-83 session in the Faculty of Arts.[2] The following seven years he spent studying in the Faculties of Arts, Law, and Medicine at the University of Edinburgh from which he graduated M.B., C.M. in 1890. The post-graduation years saw Rorie experiencing a variety of medical posts: locum in Dalkeith, Resident Clinical Clerk at Dundee Royal Asylum, ship's surgeon with the City Line, assistant briefly in Cowdenbeath, assistant in a country practice at Newburgh-On-Tay in Fife and in an industrial town practice at Barrow-in-Furness in northern England, and country doctor at Old Deer in Aberdeenshire. In 1894 he moved to Auchterderran in Fife as medical superintendent for a group of collieries and there he stayed for more than ten hardworked and energetic years; when he left, he signed twenty-three letters of resignation from his various posts, ranging from Chairmanship of the School Board to captaincy of the golf club. In 1905 he took up a country practice at Cults, a village just outside the city of Aberdeen, where he practised, with a break for service in World War I, until ill-health compelled retirement at the age of sixty-six in 1933. The retirement years were, however, far from idle, involving as they did a diversity of ploys, such as the chairing of the Aberdeen Medical

Board of the Ministry of Labour and National Service throughout the next war, until a few months before his death in 1946. In his lifetime he achieved a number of distinctions and honours. In 1908 he was awarded the research degree of M.D. by the University of Edinburgh for a thesis on 'Scottish Folk-Medicine', and in 1911 he gained the Diploma in Public Health from the University of Aberdeen. For his war service, during which he was twice mentioned in dispatches, he had conferred on him the D.S.O., and the Croix de Chevalier of the Légion d'Honneur. At a less official level he was honoured by public testimonials and the presidencies of such organisations as the Aberdeenshire Branch of the British Medical Association, the Aberdeen-Edinburgh University Association, and the Buchan Club, carefully engineered by the Secretary, J.F. Tocher, to include the Jubilee Year.

Doctor and Writer
The bare facts of biography, however, do not convey adequately the nature of Rorie's involvement in many spheres of activity, let alone his humoursome personality or the liking and respect in which he was generally held. He was first and foremost a doctor but from his day-to-day professional life evolved his interests in the life and welfare of mining communities, in medical soldiering and the welfare of ex-servicemen, in writing, and in folklore. In Fife, where the parish population was rising by 1000 people each year, Rorie took practical measures to mitigate some of the effects of the modernising expansion of the coal industry. A letter to the *British Medical Journal* headed 'Colliery Accident Stations' is designed 'to emphasize the necessity for such stations becoming universal at all pit-heads'. In it he describes the one constructed on his initiative some years before at Bowhill Colliery, where he also trained an ambulance corps from which, he adds with atypical but justifiable pride, 'a team of pit-head men in one year gained the Fife miners' ambulance cup, the Dunfermline Matheson cup, the Dundee silver challenge shield, and was second for the President of the St. Andrew's Ambulance Association's cup at Glasgow'. The colliery accident stations, he declares, 'should not fall to be provided by private philanthropy, but should be secured by legislative enactment. They are a necessity at every pit-head'.[3] While in Fife he became a member of the Parish Council (the first elected under the Scottish Local Government Act 1894), chairman of the Auchterderran School Board, and a Justice of the Peace, and worked for the establishment of a library, a reading-room, and a Gothenburg Public House (one intended to

present the convivial attractions of the pub, but without the alcohol). According to A. Greig Anderson in his *BMJ* obituary, this is 'a period of his life to which he frequently referred', when 'he laid the foundations of that deep understanding of human nature and sympathy with the underdog which was so characteristic of him in his later years, and which so deeply coloured his life's work both in medicine and in literature'.[4]

Rorie's interest in ambulance work led to his formation of a Fife section of the Black Watch Brigade Bearer Company, work he continued, when he moved to Cults, in the 1st Highland Field Ambulance of the Territorial Force. He was consequently mobilised in August 1914 at the age of forty-seven, was sent to France in April 1915, and served there till the end of the war and six months beyond, having attained the rank of (Temporary) Colonel and the position of A.D.M.S. (Assistant Director Medical Services) of the 51st (Highland) Division. His account of those years, *A Medico's Luck in the War* (published ten years after) is a 'plain unvarnished tale of some Territorial Field Ambulances in France and Flanders' designed to give due credit to the unsung stretcher-bearer, who 'was never treated to the limelight and . . . never asked to be: but . . . is well worthy of the highest tribute that can be paid to his pluck and endurance. So it is mainly for him and his comrades that the yarn is spun. . . .' And a racy yarn it is at times, with an unhackneyed angle on the war experience and a stress 'on the cheerful side' of an often cheerless existence, highlighted by quite hilarious anecdotes of his bestings of army blimps and bureaucracy (a selection of which is reprinted in *Poems and Prose*).[5] After the war, in 1922, he was instrumental in founding the Aberdeen branch of the British Legion, of which he was president for over twenty years, besides serving on the national council. Until his death, says Greig Anderson, 'he maintained his interest and affection for the ex-Servicemen and became one of their doughtiest champions'.[6] Out of his doctor's experience in mining areas and in the war Rorie developed a pronounced sympathy for the underprivileged and, more to the point, devoted time and energy to ensuring for them fairness of treatment and amelioration of conditions.

Doctoring provided both subjects and impetus for his prose-writing. Early in the Auchterderran years he published in the *People's Friend* under the general heading of 'Some of my Patients' a series of vignettes, each with the sub-title 'A Humorous Reading' suggesting they were intended for recitation. Three of the four pieces are signed 'Easton Weston', a *nom de plume* he employed frequently

[3]

later on. Rorie was not the only young doctor to augment his income with magazine writing, for a predecessor as assistant in the Newburgh-on-Tay practice, Dr Clement Gunn, had also published a number of pieces in *Scottish News*, as he reveals in a book of reminiscences, *Leaves from the Life of a Country Doctor*, later reviewed by Rorie.[7] Rorie himself published his reminiscences, largely humorous accounts of incidents and characters, in the *People's Journal* in 1937, the twelve-part series having the general title 'Recollections of a Scottish Doctor'. The war years are portrayed with customarily adroit humour in the last of these articles, 'With the Men in the Trenches', as well as in *A Medico's Luck in the War*. In the year the Second World War broke out, he edited for the British Medical Association, and contributed two articles to, *The Book of Aberdeen* for its meeting in the city.

Involvement with his profession also led to Rorie's becoming a journal editor for close on thirty years. Previously a contributor of articles to the *Caledonian Medical Journal*, he was confirmed as joint-editor in 1911 and presented his resignation in 1937, although he seems to have carried on in office until 1940. The Caledonian Medical Society had its beginnings among medical students at the University of Edinburgh who had particular interests in Celtic culture, and had developed into a forum for not simply medical but also social, literary, historical, antiquarian, and folkloristic writings; the culture of Scottish Gaeldom, especially in the early years, and folklore were consistent concerns. On the page facing the announcement of Rorie's election as a member of the Society in 1901 appears a review of the Folklore Society publication *The Games and Diversions of Argyleshire* by Robert Craig MacLagan, a member of the Society and contributor to the *Journal*, as was the premier British folklore theorist of the day, Andrew Lang.[8] Lang numbered among the Honorary Members of the Society along with such other folklorists as Alexander Carmichael, editor of the six volume *Carmina Gadelica* and Dr Alexander Stewart, author of *Nether Lochaber* and *Twixt Ben Nevis and Glencoe*.[9] After the war an Honorary Membership was conferred on Charles Murray, the leading poet of the Northeast of Scotland and a close friend of Rorie. Beyond his many article contributions, largely but not exclusively on folk medicine topics, Rorie performed the standard editorial work of his office, and flourished as a belleslettrist. Throughout his tenure as joint editor, from volume 8 (1909-11) to volume 16 (1937-40), he produced a regular miscellany entitled 'At the Sign of the Blue Pill', a pot-pourri of anecdotes, essays, reminiscences, jokes, disquisitions, poems and verses; one

sampling appears in *Poems and Prose*, and another follows below
(II:41). These show throughout a light ironic touch that conceals
rather than flaunts his eclectic interest in the manysidedness of
humankind, and latterly employ for comic effect the pose of the
genial old curmudgeon afflicted by a newfangled modernity.

Poet, Songwriter, and Performer

As a poet Rorie had a rather modest view of his own productions.
They were written for social occasions, for friends, for the University
of Aberdeen *Alma Mater*, and for medical journals such as the
Caledonian MJ, and he entertained serious doubts that they were
'too medical and too "strong" for a general readership', doubts
discussed with Charles Murray who helped allay them by arranging
for his publisher, Constable, to publish *The Auld Doctor and other
Poems and Songs in Scots* in 1920.[10] The doubts were dispelled by a
warmly favourable reception. An unsigned review in the *Aberdeen
Weekly Free Press* for 27 November 1920 may serve to indicate the
local view of his poetic status and his standing in the community:

> Dr. David Rorie, of Cults, has already won fame as the
> laureate of Scottish doctors. In his own Deeside parish he has
> built up a high reputation as a medical practitioner—a rural
> Gideon Gray, esteemed alike from his skill as a physician and
> his warm personal interest in the social life of the district,
> and deservedly popular among all classes because of his kindly
> human sympathy and his quiet and pawky Scottish humour.
> During the war he did notable work as an army doctor on
> the Western front. But perhaps to an even wider public he is
> known as the author of some delightful Scottish verses which
> have appeared from time to time in the Scottish medical press
> as well as in *Alma Mater* and kindred publications.

The Auld Doctor was incorporated in his other book of poetry
published in 1935, *The Lum Hat Wantin' the Croon and other Poems*,
which achieved such success that it had to be reprinted within five
months. Rorie's poems are funny, perceptive, exhilarating in their
use of Scots, and display a mordantly comic view of people and
their existences, from the standpoint of someone not aloof from but
very much engaged with humanity. In the introduction to *Poems
and Prose* William Donaldson provides a just estimate of Rorie's
poetry; here the primary concern is the relationship of the poet to
the folklorist.[11]

Rorie the poet is an ethnographer, accurate and humoursome,

whose strengths lie in the depiction of characters and incidents from the regional cultures of Eastern Scotland. Like Charles Murray he is a masterly engraver of character: not of the eccentric individual but of the representative type. Even more than Murray he utilises the monologue as technique, both as a suitable vehicle for the Scots and as a means of revealing character. The monologues are not introspective communings, but often one half of a conversation, idiomatically vigorous and dramatic in their rendering of personality in action. In short, Rorie portrays character-types who embody defining features of the culture and he employs in the portrayal typifying lines, often proverbial, that encapsulate the attitudes of the culture. Frequently the poems also present in poetic form such elements of the traditional culture as folk belief and folk medicine. The language of the poems has a pronounced proverbial quotient, not however sprinkled on as top dressing but comprising the kernel of many a poem. Some pieces in fact seem attempts at poetic marination, efforts to soak from a polished lump of traditional verbal concentrate all the possible juices of meaning. For the ethnographic analyst the proverbial language both conveys traditional world-outlooks and illuminates contextual usage.

Rorie also re-works for his high-cultural poetic medium material from traditional expressive culture. The 65 stanza 'The Deil and Jock MacNeil', a magnificently comic wondertale involving a Devil-contract, St Peter's three wishes, and a trickster blacksmith, is 'a free rendering in verse of a Scots folk-tale which was a favourite recitation of the late Professor Crum Brown'.[12] The story in fact is a version of the international folktale type Aarne-Thompson 330A, which is not listed in the standard type-indexes as having been recorded in Scotland. 'Isie' records in verse a jocular anecdote and 'Tam and the Leeches' a legendary incident for the medical profession, given prose form by Rorie's predecessor at Newburgh, Dr Clement Gunn:

Tinctures and infusions, too, had to be filtered; and our leeches exercised along the counter. Regarding these animals, the following tale was current at the time. A doctor had ordered six leeches to be applied to a man's stomach after bathing the skin in sweet milk. Accordingly, to an inquiry as to her method of procedure, the patient's wife answered: 'Dinna be angry, Doctor; we first of all poured the milk down to his stomach, but he couldna swallow a' the leeches raw, so we just fried the other three'![13]

[6]

Rorie, then, is in a sense a performer of traditional expressive material, but in a different medium and in a different cultural context. Conversely, however, many of his poems have gone into tradition as recitations (a fine exponent being Mr Stewart Farquhar of Troup Head, Aberdeenshire), and even as localised legendary truth, like 'The Seelie Knowe' which is printed in a recent book about Upper Donside following the comment: 'There is a fairy hillock at Tornashean and another at Deskryside, but this is the original "Seely Knowe" attracting several serious claims by those with second sight'.[14]

A closely allied activity to his poem-making was his songwriting. From his account of his student days at Edinburgh, 'The Weighty Eighties', one can infer that verse-composition of the parodic kind, with or without a tune, provided a standard exercise of the mind, particularly during the more unenthralling lectures. Three fellow-students composed a comic imitation of the then popular Gilbert and Sullivan song, 'Titwillow', and ascribed it in the annual poetry competition to a humourless class member who was suitably mortified when 'his' creation was commented upon by the Professor (David Masson, the Milton scholar, and himself the subject of a student poem in 'Standard Habbie' stanza form). In another class, Rorie and a friend narrowly escaped retribution when their parody of Kingsley's 'The Sands of Dee' satirising the idiosyncrasies of the Professor of Logic and Metaphysics was intercepted in its circulation round the class members by the man himself.[15] Rorie then found a less hazardous outlet for his talents in publishing verse and songs in *The Student* and the first edition of *The Scottish Students' Song Book*. His two most famous songs—'The Lum Hat Wantin' the Croon' and 'The Pawky Duke'—later appeared in *The British Students' Song Book*; the same two were still included in the *Aberdeen Students' Song Book* of 1956 but had disappeared from the 1959 edition.

When Rorie became a member of the medical profession, his fellow-doctors constituted a new audience. Many poems and songs appear in the *Journal* of the Caledonian Medical Society, and in the accounts of the annual dinner of the Society one finds: for 1904, that Dr Rorie and others 'contributed songs'; for 1912, that 'the enjoyment of the evening was greatly enhanced by songs and musical items contributed by . . . Dr Rorie'; and for 1923, that 'musical renderings' were provided by Dr. Rorie (this after, as President for the year, the Presidential Address, the address of welcome, and the reply to the toast to the Society).[16] In like fashion, with his 'songs and recitations' he had by 1910 'become a feature of the Annual Dinner' of the Aberdeen Medico-Chirurgical Society. On these occasions 'he generally contributed a poem composed for the occasion, in which, with great good humour and wit, he satirized the foibles and failings of his best friends and of medicine generally, all in the classic tradition of François Rabelais'. In 1931, for example, 'he brought the house down with a series of "cryptic rhymes to replace existing referral letters between the medical profession"'. At the Annual Dinner of the previous year Rorie had been formally crowned Poet Laureate of the Society with as his 'chaplet of bay, "the lum hat wantin' the croon"'.[17]

During the war Rorie found yet another audience. He became chairman of the committee responsible for the concert party of the 51st (Highland) Division, 'The Balmorals', and furnished them with items for performance. In a more informal capacity he supplied the troops with many well-used marching songs, 'amongst them', says Alexander Keith, 'if Rumour is not always a lying jade, the British reply to the German Hymn of Hate'. According to Greig Anderson he attained the status of 'unofficial poet laureate of the 51st', although 'he would never admit' to the authorship of the songs sung by the soldiers.[18] In the absorption of his songs by anonymous army tradition Rorie is paralleled, one war later, by Hamish Henderson, so that, rather strikingly, both the First and Second World Wars had a Scottish folklorist and poet who, as a serving officer, contributed songs that gained currency and fame in the occupational folksong of the Tommies and the swaddies.

Rorie's songs, then, went into tradition in three specific groups—students, doctors, and soldiers—but they also achieved popularity with a much wider audience. Many never appeared in print, having been written for friends and social occasions,[19] and some appeared only in ephemeral form, like 'Tam and Tib or Maun dae is aye maisterfu'', a 'poem' composed and sung by him for a 'banquet given to the Canadian curlers' which exists in a 1909 broadside.[20] The songs achieved their widespread popularity essentially because they are very funny, with a humour sharpened by the fluency of the language and the perceptiveness of the human observation, and reinforced sometimes by a strong satirical intent as in one of his two best-known songs, 'The Pawky Duke', which sets out to satirise the ethnic stereotype of the Scotsman held by the Southron. The best-known song of all, 'The Lum Hat Wantin' the Croon', was sung, Rorie was able to testify in the preface to the book of poems with the same title, by Scotsmen all over the world, and was described in obituaries as having 'probably been sung at more convivial entertainments than any other contemporary lyric' and as 'next to "Auld Lang Syne" . . . the song most sung by Scotsmen the world over'.[21] There may be a touch of regional chauvinism in these declarations, but popular it certainly has been in many contexts, past and present: it was performed frequently on Scottish radio and television in the '50s and '60s by Ann and Laura Brand, it is sung every year at the annual dinner of the Aberdeen Medico-Chirurgical Society, and it occurs to this day, as song and recitation, in social forgatherings. The song was created by Rorie in the early 1890s during a rather trying year in the Northern England exile of Barrow-in-Furness; he composed both words and tune, the latter by the necessary expedient for a man 'who does not know a note of music' of humming it over to his sister Jean, who then wrote it down.[22] 'The Lum Hat' later attained the unusual distinction of being translated into French, and published as 'Drole de chapeau' in a French periodical of the '30s, *La Hune*, next, coincidentally, to an article by the eminent French folklorist, Arnold van Gennep.[23]

Poet and songwriter, Rorie was also performer. Besides delivering his own poems and songs, often composed for the specific occasion, he made radio broadcasts and performed in yet another mode: 'he was much in demand as an after-dinner speaker, an art in which he was highly proficient'; the style was characterised by 'his quick intelligence, his deft handling of audiences, and that gift of humour'.[24] Clearly, Rorie was in many ways an intensely social, highly clubbable, man. This shows not only in the long list of organisations where he served as office-bearer but also in his membership of two clubs composed of creative and convivially-minded spirits: the Calm Soughers and the Sit Siccars. The former were 'a group of Aberdeen doctors that arose from the ashes of the Garioch Medical Association, and met for week-ends at James Cruikshank's far-famed hostelry, incidentally a temperance house, the Kilmarnock Arms Hotel, Cruden Bay'.[25] The moving spirits were Rorie and Sir Ashley Mackintosh, who 'once engaged in a remarkable literary partnership directed to persuading a professional colleague that Pope's celebrated lines run actually thus:

> Lo! the poor Indian, with untutor'd mind,
> Wears all his clothes before, and none behind'.[26]

The other club, the Sit Siccars, were 'formed by and of the close friends and associates of Charles Murray when he returned for good to Scotland on his retirement from South Africa. "Sit Siccar" is the Aberdeenshire name for *Ranunculus repens*, the creeping buttercup, and was suggested by Murray as an appropriate title for a fraternity who were probably at their best when sitting'.[27] Its members included, besides Murray and Rorie, Professor Sir Ashley Mackintosh again, Sir Alexander Gray, poet and economist, J.F. Tocher, county analyst and secretary of the Buchan Club, Lord Boyd Orr, scientist and nutritionist, Fred Martin, a blind MP, William Tawse, public contractor and engineer, and on occasion a brace of Governors-General, Sir Patrick Duncan and John Buchan, Lord Tweedsmuir, the novelist. The titles reflect not aristocratic origins but the recognised merit of self-made men, who all had firm rootings in Scottish, and especially Northeast, culture. The youngest member of this sodality and the secretary who never called a meeting or penned a minute was Alexander Keith, journalist, farmer, and editor of Gavin Greig's *Last Leaves*, who later recalled vividly 'the inaugural dinner of that distinguished body when [Major Malcolm Hay] and Rorie argued for two solid hours without repeating themselves upon the proposition whether the resolution that the Society should have no rules in itself constituted a rule'.[28]

Poet, songwriter, performer, and lover of good company, are all expressive facets of the same personality. That personality, however, could take on a more sedate appearance in the quotidian context of his practice: 'His small, rotund, beautifully dressed and immaculately coiffured figure was a familiar and welcome sight in the chauffeur-driven large two-seater Humber that eventually displaced his horse and gig. He was thorough, painstaking and naturally conservative, especially where drugs or surgery were concerned. Oddly enough, for a man who could be so much at his ease socially, he could seem abrupt to those who had yet to discern his underlying warm and kindly nature'.[29] Many patients, however, remember 'this lovable personality' with some warmth. May Thomson recalled for a journalist an incident from her childhood when she had broken and cut her nose: 'Rorie was summoned to carry out repairs and the stitches happened to form themselves into a distinctive pattern. The medic left the house saying cheerfully, "I'll aye know you May from the cross on the bridge of your nose"'. Elsewhere May Thomson writes in summation of Rorie's doctorly qualities: 'David Rorie always brought a smile to his patients' bedside—in fact his personality often did more good than anything else'.[30]

The Folklorist

From his engagement with medicine and the lives of his patients—miners, soldiers, country folk—there derived Rorie's multifarious activities and creativities. From the same roots there sprang his involvement with folklore, the traditional expressive behaviour of the people he lived among. His writings on folklore span forty years, from the 1899 piece 'On some Scots Words, Proverbs, and Beliefs bearing on Diseased Conditions' in the *Proceedings of the Royal Philosophical Society of Glasgow* to the 1939 article 'Some Folklore and Legends of Lower Deeside' in *The Book of Aberdeen*. For these writings he had three distinct, though sometimes overlapping, audiences: his medical peers, for whom the main outlet was the *Caledonian Medical Journal*; folklorists, for whom the main outlet was *Folklore*; and, later, a more popular, general Scottish audience, for whom the main outlet was the *Scots Magazine*. Not infrequently the same material was recycled for the different audiences. The forty years saw an evolution in the writings from a sharp focus on tradition as it relates to health and medicine to a more relaxed discursiveness suitable for a wider audience who can jointly enjoy an interest in things past, perhaps quaint, perhaps queer, but of a shared past. The medical graduate's initial irritation at the 'superstition' and ignorance that oppose his trained skills recedes rapidly before his natural sympathies, once reinforced by exposure to the concept of folk medicine and the discipline of Folklore, to be replaced by an intellectual interest in tradition, which develops into a wryly genial acceptance of the endlessly fascinating vagaries of folk and their doings. The cynical tone of the young doctor, sometimes rather arch for present-day tastes, gives way quite soon to the well-tempered scepticism and cheerful irony that mark the mature writings.

David Rorie was the first folklorist in Scotland, and one of the first anywhere, to record the culture of an industrial community: that of the Fife miners. It was a rural-industrial not an urban-industrial community but nevertheless his work marks a crucial stage in the international evolution of folkloristics away from a concentration on peasant agricultural life towards the modern wide-ranging concern with traditional expressive behaviour in all sectors of society. His 'Mining Folk of Fife' (II:36) derives from his twelve years residence in Fife, and primarily from the 1894-1905 years at Auchterderran. Though an 'incomer' and a professional man, he was not an outsider, having intimate access to his patients' lives and being thoroughly involved in community affairs; it was at Auchterderran that he had to write his twenty-three letters of resignation on leaving for Cults. His presentation of his recorded material in this piece (reduced in size in this volume to avoid duplication) indicates his innate scholarly good sense. He begins by giving his own credentials as ethnographer, then, unlike some contemporaries, makes a scrupulous disclaimer:

> It is not pretended that all the customs, etc., mentioned were universal. Many of them were dying out, and many more were referred to jestingly, often with the semi-apologetic remarks, 'that's an old freit, that's what the auld folk used to say, or do.' But everything I have set down I have tested as having been at one time or another common in the district.[31]

Then he provides the essential context for an understanding of the mining community: the nature of the group and its sub-groups, its history, the nature and conditions of the mining (including a miner's memory of 'working below ground by the phosphorescent light of decaying fish-heads'), and, from the emic viewpoint, a life-experience account of a miner born in the 1820s. Like a modern folklorist, only after providing the context does he give the recorded material. It is informed by his doctor's experience, for at its heart is the segment on folk medicine or 'leechcraft', comprehensively covered through its sections on the leech, popular physiological ideas, pathological ideas, health maxims, hygiene and general treatment, diseases and remedies, and materia medica, and the segments on the rites of passage of the human life cycle: birth, marriage, death. The extent to which childbirth figured in the daily, and nightly, round of physicians in those years is reflected in the substantial segment on birth and infancy, with its inclusive sections on pregnancy, childbed, the newborn infant, first ceremonies, the cradle, early infancy, and families. Clearly Rorie recognised the importance of language in carrying culture, and had a keen ear, since he not only records the linguistic subgenres like proverbs but also portrays much traditional belief and behaviour through the associated proverbial formulations. In this there is a direct link between the ethnographer and the poet for, as has been pointed out earlier, his poems frequently have at their core one radiating proverbial statement. Notably absent from his survey are the genres of song and story that engaged so many of his contemporaries, and which, as Peter Kearney has shown, are and were not lacking in the Scottish mining communities.[32] Evidently Rorie felt that his depiction of custom, belief, and language, genres with a concrete and observable relationship to the daily life, would represent more effectively the essentials of this mining culture. Later industrial folklorists expanded the generic range and the contextual coverage, but to Rorie goes the credit of taking the important pioneer steps in industrial folklore.

Rorie's great merit as a folklorist is that he brings to ethnography his trained clinician's skills: he observes the phenomenon closely and records with factual precision its presenting symptoms; he is careful to divine how the patient feels about it; and in his report he abjures all fanciful speculation. Physician and ethnographer, he keeps his eye on the subject, and his ear primed, and reports accurately and succinctly what is observable. He limits himself to facts but, flexibly, has no hesitation in furnishing, with an ironic smile, such fancy-based facts as folk etymologies when they constitute cultural information (II:41). Where principles governing sets of behaviours or beliefs have been adduced, as for example Frazer's on sympathetic or imitative magic, he will utilise them and refer to them, but where he suggests a possible generalisation he makes it very clear that is what he is doing; he brings, as it were, the issue to the notice of his peers and calls for opinions. Rorie abjured sweeping theories, ruminations on origins, diffusion, and Graeco-Roman parallels, and in general any kind of indulgent speculativeness. It is a testimony to his practical good sense how little he was affected by the now largely discredited theories of the century's early decades. He uses the term 'survivals' but in a factually true manner to refer to that in tradition which has survived from the past into the present; he does not subscribe to any doctrine maintaining that all traditional materials are survivals from ages of savagery and barbarism. He refers to parallel manifestations of phenomena in other cultures though not out of any belief in the doctrine of unilinear cultural evolution or for grandiose theoretical purposes but simply to extend the empirical field of interest of an observed phenomenon, or its simulacrum.

Rorie occupies an important, though not widely recognised, place in the history of medical folklore study.[33] When the extent and calibre of his work is acknowledged, however, he can be assessed, quite justifiably, as Britain's premier medical folklorist, the only rival for such a title being William George Black whose *Folk Medicine* was published by the Folklore Society in 1883. Rorie's major work is 'Scottish Folk-Medicine', presented as an M.D. thesis to the University of Edinburgh in 1908 but not published until it appeared, essentially unchanged, in the late 1920s as a series of nine articles in the *Caledonian Medical Journal*; it is printed here intact for the first time (I:9-17). The writer of this work is no medical amateur attracted by the culturally exotic, but a folklorist who is a medical professional bringing to bear on the study of traditional medicine the honed skills of the clinician, humane sympathies, acute powers of observation, and a sound empiricism of approach.

Rorie's writing on medical folklore is characterised by a certain modernity. In the introduction to 'On Scottish Folk-Medicine' (I:9), for example, he stresses that a knowledge of folk medicine provides a doctor with pertinent cultural information: 'apart altogether from its scientific interest, a knowledge of folk-medicine is of distinct practical value, more especially perhaps to the country practitioner, and certainly at times to the medical jurist as explaining the otherwise inexplicable'. Despite its usefulness, however, 'in many cases the newly-fledged graduate leaves his university without knowing even of the existence of folk-medicine'. For the benefit of the young and, one suspects, some of the not-so-young practitioners Rorie supplies some basic advice that accords in essence with what modern writers conscious of the cultural dimensions of medicine would say today. He points to 'how carefully organised' 'superstitious customs and practices' are, and to 'the age and deep-rooted strength of beliefs which have been handed down orally from generation to generation' and declares that, in consequence, 'the man who scoffs openly at what his hearers hold to be indisputable truth sanctioned by age exposes himself to the risk of being held unlearned and unskilful'; he then suggests how the young physician should modify his behaviour. Likewise he counsels an understanding of the patient: many a person, even with education, has a certain ambivalence towards orthodox medicine because he or she retains 'a lingering faith' in the traditional ways 'and this faith may have a distinct bearing on the progress of an illness'. Historically, he adds later, 'there has been a constant give-and-take between the orthodox and unorthodox; for when the former fails, the sufferer and his friends readily betake themselves to the latter, which usually has, as an additional attraction, a spice of the supernatural about it'. This occurs as part of an answer to his own posed question of how much present-day folk-medicine is genuinely oral and traditional which demonstrates a very contemporary awareness of the interrelations of the folk, popular, and high registers of culture.

Underlying his statements is the modern truism that it is necessary to understand the patient as well as the disease, which parallels the modern folkloristic adage that it is necessary to understand the culture as well as the item or artefact. To understand the culture one must first try to understand the native or emic outlook, and this issue Rorie addresses in one of his early, and youthfully abrasive, articles: 'Popular Pathology: Being an Essay on What the Patient Thinks' (I: 2). In it he discusses terms popularly employed—'dumb fits', 'hives', 'nerves'—and their possible range of referents, information not to be found in the textbooks, and explores some of the factors governing the methods of thinking, like the pseudo-rationalism that dismisses infection by contagion with the rhetorical question 'But who infected the first person?' and the fatalism that views illness or deformity as punishment visited upon people by Providence.[34] The practitioner, he warns in a perceptive comment on small-group dynamics, must be prepared for the rejection of his diagnosis of, say, a child's illness in favour of 'the finding of the inevitable jury of old women that the child has "dumb fits"', with the mother consequently gaining 'satisfaction and distinction in her own circle by disbelieving you, and falling back on the more ancient beliefs'. In much of his thinking on culture and medicine Rorie proves himself to be arrestingly modern, and indeed anticipates the concerns of Transcultural Health Care, a relatively new subdiscipline of Medicine dealing with the cultural dimension of health care.

Rorie did the bulk of his medical ethnography before 1914, the year when at forty-seven he set off for war. That year marks a stage in Rorie's life, viewed historically, for while the preceding twenty-five years produced his field research and both 'Scottish Folk-Medicine' and 'The Mining Folk of Fife', the succeeding twenty-five years saw a more discursive scholarship. Rorie began his field research after graduation in 1890: 'for some time thereafter I collected popular medical beliefs from the lips of the country people amongst whom I was working before I was aware that it was a subject with a considerable literature of its own; and although this may be a confession of ignorance to start with, it may also serve, to some extent, as a guarantee of original research' (I:9). Some slight evidence of this work is contained in a page headed 'Superstitions' and dated 5.11.96 among the papers deposited in Aberdeen Public Library.[35] It is possible that his research may have received a stimulus from one of his patients at Newburgh-on-Tay (1891-92), for there he ministered to the retired banker and folklorist-antiquarian Dr Alexander Laing who had provided Francis James Child with a small group of ballads, collected about 1873, for *The English and Scottish Popular Ballads*. Certainly, he found the district very congenial, as he records more than forty years later: 'Like all old places whose roots go deep down into the past, Newburgh had much to intrigue the collector of folk-lore, with many a popular tale or rhyme in which he could savour that pleasant grafting of fancy on to fact which so kindly brightens the stark drabness of more orthodoxly chronicled history. . . . Documented and dry-as-dust records can usually be got readily enough but the other tales have to be gathered slowly

[15]

and appreciatively by "word o' mou'", and possess a flavour and a spirituality not always found in the printed word'.[36] It was probably not until he joined the Caledonian Medical Society and the Folklore Society (1901 and 1903 respectively) and became a regular subscriber to their journals that he discovered folk medicine 'was a subject with a considerable literature on its own' and gained a framework and foci for his research and writings.

As a medical folklorist Rorie was not only an ethnographer but also a gleaner from all kinds of sources: old books, medical literature, local books, journals, and even committee reports. A number of his smaller publications are simple notes culled from an out-of-the-way place and shared with interested peers (e.g. I:5, I:7, I:8, I:19). Whatever the provenance of the material, whether fieldwork or library research, Rorie had throughout his life certain consistent concerns, primarily the traditional expressive genres of language, belief, and custom and their relation to the patterns of thinking and behaviour in folk culture, for behind the presentation of the recorded items of tradition lay his interest in people, in the participants of the traditional processes. Early on, Rorie wrote a piece on one of the 'performers' within these processes, the bone-setter, portrayed, with understandable professional scorn, as an incompetent and potentially dangerous rival: a portrayal that helps explain historically why chiropractors are viewed less than favourably by many contemporary medics. It would have been instructive to have had a parallel essay on the howdies, skeely wives and canny wives of his experience but just as there is a (very funny) poem on 'The Bane-setter' so there are poems on other performers playing their roles in the traditional processes. After retirement Rorie wrote as a cultural historian for a popular audience on how people dealt with the plague (I:18) and why people formerly passed the sick through circles (I:20).

Some of the topics in medical folklore raised by Rorie have a decidedly contemporary relevance. In many western societies where the elderly constitute a growing percentage of the total population and where advanced medical technology allows prolongation of life, and half-life, the issues of euthanasia and voluntary euthanasia have come in for considerable debate. In 1933, the year ill-health forced him into retirement, Rorie published in the *BMJ* a sober article on 'Hastening the Death of the Aged, Infirm, and Sick' (II:32) in which he assembles evidence from Scotland, England, and Brittany of 'a once prevalent and long-persisting custom' for such hastening. This and a piece by one of Rorie's contributors to the *Caledonian Medical Journal*, Dan Mackenzie, on euthanasia in British folk medicine, constitute rather important contributions to the otherwise sparse literature on this subject.[37] Another topic of, unfortunately, widespread contemporary concern is child abuse. In 'On Scottish Folk-Medicine VIII: Disease and its Cure' (I:16) Rorie states that 'the old belief of ridding oneself of disease by transference is always cropping up' and then declares as if it were common knowledge (which it may have been to his medical peers) that 'the commonest cause, of course, of criminal assaults on young children is the wish to get rid by transference of venereal disease'. This matter-of-fact statement raises the possibility that traditional patterns of behaviour may lie behind action that causes serious contemporary concern, such as, in this instance, sexual assault of children. Although the rationale for the act may have gone, it is conceivable that for some offenders there still exists a subliminal sense of traditional validation for the behaviour.

From his initial interest in medical folklore there developed, evidently quite early, an interest in all folklore. The width of his generic range is represented in Part II: Folk Tradition. The second section of Part II illustrates the varied topics in belief and custom but the first section's list of contents hardly does justice to his abiding interest in language, which shows pervasively. His earliest published article, later subsumed in the thesis, involved proverbial language and one of his last was an essay on rhyming riddles; there may have been more unpublished proverbs for Alec Keith recounts that 'he loved fruity old sayings and curious customs, and had himself an excellent collection of medical proverbs, which incidentally he once refused to show me on the ground that I was still too young'.[38] Folk narrative was not a major concern of Rorie's but some legends and cumulative tales appear in the third section (II:35, II:39) and anecdotes occur frequently, the same one—as with many raconteurs—often turning up more than once, while 'The Lighter Side of Leechcraft' (II:40) gathers up a number of anecdotes, legendary and humorous, about doctors. Although Rorie wrote essays on folk medicine in the ballads (II:21-23), he presented little in the way of recorded folksong. The paucity appears strange at first for a man whose own songs went into tradition and who was also a singer, one who was recorded in the '30s by the American folklorist James Carpenter singing 'Gien the nowte their fodder'.[39] It would seem that for Rorie songs were for performing and composing rather than recording. On this score it is perhaps significant that when he does discuss and present song-texts he deals with comic songs and parodies of the classical ballad (II:41), and that in the introduction to one of his early rollicking poems, 'MacFadden and MacFee', he parodies the conventional ballad scholarship of his time:

> This ballad is of great interest, and, as far as we know, has not hitherto appeared in print. It is certainly not in Child's Collection. It was taken down from the singing of an aged man of one hundred and five years, in Glen Kennaquhair [i.e. know-not-where]. Internal evidence would tend to show that the incidents recorded in the ballad occurred in the seventeenth century, and that Sir Walter Scott had heard at least one verse of it. The aged singer—now, alas! no more—sang it to the air of *Barbara Allen*.[40]

In the fourth section the excerpts from the pot-pourri 'At the Sign of the Blue Pill' indicate an eclectic interest in diverse areas of tradition. His disquisition on that humble necessity of yesteryear, the chamberpot, could, by ethnologists with a sense of humour, be accepted as an essay on a little-regarded topic of material culture. The 'Extracts from Applications under the National Insurance Acts' constitute one of the earliest printed examples of what has come to be called photocopy lore.[41] As one can gather from the hints about his wartime compositions and his proverb collection, Rorie had an acquaintance with the 'roch' side of tradition; unlike many of his more mim-mou'd contemporaries, however, he also engaged, in his review of Ord's *Bothy Songs and Ballads* (II:24), in some direct speaking about bawdy tradition. Incidentally, his friend and fellow poet Charles Murray sent to the Rev. J.B. Duncan a number of 'roch' songs for the Greig-Duncan collection.[42] His understanding of tradition also subsumed a quite modern awareness of the importance of specific folk groups within the traditional process, as one can gather from his recording of groups defined by age, such as children, and district, such as Deeside and Donside, and occupation, such as the fishers and miners of Fife.

As a folklorist Rorie engaged in a variety of activities. He was first and foremost a collector, researcher, and commentator, but he was also a sub-collector and middleman for other folklorists: he contributed ballads 'from a female correspondent in the Rothienorman district' to Gavin Greig's *Last Leaves*, and he sent material to Mary Macleod Banks for her three-volume *British Calendar Customs: Scotland*.[43] He was a performer for James Carpenter, and a reviewer of such books of Northeast folklore as Ord's *Bothy Songs and Ballads*, and McPherson's *Primitive Beliefs*. He edited notes of 'A Minister's Memoirs' to produce 'Upper

Donside Fairs and Feuds' (II:37), and as editor of the *Caledonian Medical Journal* he not only wrote articles and notes over many decades but prompted others to research as well, a good example being Walter Dilling and his work on magic girdles, which was stimulated by Rorie's original questioning note on obstetric girdles (I:7). This recorder of tradition was also a songwriter whose songs went into Scottish tradition at large and the tradition of specific groups such as soldiers and students. And a poet whose poems occur in tradition as recitations. Rorie the poet, as remarked earlier, is quintessentially an ethnographer, concerned in his best poems with portraying the participants and processes—the roles, interactions, language, worldview, and behaviour—of traditional culture. To this end he will employ pervasively and perceptively such a traditional genre as the proverb. In his poetry he uses an artistic form of high culture but the language—and all that implies—of the vernacular culture, which may help explain its widespread popularity across diverse groups.

A man of many gifts, David Rorie was an outstanding folklorist; an ethnographer of sympathy and good sense, a writer of precision and perception, he pioneered research in industrial folklore and achieved a position of pre-eminence in medical folklore. Yet one searches in vain for any reference to his name in Richard Dorson's definitively titled *The British Folklorists*, an omission that underscores that book's somewhat lopsided selectivity. The texts of this volume end with an excerpt from his Presidential Address to the Buchan Club (which will suggest why he was in such popular demand as a speaker), and the Address ends with Rorie providing brief eulogies on two former Club Presidents, Walter Gregor and Gavin Greig, as folklorists of considerable stature. To that pair should be added the name of David Rorie to form an appropriately folkloric triad—minister, dominie, and doctor—of Northeast folklorists whose work's importance transcends the region.

NOTE ON THE TEXTS

Rorie often used the same material in different writings, recycling it for his three different audiences—medical, folkloristic, popular—and sometimes even, after a lapse of time, for the same audiences. Some interesting titles in the Bibliography, apparently excluded from the selection, are in fact subsumed within other articles. 'Surgery and

Medicine of the Scottish Ballads', for example, is, with very minor
alterations, 'Folk-Medicine in Scottish Ballad Literature', and both
draw extensively upon 'Folk Medicine in Scottish Ballad and Rhyme:
I. Gynaecology and Obstetrics'. The thesis utilises, though often in
compressed fashion, most of Rorie's previously published writings
on folk medicine. Likewise 'The Mining Folk of Fife' shares material
with the thesis, as well as incorporating sections of earlier articles.
On occasion I have preferred to retain the sections in the earlier
article where (as in 'Some Fifeshire Folk-Medicine') the information
is presented in its human context rather than in a list. As with the
medical, so with the non-medical material. The selection includes
the *Folklore* version of the 'Migratory Stones' but Rorie wrote on
this topic in three other places: 'At the Sign of the Blue Pill',
Caledonian Medical Journal, 11 (1918-22), 102-4; *A Medico's Luck in
the War*, pp. 238-40; and 'Stones that Wander', *Aberdeen University
Review*, 22 (1934-35), 212-21. The last contains excerpts from a local
47-stanza poem that he had seen in manuscript and which portrays
the custom in former times, when the Fordyce stone was placed at
an auld maid's door as an uncomplimentary reminder of her status:
yet another example of the way in which local poetry may serve as
a valuable ethnographic record. When articles printed below share
material the policy has been to excise the larger repetitions but to
let stand many of the smaller repetitions rather than break fluency of
discourse or coherence of narrative. The shorter excisions are marked
by . . . and the longer by. . . . . .

One can be reasonably certain that the texts printed in the
Caledonian Medical Journal accord with Rorie's intentions, but elsewhere doubts sometimes arise. Clearly the Folklore Society printer
for 'Stray Notes on the Folk-Lore of Aberdeenshire and the North-
East of Scotland' (II:35) had trouble with the language in this
piece for the published text contains some obvious errors. I have
altered 'Botriphine' to 'Botriphnie', 'tyke-wake' to 'lyke-wake',
'crab' to 'crap', and 'dreay' to 'decay'. I have let stand 'lady'
though the song normally has 'laddy', in case it is an actual
variant, and 'neadie' although the sense would seem to require
'neagie' (naigie, horse). The Glossary does not list those words
already glossed within the text. Rorie was very much of his time in
the allusiveness of his references, designed for a group of readers who
all knew the same books and journals. In the References section the
usually incomplete references given by Rorie have been expanded,
except for the most obvious (e.g. Scott's *The Antiquary*) or most
inaccessible.

REFERENCES

1. David Rorie, *The Lum Hat Wantin' the Croon, and other poems* (Edinburgh: Moray Press, 1935), p. 7. For a recent edition of his poetry and a sound introduction to it, see David Rorie, *Poems and Prose*, ed. William Donaldson (Aberdeen: Aberdeen University Press for the David Rorie Society, 1983).
2. For a detailed account of Rorie's life, see I.A. Olson, 'David Rorie of Cults (1867–1946): Poet Laureate of the Society', *Aberdeen Medico-Chirurgical Society. A Bicentennial History 1789–1989*, ed. George P. Milne (Aberdeen: Aberdeen University Press, 1989), pp. 203–11. See also 'David Rorie', *Transactions of the Buchan Club*, 15 (1934–39), 76–9, and the twelve autobiographical articles in the *People's Journal*, 23/2/37 – 15/5/37.
3. *British Medical Journal* [hereafter *BMJ*] (1909), I:753.
4. *BMJ* (1946), I:415.
5. *A Medico's Luck in the War* (Aberdeen: Milne & Hutchison, 1919), pp. 2,3.
6. *BMJ* (1946), I:415.
7. Clement Bryce Gunn, *Leaves from the Life of a Country Doctor*, ed. Rutherford Crockett (Edinburgh: Moray Press, 1935), p. 63.
8. *Caledonian Medical Journal* [hereafter *CMJ*], 4 (1899–1901), 358–9. For the beginnings of the Society, see S. Rutherford MacPhail, 'Note on the Early Issues of the *Caledonian Medical Journal*', *CMJ*, 8 (1909–11), 372–4.
9. Edinburgh: Oliver and Boyd, Scottish Academic Press, 1928–71; Edinburgh, 1883; Edinburgh, 1885.
10. Aberdeen City Libraries, David Rorie Archive, A12/17.
11. See also my review of *Poems and Prose* in *Cencrastus*, No. 18 (Autumn 1984), pp. 46–7.
12. *Poems and Prose*, p. 38. On Professor Crum Brown, see Rorie, 'The Weighty 'Eighties', *University of Edinburgh Journal*, 6 (1933–34), 13–14.
13. Gunn, p. 53.
14. Ron Winram, *The Land O' Lonach* (Aberdeen: Adelphi Press for Winram's Antiquarian Bookshop, 1986), pp. 68–9.
15. 'The Weighty 'Eighties', pp. 11–12, 10.
16. *CMJ*, 6 (1904–06), 71; 9 (1912–14), 153; 12 (1923–25), 99, 67–81, 91–2.
17. Olson, p. 206; A. Greig Anderson, *BMJ* (1946), I:416; Olson, pp. 207, 203.
18. *Trans. Buchan Club*, p. 78; *Press and Journal*, 22/2/46; *BMJ* (1946), I:415.
19. Alexander Keith, *BMJ* (1946), I:416.
20. Aberdeen City Libraries, David Rorie Archive, A12/8.
21. Alexander Keith, *BMJ* (1946), I:416; *Press and Journal*, 19/2/46.
22. *The Lum Hat Wantin' the Croon*, p. 7; Aberdeen City Libraries, David Rorie Archive, A12/14.
23. Felix Rose, 'Petite anthologie de vieilles chansons populaires anglaises', *La Hune. Cahiers Trimestriels*, Numéro 12 (Automne-Hiver 1935–36), p. 6. Arnold van Gennep 'Observation sur l'histoire du Folklore dans le département du Nord', pp. 13–19.
24. Greig Anderson, p. 416; *Press and Journal*, 19/2/46. For an example of his speaking style, see below II:42.

25. Charles Murray, *The Last Poems*, with preface and notes by Alexander Keith and appreciation by Nan Shepherd (Aberdeen: Aberdeen University Press, 1969), p. xx.

26. Alexander Keith, *Press and Journal*, 22/2/46.

27. Keith, in Charles Murray, *Last Poems*, p. xx.

28. Keith, *Press and Journal*, 22/2/46. On the clubs, see also D.G. Gordon, 'Alexander Keith, M.A., LL.D., 1895–1978' *Bennachie Again*, ed. Archie W.M. Whiteley (n.p.: for the Bailies of Bennachie, 1983), p. 185. For Keith's multifarious writings, see [Harold Watt], 'Alexander Keith: A Bibliography', *Aberdeen University Review*, 48 (1979), 61–7.

29. Olson, p. 208.

30. Maureen Simpson, 'Urbane Master of Rural Wit', *Evening Express*, 26/5/83; May Thomson, 'Doctor whose song went round world', *Evening Express*, 26/5/79.

31. See below, p. 000.

32. 'Oral Tradition and the Scottish Miners', M.A. Thesis, Memorial University of Newfoundland, 1987.

33. Modern works in English on the subject are Wayland D. Hand, *Magical Medicine: The Folkloric Component of Medicine in the Folk Belief, Custom, Ritual of the Peoples of Europe and America* (Berkeley: University of California Press, 1980), and Wayland D. Hand, ed. *American Folk Medicine: A Symposium* (Berkeley: University of California Press, 1975). Norway has an impressive record of study in this field; see Ann Helene Bolstad Skjelbred, *Bibliografi over alternativ medisin og behandling i Norge til og med 1980* (Oslo: Universitetsbiblioteket, 1983), and Ingjald Reichborn-Kjennerud, *Vår gamle trolldomsmedisin,* 5 vols. (Oslo: No. Vidensk.-Akad., 1927–47).

34. On the question of punishment, see Herbert Halpert, 'Legends of the Cursed Child', *New York Folklore Quarterly*, 14 (1958), 233–41, and 'Supernatural Sanctions and the Legend', *Folklore Studies in the Twentieth Century*, ed. Venetia J. Newall (Woodbridge, Suffolk: Boydell and Brewer, 1980), pp. 226–33.

35. David Rorie Archive, A12/1.

36. *People's Journal*, 3/4/37, p. 6, 27/3/37, p. 6.

37. 'Euthanasia in the Folk-Medicine of Britain', *CMJ*, 15 (1932–36), 304–10.

38. *Press and Journal*, 22/2/46.

39. E.C. Cawte, 'A guide to the Carpenter Manuscripts', typescript in the American Folklife Center, Library of Congress, Washington, D.C.

40. *Poems and Prose*, p. 6.

41. Since modern technology—typewriters, mimeograph, photocopying and fax machines—has been harnessed to replicate older patterns of informal transmission, contemporary folklorists have devoted some amused attention to this area of photocopy lore; see Alan Dundes and C.R. Pagter, *Urban Folklore from the Paperwork Empire* (Austin: University of Texas Press, 1975) and *Work Hard and You Shall Be Rewarded: Urban Folklore from the Paperwork Empire* (Bloomington: Indiana University Press, 1978); Paul Smith, *The Complete Book of Office Mis-practice*

(London: Routledge, 1984) and *Reproduction is Fun* (London: Routledge, 1986).

42. Aberdeen City Libraries, David Rorie Archive, A12/17: letter of 21/12/25 from C.M. to D.R.

43. p. 290; London: Folklore Society, 1937–41, pp. x–xi.

I
FOLK MEDICINE

1
The Scottish Bone-setter

[From *Caledonian Medical Journal* 5 (1902–04), 2–5]

> The smiddy stands beside the burn
>   That wimples through the clachan;
> I never yet gae by the door
>   But aye I fa' a-laughin'.
>
> Alexander Rodger

There are professors and 'professors'—of that there is no doubt. Some are born to blush unseen—and often imperfectly heard—in the classrooms and laboratories of a University. A larger number rise to giddy heights. I have even seen with my own eyes a professor descend from the skies, and he—although you might have thought it—was not a professor of Divinity. He landed (learned man!) on his back in a turnip-field; and when we, an enthusiastic crowd, surged across the Swedes to cheer him, he rose, in his shirtsleeves and his wrath, and cursed us in the high-pitched language of London. Cursed us for viewing his parachute descent gratis from the King's highway, instead of paying for admission to an enclosure from which we would only have seen him ascend and drift out of sight. Other professors, having assumed the title and temporarily laid aside the hod and the pick, insert an advertisement in an evening paper, and 'specialise.' And their skill—need it be said?—is devoted to the lower disorders of the lower orders, to the relief of those who, as the Kincardineshire ploughman euphemistically described it, are 'a' wrang doon aboot the doon-aboots.'

But if the curers of the 'nervous debility,' 'youthful errors and indiscretions,' and all the rest of that happy hunting-ground for the quack, are left out of account, the next great humbug, glorified and adored by an empty-headed and open-mouthed public, is the bone-setter. He may or he may not be a professor. . . . The Scottish bone-setter, as a rule, leaves the high-sounding title to the Southron or the Yankee, and the smoke of the 'smiddy' is a good enough background to his luminous cures. For, always a humbug, the hero of our tale is frequently a blacksmith. Why this should be so I know not.

Vulcan, although notoriously unsound in one of his lower limbs, did not thereby gain a reputation amongst his fellow gods of being 'skeely wi' banes;' nor did Tubal Cain, so far as we know, brazen out an unwarranted surgical reputation. Perchance it fell out, in days of yore and gore, that he who made the sword-blade was looked to for healing the hurt—an unthrashed-out and rudimentary idea of a Workmen's Compensation Act. But be that as it may, it is no uncommon thing in rural Scotland for wee Jock or Jean to go astride Mally when the honest mare needs shoeing, and for Robin Tamson to wipe his hands on his leather apron and 'put in' a fabulous number of the bairn's bones, to the admiration of his cronies.

Of knowledge of anatomy or of training our friend has none. Of this, more even than of his skill, he is proud. For is it not a matter of 'heir-skep'? Did not his father before him, or at least his grandfather, or at the very worst his aunt, possess 'the touch' in their day and generation? *Nascitur non fit*—'It rins in the bluid.' A medical man may study anatomy and surgery for years, he may practise with success as a howdie or a pill-giver, but 'a' body kens doctors ken naethin' aboot banes.' And so hey! for the horny-handed hammer-holder when an injured limb cries out for real heaven-given unadulterated skill.

I suppose every country practitioner in Scotland could tell of cases ruined by these charlatans. I know of one case where, after the rough handling of a tuberculous ankle-joint (three bones were, of course, 'put in,' and the medical attendant's nose—equally, of course—put out), suppuration occurred in the joint, followed by general septicaemia and death. I know of another case where, after being thrown out of a trap, a man was content for a fortnight with the ministrations of a platelayer on the railway. When the patient came to me he had a fracture of the surgical neck of the humerus, with a subglenoid dislocation of the head of the bone. This was subsequently excised in hospital, and the patient, always a weakly man, died at home some months later. And so on *ad nauseam*.

All this makes for tragedy. But the prevailing note is more often that of comedy. Take the case of the little Fife boy who had been taken by his parents to see a 'bone-doctor' about a 'sair leg.' After as much headshaking, condemnation of the medical attendant, &c., as were thought necessary, several bones were put in, and the child brought home. A kindly neighbour enquired if he had suffered much pain. 'No fear!' said the wee chap, 'dae ye think I was sic a saftie as gie him the sair leg?' And, again, not a hundred miles from the 'Lang Toon,' and not a hundred years ago either, two drouthy cronies were swaying homewards, when one said to the other—'Lie doon, Jock!

here's the bane-doctor. Sham that ye've gotten a bane oot.' Down
with great ease sank Jock, and the 'skeely' one gave his aid with such
right goodwill that the practical joker was left on the pavement with
a very genuine dislocation of the hip.

What (beyond 'heir-skep') are their qualifications? *Nil*. A bone-
setter, however, has some limit to his powers. Whatever else he can
put in, he cannot put in a certificate that will satisfy an accident
insurance company. Not long ago I was asked to see a ploughman
who had fallen off a cart. I found him with a Colles' fracture,
the injured part covered with a stinking, greasy rag, above which
were firmly whipped two leather bootlaces. The bones were not in
position, and the hand, from interference with the circulation, was
in a fair way to become gangrenous. Yet the injury had been met
with a week previously, and he and his employer had been highly
pleased with the treatment. I was only wanted to fill in the insurance
schedule.

On another occasion I was visited by a genial ploughman, who
wished me to 'tak' a look at his back.' He, too, had fallen off a cart.
When? Oh, a fortnight ago. Why hadn't he come sooner? Oh, he
had been at a bone-doctor. Why did he come here now? And then
came the story. 'Weel, ye see, doctor, he tell't me he had pit in the
bane that rins frae the middle o' the back-bane richt through to the
breist-bane, and I thocht he had dune fine! But the mistress and me,
the ither nicht, was lookin' up an auld medical buik wi' an atomy
intilt, and we fund there wisna sic a bane there. So I thocht I'd see
what *you* said aboot it!' I said a good deal about it.

A coachman, who had been flung off his box and got a bruised
elbow, had thirteen small bones put in at the elbow-joint by one
famous blacksmith still in practice. This same bone-setter (who has
had a belted earl as his patient) stated to a man who in turn retailed
it to me, that he had been offered £600 a year by a London hospital
to go there and do nothing but set bones. But what is mere money
to the true philanthropist? Jingling dross! He declined the offer!

One curious qualification for bone-setting was given me by a
collier who had been to a bone-setter with a 'staved thoom.' I
asked him why he had gone there. 'Lord, man! I dinna ken.
They a' say he's unco skeely.' But what training had he? 'Weel,
he was aince in a farm, and drank himsel' oot o't!' A rapid, easily
passed curriculum, possessed even of a certain attractiveness for
some minds.

To take a few amongst many Fifeshire bone-setters, we find
the following occupations: Schoolmaster, blacksmith, quarryman,

platelayer, midwife, and joiner. The blacksmith, the joiner and the platelayer are still with us; the others have crossed the Styx.

What is their *modus operandi*? Like the spelling of the historical name of Weller, it 'depends upon the taste and fancy' of the individual. A rough and ready massage plays an important part, as does the implicit faith of the patient. The fearlessness of utter ignorance leads them to deal with adhesions to joints in the most thorough-going fashion, and we hear of their successes—not their failures. Many of them have the gift—a gift also common to many who never use it as hereditary skill—of making a cracking noise at the thumb or finger-joints by flexion and extension. When an injury is shown for treatment, the bone-setter handles it freely, says how many bones are 'out,' and then works away at the joint, making cracking noises with his own fingers, each separate noise representing one of the patient's bones returning to its proper position. 'They maun hae been oot,' says the sufferer afterwards, 'I heard them gaun in!' Seeing may be believing, but hearing 'cowes a'.'

And who are their patrons? There's the rub! Not only the *profanum vulgus*. The duchess elbows the dustman at the charlatan's door, the clergyman lends his pony-trap to the collier to drive past the house of the doctor and go to the smithy. In my own district at present there is an old woman with an unreduced backward dislocation of the ankle-joint. Years ago, when injured in the harvest field, she was conscientiously carted in a clerical gig past four medical doorplates, and handed over to the ministrations of a joiner. Those of us who remember Sequah in his palmy days—palm-oily, prairie-oily: choose your own adjective—will remember how Edinburgh Waverley Market was hung round with ecclesiastical testimonials, and doubtless, their fervent blessings have followed the ready Red Indian to wherever he may have retired. But why blame the person when the peer gives him a lead? And why blame the peer, of all men, for a belief in hereditary gifts? If a qualification for putting out laws, why not for putting in bones?

The remedy? Legislation, of course; and, preferably, 'something lingering with boiling oil in it.'

2

Popular Pathology: Being an essay on what the patient thinks

[From *Caledonian Medical Journal* 5 (1902–04), 387–92]

Whence they had those words I know not; it may be of some doctor that never went to school.

Gerarde

The remains of folk-medicine that still linger in our midst, adorned though they now are with mangled technical phraseology derived from quack advertisements and 'scientific' school board teaching, are not altogether without their own interest. What is wrong with the patient is one thing; his own opinion of his disease is certainly another. True of the male, it is perhaps truer of the female; nor is it confined to one rank of life. Thackeray tells us how, on one occasion, the immortal Becky and Lady Jane 'had one of those confidential medical conversations about the children which all mothers, and most women, as I am given to understand, delight in. Fifty years ago, and when the present writer, being an interesting little boy, was ordered out of the room with the ladies after dinner, I remember quite well that their talk was chiefly about their ailments; and putting this question directly to two or three since, I have always got from them the acknowledgement that times are not changed.' And then he calls on his fair readers to remark for themselves when next they 'assemble to celebrate the drawing-room mysteries.' Under their skins, as we now all know well, the colonel's lady and Judy O'Grady are sisters; and there is no doubt that the latter, with a submerged-eleventh at her breast, has even a better chance of studying the clinical details of disease than her higher class relation. And more especially, perhaps, the intricate nervous diseases handed down from a job lot of whisky-soaked ancestors, and that branch of irritative dermatology not wholly unconnected with bugs.

The persistency of some of the ideas is remarkable. For although the practitioner may point out, in a case, say, of intussusception, what the true nature of the child's illness is, still, when his back is turned, the finding of the inevitable jury of old women that the child has 'dumb fits' is apt to gain more credence than his dictum. And the reason is not always far to seek; for heavy doses of castor oil are not contra-indicated in 'dumb fits'; they are, so the doctor points out, in intussusception. Hence the mother, accused by implication of erroneous treatment, gains satisfaction and distinction in her own circle by disbelieving you, and falling back on the more ancient beliefs.

It is amongst the dirtiest and most degenerate that these beliefs find fullest credence—the wastrel knows them all, and knows them well. Periodically bereft of his unpaid and scanty furniture by the sheriff-officer, he flits fitfully by moonlight from district to district. Tradesmen know him, and weep over him—him, his varying wives and kaleidoscopically changing relations. And when he has set up house anew, with an old box or two for chair and table, a spoutless teapot, some stolen straw for bedding, and what other oddments he can borrow from soft-hearted neighbours, it is only natural that disease should dog the footsteps of him and his. Blame he looks for before it is given, and tries to shift to other shoulders. 'Weel, I'm sure a' thing's been done that could be done—I've done a' that I could, ony way!' At his hovel door Death knocks not once but many times, and his philosophy of life is to say 'Curse it!' when he is sober, and 'Kismet!' when he is drunk.

Instruct people of this description as regards infection? Oh, it is 'just a bairn's tribble,' or 'my faither slep' six weeks wi' a man wi' the sma'-pox and never took it.' And your parting admonitions, founded on the microbe theory, are, to their mind, fully met by the growl, 'Ay! and wha smittit the first ane?'

Who, indeed? Here you are face to face with the fatalist, the person who believes it has been 'laid on him,' or whose neighbour suggests that it has been done 'to pit a daur owre him' for some previous misconduct. The explanation of why a man had several idiot children was satisfactorily found in the fact that 'he had been awfu' for laughin' at ither folk' when he was a young man. And the woman, again, who had unfeelingly jested at his offspring, herself, in turn, bore a child with a club-foot as a punishment for her lack of heart. 'She kent weel why it was sent her, and she aye keepit the bairn's fit happit up oot o' sicht.' I remember, too, a woman gazing awe-struck at an anencephalic foetus, and saying of the mother, 'What has she done, poor soul, that this should be laid on her?' Pathology to them cannot explain it alone; crude Calvinism must lend a helping hand, and, as a matter of fact, there is not much advance this way since the moralist hammered out his heavy ballad in 1566:

> I read how Affrique land was fraught
> For their most filthy life,
> With monstreus shapes confuzedly,
> That therein wer full rife.

And again:

> Both tender babes and eke brute beasts
> In shape disfourmed bee;
> Full manie wayes he plagues the earth,
> As dayly we may see.
> For sure we all may be agast
> To see these shapes unkynd,
> And trembling fear may press our harts
> Our God to have in mynd.[1]

So, since miracles have ceased to be served out piping-hot at every shrine, a little dash of the supernatural must be gained somehow; and, if we make our bricks with fewer straws, still, we make them.

I mentioned 'dumb fits.' We are constantly coming across them in the jargon of the proletariat. But although we get the name, we get little explanation of how 'they' work, and I have heard it applied to so many conditions—pneumonia, zymotic enteritis, meningitis, &c.—that I doubt whether there really ever was, in the minds of the vulgar, any special disease to which this term referred. Jamieson makes no mention of it at all. But when a 'skeely' auld wife has diagnosed dumb fits, death is usually not far off; and if 'dumb fits' is not a recognised cause of death with the Registrar-General, it is with the general public.

With that great and prevalent disease 'hives,' however, we have more to come and go upon. The word is constantly in use amongst the many-bairned matrons, and wonderful, according to their belief, is the power of the disease.

★ ★ ★

---

1. Written in 1566 by John Mellys, of Norwich, and entitled 'The true description of two monsterous children lawfully begotten between George Stevens and Margerie, his wife, and borne in the parish of Swanburne in Buckynghamshyre, the iij of Aprill, Anno Domini 1566: the two children havyng both their belies fast joyned together, and embracyng one another with their armes: which children were both alyve by the space of half-an-hower, and were baptized and named the one John and the other Joan.'

'Nerves,' again, with the *hoi polloi* do not rank as an anatomical entity, but as a functional, if not an organic, affection. We all know the lady who appeals for sympathy, and jerks Lot's wife into the mind's eye of describing herself as 'a fair solid mass of nerves.' Again, hysteria is frequently described as 'the nerves gaun through the body,' as if that were not habitual with them. 'Thought,' too, does not mean the result of brain energy in the usual sense, but is used to signify either worry or imagination. Of a hypochondriac it is frequently said, 'There's a heap o' thought aboot it,' equivalent to 'He's makkin' maist o' his tribble.' And a very good, and not altogether untrue, description of a female valetudinarian was given by a neighbour who said, 'It's just thocht workin' wi' nerves that's destroyin' her system.'

I have spoken of hives getting 'round the heart.' A very curious idea concerning the heart is prevalent here, an idea, or one very similar to, which I was interested to see mentioned by Mrs. Moodie in her article on 'Highland Therapy.' Mrs. Moodie states that in connection with insanity there was a belief that it was caused by a person's heart getting displaced (jumping out of its 'husk') by a sudden shock. It is not in connection with insanity that we find the idea in Fifeshire, but in connection with fatal shock, and the expression used is to 'ca' the heart aff its stalk.' For example, not long ago a child in this district died of shock following a severe scalding caused by falling into a tub of boiling water, and the popular verdict was that its heart had been 'ca'd off its stalk.' Whether this idea of the cardiac organ possessing a stalk is due to its pear shape or not I do not know, but more likely the aorta in days of old was regarded as the stalk whereon the heart hung, and as a large amount of popular anatomy has filtered out to the multitude through pig-killing and other butchery (for has not 'man got a' the puddens o' a soo but ane?'), we cannot expect it to be particular or exact. Any pain near the heart, or any cut or bruise near the heart, is regarded as being particularly dangerous, and quite small lesions of the skin in that vicinity are presented for treatment which would be passed over unnoticed in other parts of the body. Injuries, too, however slight, caused by a dog-bite also claim immediate attention, especially when the region affected is the thumb (in case of the supposed graver risk of lockjaw supervening).

Wind, too, is a pathological wonder-worker. It can affect all parts of the body, commencing as a 'prinkling' in the big toe, and next instant 'fleein' to the heid.' It can 'get into the veins and swall up the briests.' What can it not do? And who less amenable to treatment than the kail-supping old wife affected with the 'nervish' variety, who lives resignedly in an aromatic atmosphere made up of extra-strong peppermint and a 'poorin' o' spirits?'

But after you have winnowed out what little grain there is from the chaff, the present-day pathology of the plebs is usually a gloriously muddled rubbish-heap. A typical example I came across the other day when I was gingerly feeling for an irregularly distributed radial, vowing, the while, innumerable candles to St. Keating. 'I see ye're puzzled wi' my pulse, doctor,' amiably said the patient, 'and ye're no' the first by a guid wheen. Professor——, o' Glesca, says it's a pulse in a thoosand!' 'Why?' I asked. 'Weel, ye see, aboot the middle o' the airm it dips doon and runs into the alimentary canal!'

Truly physicians are in vain in such a plight, and the way is clear for Peter Puffer's Piebald Pills or Father Swindle's Syrup.

3

Some Fifeshire Folk-Medicine

[From *Edinburgh Medical Journal* 15 (1904), 513–9]

'Folk-Medicine,' says Black in his interesting work on the subject, 'comprehends charms, incantations, and traditional habits and customs relative to the preservation of health and the cure of disease, practised now or formerly at home or abroad.' Habits and customs of a more or less curious nature we have yet with us in Fife, but the charms and incantations are gone—cremated, doubtless, with the frail bodies of the half-daft beldames who were sent to the stake by an active clerical caste for trespassing on its own special preserve of superstition. But lingering with a singular persistency in most of the rural districts, and stored chiefly in the memories of the older women, we still find some curious ideas; and when we have time and inclination to study them for their own sake, they are not altogether lacking in interest. Should they run counter to our instructions to the patient, we are apt to treat them cavalierly, forgetting the accredited part woman played in the leech-craft of the past. In the more remote parts of the country, she had, like Annot Lyle,[1] some knowledge of the dressing of wounds (for, while the tuilzie lasted, man meddled only with the making of them), and in all parts of the country she had some skill in herbal simples. The lady of the 'big house' had her still-room and her cordials to dispense, had the medical books of the time dedicated to her, and even, perhaps, some of her own recipes incorporated in them. And thus she was (no tabulated statement of her results being ever called for) always ready to tackle

> The glengore, gravel, and the gut,
> And all the ills that first were put
> Into Pandora's purse.

Nowadays the craft, such as it is, has descended into hands more plebeian, and become specialised more particularly perhaps in the art of obstetrics. For has the sonsy dame, twice seven times confronter of the curse of Eve, not more practical knowledge of the handling

---

1. Scott's *Legend of Montrose.*

and the dandling and the dosing of the latest pink-skinned immigrant to this cold world, than the youthful graduate, who, big with theoretical maternity, would shoulder her to the door? 'I'se warrant she bude to hae'—unless, perchance, circumstances demand the use of 'the irons,' when she hangs back, a handless, hysterical hindrance, hinting, and more than hinting, at this unhallowed haste.

The 'Kingdom' of a hundred years ago, with its miners, weavers, fishers, and agriculturists, must have presented a wide field for research in this direction; and even yet, when the Forth and Tay bridges have removed much of the clannishness for which Fife was renowned, there are still gleanings for the folk-lorist. For, whether deserved or not, the reputation of being one of a race apart still clings to the Fifer, and the numerous proverbs applied to him bear witness to it. 'Fife for fly folk.' 'He's a whistler' (a play here on the word 'Fife'). 'Gang to Fife and get a wife' (a canny one who will guard the bawbees). 'Clever as the Fife kye—they can knit stockin's wi' their horns.' These, and many more like them, give us the outsider's opinion of the race. Some of these sayings the Fife people quote themselves, with a quiet enjoyment of the tribute to their characteristics; others, such as 'He's got the Fife complaint—big feet and sair een,' they naturally reject as unseemly. But, take him all in all, the Fifer has faith in himself, and it is thus only natural that his beliefs should be parted with slowly and grudgingly.

Now, as there is a reason for everything, there is a reason for the survival of folk-medicine. It is long since Dunbar wrote:

> Tak consolatioun
> In zour pane;
> In tribulatioun
> Tak consolatioun;
> Out of vexatioun
> Cum hame again,
> Tak consolatioun
> In zour pane,

yet the quaint jingle of the old makar still voices the quest of the many—rest from pain be it of the body or the mind. Wherefore, says the ruder son of the soil (and not altogether with unreason), if the orthodox fail to give me what I seek, and that speedily, let me deal in the open market. And straightway he does what he says.

Look at your evening paper, and see how the 'bone specialist' can, at a certain hotel in a certain ancient town, on Mondays from 11 to 2, *cure* (O illiterate wonder-worker!) 'rheumatics, sciatic, and skin diseases.' Bones, presumably, he shoves in also as an organist does his stops. Ask any druggist, more especially a country one, how many rough-and-ready prescriptions of the 'hickery-pickery' order he gets in a month. True, the paper is a dirty scrap; the writing is that of a stubby, well-bespat, and halting pencil; but what is on the 'line' has done a 'warl' o' guid' to some one else—and besides, has it not the special value of heterodoxy?

'And I got the cure frae an auld wife wha got it when she was a young woman frae a man wantin' the legs that was drawn aboot by twa black dogs.' So I was told the other day. For the tinker and the tramp, who have dodged the dominie and gained what lore they have from the foul tongues of their forebears, have still rough-and-ready cures to niffer for bite and sup at the cottage door. A hot spell draws them like flies out to the high-roads and bye-roads, padding it where the footing is softer at the roadside's fringe. Dogs are siccar at them, and after a scouther of rain they stink like any brock; but, mark you, they are 'skeelie wi' simples, and gey solid crackers: ye'd wonder what gaun-aboot folks ken.'

Note, too, the slight touch of the uncanny: 'A man wantin' the legs drawn aboot by twa black dogs.' Not quite up to the standard of Borrow's Brute Carle of the Danish ballad, for

> A wild swine on his shoulder he kept,
> And upon his bosom a black bear slept,
> And about his fingers with hair o'er-hung
> The squirrel sported and weasel clung;

nor even, I fear, of Aiken Drum, whose

> . . . wauchie arms three claws did meet
> As they trailed on the grun' by his tae-less feet.

Still, in these prosaic days, it is as near as may be; for a man with two legs drawn about by a horse you can consult any day in the week, but the advice of the other ought to be something 'by-ordinar'.' The cure, nevertheless, was neither very quaint nor very subtle; for this lousy oracle of the highway, this wandering dog-drawn Witherington, fighting fortune on his stumps, only recommended sheep's kidney fat and Archangel tar for a 'scabbit heid efter inockilation wi' bad maitter.'

Or take the case where the gude-man was laid up in his roadside cottage with a 'poisoned arm,' healing slowly—too slowly, the friends thought. To his door came an old hag, sun-tanned, dram-stained, cutty at lip. She noticed the sick man, asked for and got a sight of the arm, and then gave her sage advice—advice that carries you back into the past, how far, it is hard to say. For she advised the splitting up, and applying hot to the diseased surface, of three puppy dogs: that was all. A neighbour with a cross-bred litter doomed to the tub readily handed them over to the tinkler wife's gully; and, antiseptic dressings and all such feckless modernities being abandoned, on went the slaughtered innocents. Certainly *post*, doubtfully *propter hoc*, the arm got better.

Within the last few months, also, I came across a boy who was duly getting, thrice daily, a tablespoonful of the liquor in which a mouse had been boiled. This for enuresis. Another method is to roast the mouse after removing its head, and powder the animal down. The powder is then used for the same purpose. There is an old Fife saying, 'Go to Freuchie and fry mice,' and it may be a matter of conjecture whether this troublesome complaint was not epidemic there at one time, due perhaps to the proximity of Falkland Palace, and consequent facilities, when kings held wassail, for over-doing liquid refreshment.

To deal systematically with all these cures is not easy: one must cull them as they are happened upon, and they are often best told in the original Doric. Take, for example, the sulphur cure for cramp. You express a doubt of its efficacy? 'I was gaun ae day to M—Kirk, and I cam on an auld wife sittin' by the roadside wha couldna gang a step faurer for cramp. She telt me she had come awa in a hurry wi'oot her sulphur band, and this was the first time for mony a day she had dune't.' This sulphur band was a piece of sulphur sewed in a garter and worn round the leg, and is still in fairly common use to keep away cramp. Kept under the pillow at night, a piece of sulphur will act in the same way for all the occupants of the bed; and it is a curious mixture of old and new to see a portion of a sulphur candle, left by a sanitary inspector, promoted to this use. Or the sulphur may be tied in the 'oxter.' Flowers of sulphur rubbed into a 'flyped' stocking and then put on in proper order is a cure for 'pains,' or rubbed into blue flannel is an application for lumbago. Where 'a rush is hingin' aboot a bairn,' sulphur and whisky brings it 'to the ootside,' while sulphur and cream of tartar is a regular Spring drink for 'clearin' the blude.'

'Pains' (rheumatism), unfortunately, is a common complaint, and any cure is eagerly caught at. Many consequently exist besides the sulphur one. Black slugs 'masked' in a teapot with water and salt supply an oil that is useful for rubbing. A potato or a hare's foot carried in the pocket may work wonders. The marrow of bullocks' bones twice boiled may be well rubbed in, or the painful joints may be well switched with freshly gathered nettles. Inwardly, turpentine and coarse sugar, half and half, may be consumed freely.

[39]

Slugs have another use—white slugs this time. A quantity of them is placed in a flannel jelly-bag along with a handful of salt, and the resulting oil that drips away is carefully caught and administered like cod-oil in phthisis. I have seen this same 'cure' in Lancashire, and in many other parts of England, and the Continent slugs and snails are used in different forms for pulmonary complaints.

The expressions 'not strong' and 'in bad health' are always, amongst the *hoi polloi*, used to mean phthisical, and great offence may be unintentionally given by saying that a person is 'not strong.' It is a common and unfortunate belief, both as regards phthisis and other infectious diseases, that an older person is not liable to take infection from a younger; but the other belief, that all bedding and clothes belonging to a deceased phthisical patient should be burnt is an aid to the medical attendant. The clothes in an infectious case may thus be quite safely washed by an older person: 'I dinna think there's ony harm in her washing his claes: she's auld be's him.'

When the outset of trouble is heralded by a 'grewsin',' care must be taken not to grip any part of the body, for that gripped part is apt to 'beel.' This is a commonly assigned cause of suppurative mastitis. Further, a mother who while 'grewsin'' grips her child may thus give it a severe cold—'I maun hae gruppit it.' But more commonly the child 'has sookit the cauld' off her.

Whooping-cough being, like pains, common, has many cures. But the greatest stress is laid on the benefit of 'change of air.' The length of time the change lasts is of no moment. A Saturday to Monday visit to a distance eight miles off is quite enough; and if, through driving or travelling by train, the patient is rendered much worse, the circumstance is certainly unfortunate, but cannot be quoted against the treatment. Not long ago, a patient of mine, a mere infant, with whooping-cough, was taken down the pit by its father and held for ten minutes in a strong draught in an aircourse. It died in two days of pneumonia. But of course 'we canna help tribble.' A short change of air to a gas-works or a lime-kiln is also efficacious, while those who cannot reach these sanatoria can take advantage of freshly dug earth.

This earth cure is also advantageous to miners asphyxiated with 'bad air,' although the opportunities to practise it are limited somewhat by the spread of first-aid principles. But in days not so long gone by, a hole was dug out for the sufferer's face to lie over, and, when sufficiently recovered to be put to bed, the divot of turf was laid on his pillow, so that, in his slumbers, the gentle breath of Mother Earth might still play round him.

The old idea of ridding one's self of a disease by transference is always cropping up. I mentioned earlier in this paper the puppy-poultice, and the idea in this was undeniably that of transferring the trouble from the human body to the canine. Indeed, I think in many cases of poulticing the same idea is latent. The popular belief is that the efficacy of a poultice lies not so much in the heat and moisture of it, as in its power to 'draw the tribble.' The disease is 'in' until it is extracted; it has to be got out. Some poultices are held to be 'awfu' drawin'' things; and 'Is it no' drawin' it owre sair?' is a common query. When a blister refuses to rise readily, it is looked on as a bad sign: it is 'ill to draw, dour to draw, the tribble's deep in.' The commonest cause of criminal assaults on little children is the wish to get rid of venereal disease, and I saw lately a case where a nurse-girl deliberately 'smittit' a younger child with impetigo contagiosa to relieve herself of the complaint. When a patient is ill, too, there is always a desire not to take anything that may 'feed the tribble.' There is a fight going on between the trouble and the 'system,' and unsuitable medicine or diet may go to help the former instead of the latter. 'For ony favour,' said a woman the other day, 'dinna gie me onything that will gar me eat, for a' I tak' gangs to the hoast and just strengthens it.' Behind it all, unknown to the speaker, of course, lies the idea of demoniac possession; just as Zoroaster believed that while a woman suffered from the menstrual flow (which was the work of Ahriman, or the devil) she was not to be allowed to eat as much as she wished, 'as the strength she might acquire would accrue to the fiends.' Her food even was not to be given by hand, but passed to her with a long spoon, a method of intercourse with devils still quoted by politicians on delicate occasions of international diplomacy.

Hence it is, perhaps, that we get also the idea that those who are not afraid of a trouble will not take it, on the principle of resisting the devil and him fleeing from you. It is an idea which has frequently to be combated when dealing with infectious disease; plenty people, otherwise intelligent, believing that the 'trouble's no' catchin'' so long as they 'are no' feared at it.' The belief is of course an old-standing one. In *Helps for Suddain Accidents* (London, 1633) we find that 'Fear corrupts the juices of the brain (through the force of imagination), and makes them fall down and disperse themselves into all the parts of the body filled with a sickly quality, and so contrary to nature. This is the reason why fearful men are apt to die of slight wounds; whereas a valiant spirit has always flesh apt to be healed.' An echo here of Ecclesiastes, when he says, 'A merry heart doeth good like a medicine, but a broken spirit drieth the bones.'

[41]

An infectious disease is described as a 'catchin' complaint,' while for contagious the word 'smittle' is properly used. Often, however, 'smittle' is used loosely to cover both, and a common expression of disbelief, as regards modern theories of infection, is the question, 'Wha smittit the first ane?' And the belief (as regards measles, scarlatina, whooping-cough, etc.) that they are merely 'bairns' troubles' and therefore as inevitable as teething, is responsible for much infant mortality; for 'Pit them a'thegither an' hae dune w'it,' is still occasionally practised. Measles, also, 'maunna be wet,' and this axiom is frequently made the excuse for leaving the patient in a lamentable state of dirt.

In a slight case of one of the exanthemata, where medical aid has not been invoked, and where the omission has resulted in more of the same kind occurring, the excuse may be offered, that the parents thought it was 'only a burst.' 'He's burst himsel',' explains all skin eruptions, from 'plooks' to pemphigus, although an English locum might well be alarmed if summoned to such a case, and forgiven if his mind ran on gunpowder or boilers. The usual cause of a 'burst' is a chill following sweating, but the same result is got by a 'rash drink o' water,' the drinking of which dangerous fluid will either 'burst' or 'foonder' you. Cold water as a drink in illness is regarded with holy horror by the average female friend in attendance on a sick-bed, who recites with pride how she has refused the natural craving of the sufferer. It is a forbidden fluid, too, in the puerperium, and the medical attendant who permits its use assumes a direct responsibility for all illness that may ensue, be it 'chacked' nipples or sudden death. The genuine old-fashioned miner in this country always misses out his back and his knees from his daily ablutions, on coming off his shift, for the reason that washing weakens them. There are thus well-grounded and old reasons for believing that water is not the harmless thing which teetotalers assert.

Change of water is frequently assumed to be as bad for the health as change of air is good. People coming to a new district often blame this for causing illness, especially boils; while living too near running water is supposed to cause decay in teeth. Boils, however, by many are looked on as a sign of rude health, or at any rate, as only liable to come out on those who are exceptionally well. Another belief of the same nature is that *pediculi capitis* only appear in strong children, and I have known a case of a woman actually collecting these undesirables and transplanting them to the head of a sickly child, under the belief that the invalid would gain strength thereby! Truly a curious piece of muddled reasoning.

4

Some Survivals of Folk Medicine in Scotland

[From *British Medical Journal* (1906), I: 385]

Aberdeen Medico-Chirurgical Society. At a meeting on February 1st, Dr. A.R. Galloway, Vice-President, in the chair . . . Dr. Rorie read a paper on *Some survivals of folk medicine in Scotland*, in which he stated that what of that nature had been left chiefly centred round obstetrics. It was still believed in places that a menstruating woman was a source of uncleanness; anything, such as preserves, made by her would inevitably go bad. There was a popular belief that when a wife became pregnant her husband was liable to suffer from the minor ailments incidental to that condition. This was called 'breedin alang wi' her.' An old woman stated that her husband 'aye bred alang wi' her wi' a' her bairns,' and it was the persistence of toothache in her unmarried adult son which led her to the correct belief that he had broken the seventh commandment. A reference to the old calendar or tally stick was found in the expression 'to have lost her nick-stick,' referring to a woman who was out of reckoning as to the time of her confinement. The old belief in the harmful influence of crossing anything in the presence of a sick person still found a home here and there. To sit cross-legged and, still worse, to nurse one's knees in the presence of a pregnant woman or during confinement was a sure way of causing difficulties or delaying labour. This belief, common in the time of the Romans, was found in old Scottish and Dutch ballads. No belief was more common, perhaps, in the popular mind in connexion with pregnancy than that regarding maternal impressions; as, for instance, to slap a pregnant woman on the face with a red hankerchief resulted in a child with a red mark on the forehead. To throw anything at a pregnant woman was fraught with danger to the expected offspring; it might cause birth mark or serious deformity. In the popular belief a 'lassie' was got from post-menstrual coitus, while the 'laddie' was the outcome of premenstrual connexion. It was good luck to be born with a caul. If the caul were lost or destroyed the luck went too. If the cord were cut too short the child would be in adult life childless. To prevent this misfortune a popular prophylactic was to wrap the laddie in a woman's petticoat and the lassie in a man's shirt. It was common to see both articles in readiness for the expected stranger. Another popular saying was 'They that get their teeth abune shall never wear their marriage shoon,' referring to the upper teeth appearing first. As regards folk medicine proper, it generally took the form of herbal simples, endowed, where possible, with a picturesque touch of the supernatural. Animals were occasionally called upon to provide the necessary substance, such as black slugs 'masked' with salt in a teapot and the oil used for rheumatism. A curious belief in the power of the earth was shown in the habit of digging a small pit beside the head of a miner asphyxiated with choke-damp with the idea that the earth drew all the bad air from him. As for folk surgery it was confined to the history of the bonesetter. He was very frequently a blacksmith, but might be of any trade; the one necessary point being that his skill should be hereditary.

5

Scottish Amulets

[From *Folklore* 20 (1909), 231–2]

As regards present-day survival of amulets for protection against diseases, I may note that I still find them in use, but not commonly. Red silk round the wrist for rheumatism I have seen in Fife,—(although the wearer was a 'gangrel' and perhaps had Irish blood in his veins),—and in Aberdeenshire of old days red worsted would be tied round a child's wrist to keep away the 'witches.' The chief thing, however, for the latter purpose was the little heart-shaped silver 'witch-brooch.' It was pinned to the child's underclothing at its first dressing. The shape was probably derived from its being originally the mounting of an 'elf shot' or 'fairy dart,' *i.e.* flint arrow head. An old man in Kincardineshire some thirty years ago had such a 'fairy dart,' which he kept as a safeguard against warlocks and witches. It would lose all efficacy if allowed to touch the ground, and in showing it he always held his hands below those of the person looking at it, in great anxiety lest it should fall. The use of sulphur as an amulet for cramp is common in Fife and Aberdeenshire. In the former county I have seen it often as a 'sulphur band,' *i.e.* a piece of rock sulphur sewn into the garter and worn round the leg. I have seen a piece tied in the armpit, while a piece of it under the pillow would be expected to keep a whole family from the affliction. A homoeopathic chemist in Edinburgh had, some years ago, sulphur balls which he sold for cramp.

6

The Stone in Scottish Folk-Medicine

[From *Caledonian Medical Journal* 8 (1909–11), 410–15]

The accompanying photograph shows a large stone, hollowed out by natural processes, in the bed of the Aberdeenshire Dee, between Dinnet and Cambus-o'-May. It is known locally as 'The Deil's Needle.' The aperture is now visible from bank to bank; but, until the occurrence of a big spate some years ago, it lay parallel with the course of the river.

Apart from its peculiar appearance, its interest is due to the fact of a folk-belief (fading like many others, and even now not generally known locally) in its efficacy as a cure for sterility in the female. If a barren woman crawl through the stone she is held thereby to have increased her chances of pregnancy.

Sympathetic and imitative magic are, of course, at work here; the act of birth being imitated by the passage of the devotee through the stone. It is stated to have been so used within comparatively recent years. The 'Holed Stone' and the 'Crick Stone' in Cornwall are associated with a similar folk-belief.

Keeping first to imitative birth, we find it used for the child as well as the mother. Hope[1] refers to a granite block in Cornwall in the same parish as that in which St. Madron's spring is situated. In the centre of this block is a hole. It is known in Cornish as 'Man-an-Tol,' *i.e.,* 'The Stone of the Hole.' Its name in English is 'The Creeping Stone.' Sickly children were at one time passed through the hole a certain number of times, in the belief that a cure would follow. The same writer also refers to St. Paul's Well, in the parish of Fyvie, Aberdeenshire. 'Close to the well were the ruins of an old church. One of its stones was supported on other two with a space below. It went by the name of 'The Shargar Stone'—'Shargar' signifying a weakly child. The stone in this instance got its name from the

---

1. *Holy Wells.* Quoted by Mackinlay, *Folklore of Scottish Lochs and Springs.*

custom in the district of mothers passing their ailing children through the space below the stone in the belief that whatever hindered their growth would be thereby removed.' Here, then, we again have the new birth idea.[1]

Martin[2] has a reference, unfortunately without sufficient detail, to a stone 'for providing speedy delivery to a woman in travail.' This was on the island of Rona, where, again to quote Martin, 'there is a chapel dedicated to St. Ronan, fenced with a stone wall round; and they take care to keep it neat and clean, and sweep it every day. There is an altar in it, in which there is a big plank of wood, about 10 feet in length, every foot has a hole in it, and in every hole a stone to which the natives ascribe several virtues.' One of these stones had the obstetrical value mentioned, but we have no reference as to technique. Quite possibly these stones had black magic virtues as well as white, as in the case of similar stones at Kilmoon in Ireland. These stones lie on a dry stone wall under an old wind-bent tree at the Holy Well. Some fifteen or sixteen years ago a farmer was prosecuted by a beggar woman for beating and laming her. In defence he urged that 'she swore to turn the stones of Kilmoon' against him.[3] It was believed that if a person went fasting to the place and did seven rounds 'against the sun,' turning each stone in the same unlucky direction, the mouth of the person against whom the stones were turned would be twisted under his ear, and his face permanently distorted. The magistrate regarded the farmer's act as one of *bonâ fide* defence. How the stone that caused 'speedy delivery to a woman in travail' was used we do not, as I have said, know. But in that extraordinary miscellany of medical myths, *The Poor Man's Physician or The Receits of the Famous John Moncrieff of Tippermalloch*, we find as the two last of twelve expedients to help 'hard childbirth,' that these are given: '11. Eagle-stone or Load-stone or Storax and the rest, fastened to the hips. 12. See that the woman have no precious stones about her, either in rings or otherwise.' And in abortion we have the following recommendation: 'These things which are accounted, by a secret property of their Nature, to retain

---

1. Dr. Greig, of Fyvie, who kindly made local inquiry regarding this, states that the well is now a watering-place for cattle. All that an old resident can recollect is that 'many stones were there, and a well. By leaving a token (coin or pin) there you got what you wished for on the first Sunday of May.'
2. *Description of the Western Islands* (*circa* 1695).
3. *Folklore*, vol. xxii, p. 50.

a child in the womb, are, an Eagle-stone worn about the neck, a Load-stone applied to the navel; Corals, Jaspers, Smaragds, Bones found in the Hearts of Stags, or such like, worn under the arm-pits or hanged about the neck.'

The popular interest in and respect for stones is world-wide. Almost every travelled boulder has, locally, some history, usually not unconnected with athletic feats on the part of 'The Auld Smith Himsel'.' The 'yird-fast stane' is a recognised factor in Scots folk-medicine. Water collected in the hollow of such a stone is efficacious as a cure in whooping-cough; and an oath taken, or a bargain made, over it is binding.

Gregor, in his *Folklore of the North-East of Scotland*, mentions *Clach-na-ban* ('stone of the woman'), a huge granite rock on the top of Meall-ghaineaih,[1] a hill on the east side of Glenavon, as also possessing an obstetrical interest. Near the top of this rock a hollow has been scooped out by the influence of the weather somewhat in the shape of an armchair. Women about the time of their confinement ascended the hill, scaled the rock, and seated themselves in the hollow, under the belief that such an act secured a speedy and successful birth. Unmarried women also made pilgrimage to it, in hopes that such an act would have the effect of bringing husbands to them. Milne,[2] from a philological point of view, throws cold water on the belief, wishing to show that the *clach ban* is 'the white stone.' He says, 'An absurd story attached to the stone assumes that *ban* is the Ga. pl. of *bean*, "woman", making *clach bhan* mean the "stone of women."' But folk-belief existed long before philology, and, quite possibly, may long survive it. That the stone was so believed in there is no doubt.

Stone-worship in Scotland, 'the worship of stones as the embodiment of nature deities,' must have existed to a wide extent as well as over Europe. Lubbock, in his *Origin of Civilisation*, points out that in Western Europe during the Middle Ages there are several instances of denunciation of stone-worship, proving its deep hold on the people. Mackinlay[3] mentions that as late as the seventeenth century the Presbytery of Dingwall sought to suppress, among other practices of heathen origin, that of rendering reverence to stones, the stones in question having been consulted as to future events.

---

1. Thus Gregor. But Milne (*Geology of Strathavon*) gives *Meall-na-gaineimh*, 'sandy hill.'
2. *Geology of Strathavon*, p. 33.
3. *Loc. cit.*

When we consider the permanence of a large rock or boulder as a feature in the landscape, its power of successfully withstanding storms before which trees and other landmarks go, and the peculiar shape of some rocks, suggesting the human form or some part of it—the face, leg, pudenda, &c.—it is not to be wondered at that the primitive mind, more especially, perhaps, in its phallic developments, was early led to regard stone with veneration.

Napier, in his *Folklore in the West of Scotland*, says that a belief in the virtues of precious stones existed in his youth. Each stone had its own symbolic meaning and its own peculiar power to protect its possessors from sickness. This belief existed widely amongst the ancients. But when, in time past, the rural population of Scotland required such protection they had, of necessity, recourse to other stones than the topaz, the diamond, the amethyst, and the emerald. The 'elf-shot' (flint arrow-head) was a favourite, and protected against all evil-eye influence or witchcraft, if not allowed to touch the ground. Fifty years ago an old man in the parish of Banchory Devenick, Kincardineshire, was in possession of such a talisman, and, while willing to show it to youthful visitors, always carefully held his own hands below theirs in case of its being accidentally dropped. Amongst many other objects of a similar nature in the museum of the Society of Antiquaries of Scotland is an oval-shaped pebble measuring $2^1/2$ inches in its greatest diameter. This was kept suspended in a small bag with a red string (the red string, of course, having also its special protective virtues) round the neck of an old Forfarshire farmer who died at the age of 84.

Mackinlay, in dealing with the subject of charm-stones in and out of water, mentions that Martin refers to a certain stone in Arran called *Baul Muluy, i.e.,* 'Molingus, his Stone Globe.' It was green, and about the size of a goose's egg. Used by the islanders when great oaths were to be sworn, it was also employed to disperse an enemy. When thrown amongst the front ranks the opposing army would retreat in confusion. In this way the Macdonalds were said to have gained many a victory. (Would they had carried it when they met bloody Cumberland!)

When not in use, the *Baul Muluy* was carefully kept wrapped up in cloth. Are there other records of the existence of this stone? And is it known what became of it? In addition to its usefulness in jurisprudence and war, the *Baul Muluy* cured stitches in the side. 'When the patient would not recover, the stone withdrew from the bed of its own accord.'

'Curing-stones' are still in use (more or less guardedly) in connection with irregular veterinary medicine, being either rubbed over the affected part and washed in water, or dipped in water and the animal then washed with it or made to drink it.

'Cramp-stones,' for curing cramp in cows, and the *lapis hecticus* for 'consumption' in man and beast were in use till recent years in Skye. This last stone was made red hot, cooled in water or milk, and the liquid given to the patient to drink.

Reference was made by a writer in a previous number of the *Caledonian Medical Journal* to the curing-stones at Killin, kept at a mill there. Mackinlay says that 'whenever a new mill was built to replace the old one a niche was made in the wall for their reception. They are some seven or eight in number. The largest of them weighs 8 lb. 10 oz. . . . On the saint's day (the 9th of January) it was customary, till not very long ago,[1] for the villagers to assemble at the mill and place a layer of straw below the stones.' He then goes on to refer to a reference by Tylor in *Primitive Culture* to the Norwegian habit in certain mountainous districts of preserving round stones, washing them every Thursday evening ('which seems to show that they represented Thor'), smearing them with butter before the fire, and laying them on fresh straw. At certain times of the year they were steeped in ale that they might bring luck and comfort to the house. Whether the straw bed of the Tayside stones was gained from Thor-worship who can tell? When we consider that no part of our land can boast a pure race, and that even the Highlands has a blend of Danes, Picts, Gaels, Norsemen, and Saxons, it is little wonder if popular custom becomes a palimpsest, and requires some scraping before we get to the original meaning.

---

1. This was written in 1893.

7
Queries, Notes, and Extracts

[From *Caledonian Medical Journal* 9 (1912–14), 46-8, 222–3]

An obstetric girdle

Brand, in his *Popular Antiquities*, under 'Child-bearing Customs,' says, 'According to Henry, the ancient Britons, in the event of a birth being attended with any difficulty, put a girdle made for the purpose about the woman in labour, which they imagined gave immediate and effectual relief. Girdles of this kind were, till lately, carefully preserved in many families in the Highlands of Scotland. They were impressed with numerous mystical figures, and the ceremony of binding them about the waist was accompanied with words and gestures, indicating the great antiquity of the custom and its original derivation from the Druids.'

Can any member of the Society give a further reference to such a belt? Or is there one now known to be extant? The putting on of such a belt at such a time is contrary to the general popular idea of unloosing all clothing, knots, hair-bindings, &c., during labour. And behind it there is not, apparently, the idea of mechanical aid, as in the case of the Zulu habit[1] of tying a grass rope round the parturient woman's middle, 'to keep the infant from slipping up again.'

A highland bonesetter

The following cutting from a northern newspaper is not without interest. The dwelling on the necessity of heredity[2] in the matter, and the naive references to the effect of opposition on his 'practice,' are worth noting:

> Mr. Donald M'Conachie, farmer, Haugh of Elchies, Knock-ando, died yesterday. Deceased had been in indifferent health for about two years. He was born at Oldhall, Easter Elchies, in 1829, the year of the great Morayshire floods, and was 82 years of age. He was the first cousin of the late Mr. James

---

1. *British Medical Journal*, 28th October, 1911, p. 1144.
2. 'The Scottish Bonesetter,' *Caledonian Medical Journal*, January, 1902.

M'Conachie, Haugh of Elchies, the famous bonesetter, whom he succeeded as the tenant of the farm in 1875.

His father was a very skilful bonesetter in his day, and deceased not only acquired the gift of bonesetting by heredity, but also by assisting his cousin James with his numerous patients. After the latter's death in 1875, Mr. M'Conachie had an extensive practice as a bonesetter, and on a Saturday he would have had as many as from 20 to 30 patients. He also attended patients at a distance, travelling as far south as Glasgow and as far north as Forres, as far east as Fraserburgh and as far west as Badenoch.

Since Mr. James M'Arthur, however, commenced bone-setting on the opposite side of the river the number of his patients greatly decreased, and within recent years, owing to the infirmities of old age, he had practically to retire. He was a splendid hand at treating sprains and dislocations. He was a successful farmer, and was much respected by his neighbours. His wife predeceased him many years ago.

Folk-mediciners

In the graveyard of St. Fergus, Aberdeenshire, is a tombstone with the inscription, 'Here lyes the corps of George Purdie, sometime gardener at Inverugie, who departed this life the 11 of June, 1738, aged 73 years.' Henderson[1] says of him, 'George Purdie, besides being skilled as a gardener, attained considerable fame as 'an herbalist and district leech.' Large numbers of people waited upon him periodically for the purpose of being bled and treated to his innocuous herb ale and other concoctions. The site of his garden at the back of the Castle (of Inverugie) is pointed out; and in it herbs are still found.'

Another folk-mediciner of the same type, and of perhaps wider notoriety, was Adam Donald,[2] 'The Prophet of Bethelnie.' He was 'a deformed eccentric native of the parish, known by the familiar titles of Satey, Prophet, and Doctor. He conducted an extensive business, not only as a doctor and herbalist, but as an exponent of the powers of divination. His ointments and medicines were prepared by himself from herbs gathered in the country, and it was firmly believed by the credulous that he could give an infallible remedy for every ailment under the sun. As a necromancer he frequented

---

1. *Aberdeenshire Epitaphs and Inscriptions*, vol. i, p. 227.
2. *Loc. cit.,* vol. i, p. 49.

the lonely graveyards, professing to get disclosures and advice from departed spirits. When an article was stolen or went amissing, and when misfortune or loss occurred, who could so well reveal the secret, or prescribe the remedy as the redoubtable prophet? When so consulted he took care to give cautious, general answers, capable of various interpretations, and having private facilities at his command for knowing something of the history of the applicants, he was able to impress them so favourably that persons from all parts of the shire repaired to him. With the fishing population he was extremely popular, and his wonderful cures and still more wonderful revelations were retailed and multiplied to an extraordinary extent. His usual consultation fee was sixpence, and, small as this sum may seem, he gathered as much as enabled him to win the affections of a good-looking country maiden, whom he ultimately married. After a time a daughter was born, but as she grew up she laughed at the imposition practised by her father, and divulged the secret of it. After this, business fell away considerably, and poor Adam spent his latter days in anything but affluent circumstances. A picture of him was painted, and he expressed the desire that the following lines, which he had composed, might be placed at the foot of it:

> Time doth all things devour,
> And time doth all things waste;
> And we waste time,
> And so we are at last!

He was born in 1703, and died in 1780.'

The Couvade in Japan

I find that the interesting custom known in Europe as the couvade exists in a modified degree in Japan. In some fishing communities the wife usually goes to the home of her parents to be confined, but whether or no, the husband is not permitted to be present at the birth of the child, but is obliged by 'ancient custom' to keep indoors for one week. This period is called *Nana-ya* or Seven Nights, which clearly intimates a fixed period for this compulsory housekeeping. Among the Ainus, as Batchelor I think was the first to observe, the couvade is an established custom. The father stays at home for one week, and occasionally takes to his bed or rests like an invalid. Sometimes he spends this interval in a neighbour's house, but the idea of resting is prominent. Batchelor tells us that this performance is called *yainnu-nuke*, and that it signifies 'comforting,' or 'blessing,' or 'resting oneself quietly.' On the morning of the seventh day he is said to 'Shotki chupu,' *i.e.*, 'fold up his bed.' On this day he returns to

[53]

his own hut. But even then he must abide quietly at home for another six days. It is evident that in both these cases we have substantially the same custom, which may be taken as a vestige of sympathetic magic, connecting the present with the days of the matriarchate. In the Japanese form of this custom the return of the wife to her parents' house is decidedly reminiscent of the separate establishment, if not of the matriarchate. NEIL GORDON MUNRO, M.B., in *Prehistoric Japan.*

8

Folk-Medicine in the Report of the Highlands and Islands Medical Service Committee

[From *Folklore* 24 (1913), 383–4]

Paragraph 21 of this Report reads thus: *'Primitive Customs and Habits.* In some parts of the Highlands and Islands there still remains a belief in inherited skill and traditional "cures." And, as might be expected, we found that this obtains the more firmly the more difficult it is to get proper medical attendance.'

A witness from the remote island of Rona (Skye), which a doctor rarely visits, was particularly interesting in a description in Gaelic of some of the various 'cures' which in default or disregard of medical advice are frequently resorted to. He told, for example, of a 'cure' recently applied in the case of an epileptic. A black cock was buried alive beneath the spot where the patient had had the first attack of epilepsy. He also described the successful treatment of a woman suffering from the *tinneas an righ* ('king's evil,' *i.e.*, bone or gland tuberculosis) by a seventh son to whom she had gone all the way to the island of Scalpay, Harris.

Referring to the prevalence of this form of treatment Dr. Tolmie, South Harris, says: 'When they have bone disease they use the old remedies. There was a man suffering from keratitis and he was not getting well. It is a difficult disease to cure in an old person. He was not getting on, and I had to go over one very wild day to see him, and when I arrived he was away from home—it was a fearful day—and he had to drive nine miles and walk about another six to an old lady at Licisto. The old lady made up some rhyme, and mixed some grasses with water and sand, and sung. He came back and said he was a little better. The seventh son is supposed to be able to cure such diseases. I know of one case of a person who had a carbuncle on the back of his neck, and it did not heal, and he got a seventh son to come to his house, and every night for a long time he put cold water on it and a sixpence round his neck. It is in such a field of ignorant

[55]

faith that the "skilly" woman can practise all her arts at will and with greatest danger when she is most in demand—and that is, in cases of maternity.'

Paragraph 57 reads: 'The persistence of the traditional "cures" and superstitious practices in remote districts referred to in par. 21 is undoubtedly due largely to the want of medical attendance.'

[From *Caledonian Medical Journal* 13 (1926–28), 70–6, 85–102, 153–63, 231–7, 259–68, 375–81; 14 (1929–31), 20–7]

9
Introductory

Within the last thirty years several papers have appeared in the *Caledonian Medical Journal* dealing directly or indirectly with Scottish folk-medicine, and founding on these and on notes which I have made over the same period, I think it is possible in a short series of articles to bring together a fair amount of information on the subject. In a Society such as ours, with a membership thoroughly representative of country practice in all parts of Scotland, many must be able, if they so desire, to send in information on folk-beliefs bearing on medical practice, and such information would be warmly welcomed and duly acknowledged. No note is too small to be of value, and the post card is suggested as a ready method of 'doing it now.'

Excuses are not needed at the present day for dealing seriously with folk-lore as a branch of anthropology—that branch of it which treats of the mental and spiritual side of humanity. And the department of folk-medicine has a special claim upon the attention of the medical practitioner, making up as it does no small part of the superstition and ignorance against which he has frequently to war in the course of his day's work. Yet, in many cases the newly-fledged graduate leaves his university without knowing even of the existence of folk-medicine. Such at least was my own experience in 1890; for some time thereafter I collected popular medical beliefs from the lips of the country people amongst whom I was working before I was aware that it was a subject with a considerable literature of its own; and although this may be a confession of ignorance to start with, it may also serve, to some extent, as a guarantee of original research.

That he will have to fight against ignorant and superstitious customs and practices the young practitioner knows well enough; he has learnt that fact in his dispensary work. What he does not at first recognise is how carefully organised these are, nor the age and deep-rooted strength of beliefs which have been handed down orally from generation to generation. To attempt, therefore, to deal a knock-down blow in an off-hand way to such beliefs is an impossible task; they have lived too long to be easily killed.[1] The man who scoffs openly at what his hearers hold to be indisputable truth sanctioned by age exposes himself to the risk of being held unlearned and unskilful; whereas, as Hartland says,[2] 'The more perfect your interest in and sympathy with them [*i.e.*, the peasantry and uneducated classes] the more completely you can identify yourself with their mode of thought, and the greater your influence for good upon them.' For one cannot too early recognise that the same belief or the same 'cure' is constantly cropping up; that one is not dealing with the individual vivid imagination of the garrulous old woman who repeats it, but that she is a retailer and not a manufacturer. And I would therefore plead that, apart altogether from its scientific interest, a knowledge of folk-medicine is of distinct practical value, more especially perhaps to the country practitioner, and certainly at times to the medical jurist as explaining the otherwise inexplicable.

It is difficult, of course, to separate by a hard and fast line the present from the past; it is not easy to say what is really believed and what is merely regarded with sympathy as an 'old frait.' And in what follows I wish to make no claim that the habits, customs, beliefs, and superstitions which are detailed are in any sense universal throughout Scotland. How far-spread they are fellow-members of our Society can help me to say. All that can be definitely said of them is that they still crop up here and there with a singular persistency; that even those whom a compulsory 'education' has taught to 'know better' have, at the back of their minds, a lingering faith in it all; and that this faith may have a distinct bearing on the progress of an illness. Within the

---

1. In 1773, Mr. McQueen, the minister of Raasay, complacently informed Boswell that he had destroyed the local belief in charms and witch-craft by occasional sermons on the subject. 'He told us,' says Boswell, 'that since he came to be minister of the parish where he now is, the belief of witch-craft and charms was very common, insomuch that he had many prosecutions before his session against women, for having by these means carried off the milk from people's cows. He disregarded them, and there is not now the least vestige of that superstition.' But Boswell evidently took the old gentleman's word for it; he does not give us the pew's opinion of the Raasay pulpit; and careful enquiry in that parish to-day would show the old beliefs have long survived the worthy old minister.
2. *Folk-lore, what it is and what is the good of it.*

[58]

last twelve years I attended a woman whose gloomy view of her condition and her chance of recovery was quite out of proportion to the severity of her disease; and this I found was due to the fact that, shortly before, she had broken a mirror—an accident which condemned her to ill-luck for seven years.[1] An illuminative flash is also thrown on this mode of thought by the remark once made to me by an old Fife fisherman. I had been talking to him about the prevalent custom of skippers of fishing boats 'treating' certain old men—'the canny men'—of the village whose goodwill is held to be valuable before the boats sail. 'Of course,' said my friend, 'it's a heap o' blethers.' And then after a pause he added, 'But a' the same, I've kent us get some extra gude shots when the richt fowk was mindit!'

Black,[2] in his interesting work on the subject, defines folk-medicine as 'comprehending charms, incantations, and traditional habits and customs relative to the preserving of health and the cure of disease, practised now or formerly at home or abroad.' Charms and incantations are not common amongst the Lowland Scots, and to get them nowadays one would need to go into the more remote glens and islands amongst the Gaelic-speaking part of the population. The chief repositors of folk-medicine are—and always have been—the older women of the hamlet, village, or town, and, in recognising this fact, we must also bear in mind the accredited part that woman played in the leech-craft of the past. As Neuberger[3] says, 'Woman was the first physician.' In these far off and ruder days she usually had some knowledge of the dressing of wounds when man meddled only with the making of them, and she had always some knowledge of herbal simples. The lady of the 'big house' had her still-room whence she dispensed her cordials; had the medical books of the time dedicated to her on occasion; had even perhaps some of her own recipes incorporated in them.[4]

How much present-day folk-medicine is genuinely oral and traditional? It is hard to say, because, even now it is still receiving contributions from half understood 'health lectures,' 'medical'

---

1. Common throughout Europe; in Picardy, extended to the breaking of a drinking-glass.
2. *Folk-Medicine.*
3. *History of Medicine.*
4. William Bulleyn (Elizabethan era), in his *Book of Simples,* says, 'The Lady Tailor of Huntingdonshire and the Lady Darrel of Kent had many precious medicines to comfort the sight, and to heale wounds withal, and were well

articles in the lay press, and physiological explanations in the elementary schools. Much of the older lore must have trickled down from the monasteries, while such books as *The Poor Man's Physician* and *A Thousand Notable Things* collected together and again scattered abroad a whole museum of curious lore partly gathered orally and partly drawn from the now out-of-date medical ideas of their day. All through the past there has been a constant give-and-take between the orthodox and the unorthodox; for when the former fails the sufferer and his friends readily betake themselves to the latter, which usually has, as an additional attraction, a spice of the supernatural about it. Thirty years ago an old woman showed me a curious and evil-smelling 'sau,' of which she said, 'My grandmother got the cure frae a man wantin' the legs and drawn aboot by twa black dogs'—probably an ex-serviceman of the Peninsular campaigns. Here you have the necessary touch of the uncanny; advice from a man *with* legs and drawn about by a horse (or propelled by petrol) one can get any day, but the other gentleman's knowledge must have been a 'gift.' As Clifford Allbutt[1] says, 'Folk-medicine, whether independent or still engaged with religion and custom belongs to all peoples and all times, including our own. It is not the appanage of a nation; it is rooted in man, in his needs and in his primeval observations, instinct, reason, and temperament. . . . To folk-medicine, doubt is unknown: it brings the peace of security.' Hence the vogue of the potato in your pocket for rheumatism, the 'electrical' belts (with no electricity in them), the ring on your finger or the plate on your sole (both of which 'draw out the poison from your system' as well as the money from your purse). And of these the ring alone has a poetic touch about it. One recollects how in the ballad of 'Young Ronald' the lady gives her lover, setting out for the war, a talisman and

> Likewise a ring, a royal thing,
>   The virtue it is good,
> If ony o' your men be hurt
>   It sune will stem your blude.

---

seene in herbs.' Take also Markham's *The English Housewife, containing the Complete Women's Skill in Physic, Surgery, Cookery, Distillations, Perfumes, Brewing, &c., with Curious Receipts* (London 16—); *vide* also Paul's *Past and Present in Aberdeenshire* for the minister's part in more recent years as 'mediciner' to the Parish.

1. *British Medical Journal*, 20th November, 1909.

Another ring, a royal thing
  Whose virtue is well known,
As lang's this ring's your body on
  Your blude shall ne'er be drawn.

These were the days when 'gay ladyes'—such as the Lady of
Branksome Tower— could heal by other charms than their own.
But nowadays the craft, such as it is, has descended into hands more
plebeian, and become specialised, more particularly in the dangerous
sphere of obstetrics. And so, as we are dealing as far as possible
with the survivals of Scottish folk-medicine, we may first consider
the subject as manifested in menstruation, conception, pregnancy,
labour, the puerperium, and the child.

10
Menstruation

The onset of menstruation in Lowland Scotland is variously described as 'comin' the length o' a woman,' 'turnin' no-weel o' hersel','
'alterin', or 'seein' her ain.' A woman who has missed a period will say that 'her ain has left her,' and when this happens finally she is said to be 'past the change.' In cessation of the lochia the patient is said to 'be dried up,'[1] while a woman who menstruates during lacation is called a 'green nurse.' There is a belief[2] that such a 'green nurse' should not, under any circumstances, suckle any male child, but that it does not matter if the child at the breast be a female. The underlying idea is probably that which will be dealt with later on, viz., the uncleanness of menstruation where contact with the male is concerned.

As regards menstruation, it is steadfastly believed by the folk that any substance, such as jam or preserves, made by a menstruating woman 'will not keep,' but will, for a certainty, 'go bad.' I have been told in all seriousness[3] that a newly-killed pig had been rendered quite unfit for food through being handled by a woman 'in her courses,' subsequent curing processes being useless through the rapid decomposition which set in.[4]

Similar examples might be multiplied, and the belief is universal in England as regards all meat.[5] Here, of course, we have traces of Mosaic law and that of Islam. We can follow the idea further in the taboo imposed by many savage tribes on their females at

---

1. In India, puerperal fever is called 'the dry disease.'
2. Aberdeenshire, Fife.
3. Fife.
4. The same belief exists in Brunswick: Frazer, *Golden Bough* (1st edition, vol. iii, p. 224). In the AEgean Islands a menstruous women may not come into an olive-press, or into a garden, or enter a boat. *Folk-lore* (vol. xviii, p. 330; vide also Deuteronomy, xxii, 9–14, and I Samuel, xxi, 5).
5. *Folk-lore*, vol. xx, p. 348.

the onset of puberty.[1] Zoroaster taught that the menstrual flow is the work of Ahriman, or the Devil, and a woman so suffering was not to be allowed to eat as much as she wished, 'as the strength she might acquire would accrue to the fiends.' For the same reason as the Australian black fellow kills the gin who dares to sleep on his blanket, it is believed by the folk in Scotland that a man who has connection with a woman in her courses runs the risk of venereal disease. Prophylaxis is obtained by washing the penis with his own urine immediately after coitus, and this is held to be efficacious in all cases where the male fears he has run the risk of contracting *lues venerea*.

But the deeply ingrained dread which primitive man has of menstruous blood is universal.[2] The boys of the Australian blacks are told from infancy that the mere sight of it makes them prematurely grey-headed and senile. A menstruous woman must not go near men nor touch anything they use; must not eat fish nor even go near water, lest the fish be frightened and fishing rendered impossible; must not even fetch water to the camp. Severe chastisement or even death is inflicted as penalty for breach of these rules. Amongst some South African tribes the women, in case menstruation should come on them suddenly, are not allowed to enter the camp by the men's paths. Some such idea is at the root of the Scottish miners' objection to meet the pit-head women when going to their work in the morning; it is considered to be of ill omen, and apt to presage accident to the man or his 'place' in the pit.[3] According to the Talmud, a woman at the beginning of a period passing between two men causes one of them to die; at the end of a period, causes a severe quarrel between them. In many parts of Europe menstruous blood is held to have miraculous virtues, and entered into the composition of various love-potions and charms.[4]

---

1. Frazer, *G.B.*, vol, i, p. 326
2. *Ibid.,* vol, iii, p. 222.
3. The reason of the further belief that the most unlucky woman of all to meet is an 'auld wife wi' a mutch' (a person past the climacteric) is probably fear of evil eye and witch-craft influence.
4. It was probably some such charm that Gregor (*Folk-lore of the North-East of Scotland*) refers to in speaking of love-charms when he says, 'There was another method talked of, but it was of such a nature that it must be passed over in silence.'

11
Conception

The influence of sympathetic and imitative magic[1] upon the determination of sex enters largely even at the present day in Scotland into popular ideas regarding conception.

In one case where the mother[2] had had several female children and was anxious for a son, she expected at the next confinement that the child would be a boy, because at the time of conception marital relations had been carried out with the pillows at the foot of the bed, and the husband keeping his cap on. To anyone not interested in folk-lore this seems merely ridiculous; but the idea is quite apparent. If children of the female sex had been hitherto begotten in the ordinary position of the bed, reversing its arrangement would tend to reverse the sex; while the idea of virility and activity suggestive of the male, was maintained by the man keeping on part of his outdoor working garb. This latter idea of work-a-day dress suggesting and influencing masculinity was more marked in another case where the child (illegitimate and not the first) was a male. The mother on hearing of its sex said in a matter-of-fact tone, 'It couldna but be a boy; it was gotten amang the green girss

1. 'Sympathetic magic plays a large part in most systems of superstition. Manifold as are the applications of this crude philosophy - the fundamental principles on which it is based are reducible to two – first, that like produces like, or that an effect resembles its cause; and second, that things which have once been in contact, but have ceased to be so, continue to act on each other as if the contact still persisted. From the first of these principles the savage infers that he can produce any desired effect merely by imitating it; from the second he concludes that he can influence at pleasure and at any distance any person of whom, or anything of which he possesses a particle. Magic of the latter sort, resting as it does on the belief in a certain secret sympathy which unites indissolubly things that have once been connected with one another, may approximately be termed sympathetic. Magic of the former kind may be described as imitative or mimetic.' (Frazer, *G.B.*, vol. i, p. 10.)
2. Aberdeenshire.

(grass) by a man wi' his boots on.' And on another occasion[1] I heard the reason of the male sex of the child attributed to the fact that it was 'gotten under a green tree.' In Scottish ballad literature the children begotten and born 'in gude greenwood' are invariably of the male sex.[2] Apart altogether from the question of sex, intercourse carried out on the ground, and better under a tree, is popularly supposed to be efficacious in a barrenness, as trees are supposed to have a fertilising effect both on women and cattle.[3] In an old Scottish book of popular medicine[4] (a book which had a wide circulation in its day, and, as a collection of folk-beliefs doubtless spread afresh many that were being forgotten) we find sympathetic and imitative magic ideas well marked. Impotency was cured by the gall of a boar[5] anointed on the penis. Satyrion root 'holden in the hand' during coitus was recommended. 'If the woman shall eat the great and hard stone of Satyrion she shall conceive a male child, and if she shall eat the lesser stone, a female child.' And again, 'juice and seed of male mercury having round seeds hanging in pairs, in form of testicles, anointed on the woman's privities cause her to conceive male children.' So in the Torres Straits Islands[6] a woman will press to her abdomen a fruit resembling the male organs of generation, which she then passes to another woman who has borne nothing but boys. The Chinese woman of the present-day wears[7] 'male money' to procure the much desired male offspring. This is a coin inscribed on the one side 'health and long life,' on the other a fir tree and the mythical

---

1. Fifeshire.
2. *E.g.*, in 'The Earl of Mar's daughter':
    Then he has staid in bower wi' her
        For sax lang years and ane,
    Til sax young sons to him she bare
        And the seventh she's brought hame.
3. In the Isle of Man, on May Day, branches of trees, especially of the mountain ash (the rowan), were strewn on the thresholds (*Folk-lore of the Isle of Man*, p. 146). Everyone in Scotland knows the virtue of the rowan as a protective against witch-craft and evil-eye influence and to bring good luck. 'Luck' in marriage always meant one thing amongst the folk — fertility.
4. *The Poor Man's Physician, or, The Receits of the famous John Moncrieff of Tippermalloch*. The copy from which I quote is the third edition, Edinburgh, MDCCXXXI.
5. The boar and the goat in popular belief stand for lust and procreative power.
6. Frazer, *G.B.,* vol. i, p. 20.
7. *Folk-lore*, vol. xiv, p. 295.

beast 'Kylin,' which appeared to the mother of Confucius before his birth.

At the present day in Scotland the folk-idea prevails that the right testicle is concerned with the production of male children, and the left with female. It is believed that having one testicle or the other bandaged up during coitus (according to the wishes of the parents as regards the sex) will successfully determine the issue. The right and left idea is further seen in the belief that if the woman after intercourse goes to sleep on the right (or left) side the future child will be a boy (or girl). Similarly, women who habitually sleep on the right side are held to be more apt to bear male children, and *vice versa*. Another method, if female children be desired, is to place an axe under the bed. The idea here is obvious. An old Scottish rural euphemism for the female pudenda is 'the bittie the axe fell on,' and we can also note the old English expression of 'the wound.' These beliefs are now chiefly referred to jocularly; the 'handy-wife' remarking on the birth of a girl, 'Ye maun hae had the axe under the bed,' just as in the case of a male child's arrival she will say, 'He's had his cap on this time.'

Further beliefs in the matter of sex are that the child will be male or female (1) according to whether the father or mother is fonder of the other at the time of conception;[1] (2) that the child will be like the parent who is fonder of the other during pregnancy, the question of sex being left out of account, the reason given being that he (or she) 'looks often at and thinks often o''; and (3) that the child will resemble the parent who 'has the stronger constitution.'

A common folk-saying in Scotland is, 'Any laddie can get a laddie; it tak's a man to get a lassie.' And as regards the determination of sex there is the very curious and prevalent proverb, 'A laddie will lie down in a dirty bed; a lassie in a clean ane.'[2] The reference is to pre-menstrual coitus tending to produce male children, and post-menstrual female. As most practitioners unfortunately know, it is comparatively rare for a woman of the folk to change either the bed-linen or her body-linen until the period is past, the reason given being fear of 'a chill'; and as a result the dirty linen remains in use until the cessation of the monthly flow. Hence the 'clean' and the 'dirty' bed. A variant is, 'A laddie will clean himsel'; a lassie winna':

---

1. *Vide* Lucretius, *De Rerum Natura*, Book IV.
2. It is curious that in many instances this proverb is as determinedly quoted the other way round.

but this is also interpreted by many to mean that a woman can menstruate once or twice after becoming pregnant without damage to the child should it be a boy, but with a bad result should it be a girl. In addition to the 'green tree' and 'green grass' beliefs already mentioned, mimetic magic of the 'new-birth' type is still to be found in Scotland in connection with the cure of barrenness, a condition always looked upon as a curse by our ancestors, in times when the possession of children—especially males—meant power and position for the family and the tribe. In the bed of the River Dee, near Dinnet, Aberdeenshire,[1] is a stone variously known as 'The Split Stone,' 'The Round Stone,' or 'The Deil's Needle.' It is a large stone with a circular hole in it, and it is believed that any barren woman who creeps through this will conceive. The idea is that of simulating the act of birth by her transit through the stone passage, and thereby advantageously affecting her own chance of becoming a mother. The stone is known to have been put to this use within comparatively recent years. And so with 'Clach-na-Bhan' (Stone of the Women), a huge granite rock on the top of Meall-Ghaineaih, a hill on the east side of Glen Avon.[2] 'Near the top of this rock a hollow has been scooped out by the influence of the weather somewhat in the shape of an arm-chair.[3] Women about the time of their accouchement ascended the hill, scaled the rock, and seated themselves in the hollow, under the belief that such an act secured a speedy and successful birth. Unmarried women also made a pilgrimage to it in hopes that such an act would have the effect of bringing husbands to them.' The efficacy of this stone in popular estimation would doubtless be increased by the fact that it was a 'yird-fast' stone, and that water would tend to collect in the seat of the 'arm-chair.' In Brahan Wood, near Dingwall, there is a stone which is said to be a 'knocking-stone.' Barren women were accustomed to sit on it in close contact for the purpose of becoming fertile.[4] To similar uses are put the tree called 'The Eye of the Needle,' on the Island of Innisfallen, Killarney; 'The Holed Stone,' near Lanyon, in Cornwall; and 'The Crick Stone' (a forked

---

1. *Vide* 'The Stone in Scottish Folk-Medicine,' *Caledonian Medical Journal*, vol. vii, p. 410 [see above].
2. Can any local member procure a photograph of this stone?
3. Gregor, *Folk-Lore of the North-East of Scotland*, p. 42.
4. *Folk-Lore*, vol. xxix, p. 254. Can more information, a photograph and further description, with measurements, of this stone be secured by any member of the Society?

stone) also in Cornwall.

And just as the unmarried woman might secure a husband by sitting on the stone Clach-na-Bhan, where so many women with husbands and offspring had sat, so 'for luck' a barren woman is told to 'tak' a rub' against a pregnant one. On the same principle the stocking of the bride when taken off and flung at the old custom of 'the beddin'' was supposed to mean the married state at no far-off date for the person whom it struck.[1]

Besides stones, various springs in Scotland were held to cure barrenness in women, notably those of St. Fillan's at Comrie and of St. Mary at Whitekirk and in the Isle of May. Mackinlay[2] points out that many of the Wells dedicated to Our Lady were famous for the cure of female sterility, 'which, in the days when a man's power and influence in the land depended on the number of his clan or tribe, was looked upon as a token of the divine displeasure, and was viewed by the unfortunate spouses with anxious apprehension, dread, doubt, jealousy, and pain.'[3]

---

1. Gregor; see also Allan Ramsay's first supplemental canto to 'Christ's Kirk on the Green':

    The bride was now laid in her bed,
      Her left leg ho' was flung,
    And Geordie Gib was fidging glad
      Because it hit Jean Gun.

2. *Folk-lore of the Scottish Lochs and Springs*, quoting Walker.

3. Dan MacKenzie (*Folk-lore*, vol, xviii, p. 270, art. 'Children and wells') points out that the idea connecting springs or wells with children and the cure of sterility is world-wide. In ancient Greece sterility was cured at the river Elatos in Arcadia, and the Thespian Well at Helicon. The well at Pyna on the Hymettos, near the temple of Aphrodite, possessed the same property; and at Baiae, in ancient Roman times, there were wells resorted to by women for the same reason. The same belief is found in the mythology of India and China in the fertilising power of water; and in Algeria, not far from Constantine, there is a bath beside the well Burmal-ar-rabba, which Jewish and Moorish women have used for ages in the hope of becoming mothers. Certain pools near Jerusalem are employed for the same purpose, and in England there are numerous wells of similar repute. The links binding children and wells are detailed by MacKenzie as follows: '1. Little Children are taken to wells and springs for the cure of disease, and in order to prevent disease. 2. According to the folk-belief of Germany and elsewhere, babies come from wells. 3. The deities of rain and water in many parts of the world were also the deities of fertility and birth. 4. Sterility amongst women is often treated by bathing. 5. The water spirit assumes at times the form of a child or small person. 6. Water spirits show their fondness for children by stealing them. 7. There is a certain amount

of evidence to show that in some parts of the world children used to be sacrificed in water and wells. He also points out that the origin of the connection between water and children, in early times supposed to be actual and physical, in later days mystic only, was two-fold, being based on the two natural facts that children pre-natally actually live in water, and that there is a natural association between fertility and water is seen plainly in the vegetable world.

12

Pregnancy

Pregnancy is frequently dated amongst the folk from 'takkin' a scunner' at some particular article of diet *e.g.*, fish, tea, &c., and an interesting reference to the old tally-stick is got in the saying regarding a woman who is 'oot' in the calculation of her date, that 'she maun hae lost her nick-stick.'[1] It is a folk-belief that if the lower eyelid is of a blackish or dark blue colour it is a sign of pregnancy,[2] as, for example, in the old song, 'The Bonnie Bruckit Lassie':

> The bonnie bruckit lassie
> She's blue beneath the een.

And again, in 'The Shearin' is no' for You':

> You're blue beneath the e'e,
> Where a maiden shouldna be.

Aristotle mentions this as a sign of pregnancy. Green is also a sign, as in the ballad of 'Young Tamlane':

> When out and came her, fair Janet,
> As green as ony gress.

When a woman becomes pregnant she is variously referred to as

---

1. 'There is another very curious custom which elucidates fully the meaning of the word nick-stick. Every herdsman of cattle has a staff with which he walks, and at times beats his charge if they should get lazy or troublesome, while he drives them to and from the field. If there is a bull in the herd, the herdsman receives a penny called the Bull-penny for which he cuts a notch or nick on his staff, for every cow that has been with the bull. This nick tallys with the account kept by the farmer, who on a certain day collects all the bull-money, which the mistress of the farm claims, as well as the money received for the pigs sold from the farm; with this money and that received for the butter and cheese she must pay the household expences.'--'Old Rites, Ceremonies and Customs of the Inhabitants of the Southern Counties of Scotland.' Collected by T. Wilkie, reprinted from *The History of the Berwickshire Naturalists' Club*, vol. xxiii.
2. 'If under the lower eye-lid the veins be swelled and appear clearly and the eyes be somewhat discoloured, it is a certain sign she is with child.'—Aristotle's *Masterpiece*; *vide* Kinloch's *The Ballad Book*.

'on the road,' 'muckle-boukit,' 'heavy-fittit,' 'gettin' stoot,' or, more plainly but less politely, 'breedin'.' A husband engaging a doctor for his wife's 'doon-lyin'' may delicately refer to the lady as being 'in the wey o' weel-daein'.' Amongst the Gaels[1] the pregnant state is described in the modern language by *leth-tromach*, literally 'half-heavy,' for the earlier stages, and by *trom* (heavy) for the later stage. The word *torrach* is also used; it means 'fruitful,' for *toradh* is the fruit or yield of plants and animals.

Each pregnancy is supposed to cost the mother a tooth, and there is a general belief that when pregnancy commences the husband is afflicted with toothache or some other minor ailment such as indigestion or sickness, which will continue until the birth of the child. This is a very widespread and deep-rooted belief. Some thirty years ago[2] a man came to me to have a carious molar extracted. When the operation was over he remarked in all earnestness, 'I'm feared she's bye wi't again, doctor. That teeth's been yarkin' awa' the last fourteen days and it's aye been the wey wi' me a' the time she's carryin' them.' Another patient assured me that her husband 'aye bred alang wi' her' when she was pregnant; and that it was the persistence of toothache in her adult son which led her to the (correct) suspicion that he had placed her in a fair way of becoming a grandmother. Continued proximity of the two parents is not required, only the fact that the woman is pregnant to the man; for the girl in this case resided miles from her lover. In the North-East of Scotland[3] it was believed that the one who rose first on the morning after the marriage carried all the pains and sorrows of child-bearing. The sympathy thus created between the health of husband, wife, and child brings us in touch with the underlying idea of the *couvade*. In *Aucassin and Nicolete* (*circa* 1130),[4] when the hero in search of his lost lady comes to the land of Torelore he asks for the King and is told he is 'in child-bed.' On interviewing the monarch,

> Quoth the King 'I am brought to bed
> Of a fair son, and anon

---

1. H. Cameron Gillies, M.D., 'Gaelic names of diseases and diseased states,' *Caledonian Medical Journal*, vol. iii, p. 242.
2. In Fife; common throughout Scotland. The other day in Dundee a young husband, when advised to have a carious and painful tooth extracted, said it was no use 'as anither would just start, for the wife was gaun to hae a bairn,' adding, 'Ye see it's the married man's toothache.'
3. Gregor, *Folk-Lore of the North-East of Scotland*.
4. 'As done in English by Andrew Lang' (D. Nutt, London).

> When my month is over and gone,
> And my healing fairly done,
> To the Minster will I fare
> And will do my churching there,
> As my father did repair.'

In a note, Lang says that the feigned lying-in of the father may have been either a recognition of paternity, as in the sham birth when Hera adopted Herakles, or that it may have been caused by the belief that the health of the father at the time of the child's birth affected that of the child. But in Scotland we have the sympathy between father, mother, and child commencing long before the birth occurs—dating, in fact, from the commencement of the mother's pregnancy.

While the mother is pregnant various things are forbidden. She must not at any time sit cross-legged as she may thereby cause a cross-birth; nor for the same reason should she sit with folded arms. Here, again, we come across a widespread belief. Frazer[1] states that in the North Celebes, amongst the Toumboulah tribe, the same veto is extended to the husband, who, after a ceremony performed at the fourth or fifth month of pregnancy is forbidden to sit with one leg crossed over the other, or to tie any fast knots. Gregor[2] says that in the North-East of Scotland a cake should not be turned twice on the girdle (an approach to knot tying) by a pregnant woman, for if so, her child would become 'cake-grown,' *i.e.*, bent until the belly rested on the thighs. Sympathetic or imitative magic teaches that by crossing, turning, or tying, a corresponding impediment would be set up in the body of the woman. 'Whether you cross threads in tying a knot, or only cross your legs in sitting at your ease, you are equally, on the principles of sympathetic magic, crossing or thwarting the free causes of things, and your action cannot but check and impede whatever may be going forward in your neighbourhood.' The Romans were fully aware of 'this important truth.' Pliny mentions that to sit beside a pregnant woman, or a patient under medical treatment, with clasped hands is 'to cast a malignant spell over the person; and it is worse still if you nurse your crossed legs with the clasped hands.[3] The stock instance of the dreadful consequences that might flow from doing this was that of Alcmena, who travailed with Hercules for seven days and seven nights, because the goddess, Lucina, sat in front of the house with

---

1. *G.B.*, vol. i, pp. 393–4.
2. 'Kilns, Mills, Millers, Meal and Bread.'
3. Frazer, *G.B.*, loc. cit.

clasped hands and crossed legs, and the child could not be born until the goddess had been beguiled into changing her attitude.'

Black[1] mentions the power believed to be exercised by witches over labour in Scotland. 'Owing to a supposed connection which the witches knew between the relation of husband and wife and the mysterious knot, the bridegroom, formerly in Scotland, and to the present day in Ireland, presents himself occasionally, and in rural districts, before the clergyman with all knots and fastenings on his dress loosened; and the bride, immediately after the ceremony is performed, retires to be undressed, and so rid of the knots.'[2]

Most of us know the common belief that when a boot-lace or an apron-string comes untied the person's lover is thinking of him or her. For as knots are kept tight by the evil thinking of ill-wishers, so are they unloosed by the kindly thoughts of those wishing well to you.

In the old Scottish ballad of 'Willie's Lady'[3] we find the same idea mentioned (and the editor notes that the Danish versions are numerous). Willie has married contrary to the wishes of his witch-mother, and when his wife comes to be confined no progress is made in her labour.

> He's wooed her for her yellow hair,
> But his mother wrought her mickle care,
> And mickle dolour garred her dree,
> For lichter she can never be,
> But in her bower she sits wi' pain
> And Willie mourns o'er her in vain.

All pleading with, and offering of gifts to, the mother are ineffectual, but she is at last circumvented by the sage advice of the household sprite, 'the Belly Blind,' who advises the making of a wax infant and

---

1. *Folk-Medicine*, p. 186.
2. Gordon (*Book of the Chronicles of Keith*, p. 58) mentions that in the eighteenth century before entering the kirk for a marriage every knot and string of the clothing of the bride and bridegroom was unloosed at the back of the kirk, and 'when the wedlock-knot was tied there were many willing helpers to sort petticoats, garters, mutches, neckerchiefs, and shoe-latches.' Conversely, Louandre (*La Sorcellerie*, 1853, p. 73, quoted as footnote, vol, i, p.108, of Navarre Society's edition of *Montaigne's Essays and Letters*) speaks of *les nouements d'aiguillettes*, as they were called, knots tied by someone at a wedding on a strip of leather, cotton, or silk, and which, especially when passed through the wedding ring, were supposed to have the magical effect of preventing a consummation of the marriage until untied.'
3. Child's *Collection of English and Scottish Ballads*.

inviting her to the christening. She, thinking the real child has been born, breaks angrily out with:

> O wha has loosed the nine witch knots
> That was amo' that lady's locks?
> And wha has taen oot the kaims o' care,
> That hangs amo' that lady's hair?
> And wha has loosed her left foot shee
> And looten that lady lichter be?

All this being carefully noted by the anxious husband, he hurries to his wife; and the knots and other obstacles mentioned having been removed, the labour progresses favourably:

> And noo he's gotten a bonny young son
> And mickle grace be him upon.

A prose variant of a similar subject is found in the Highland legend of Allan of the Faggots.[1] This celebrated West Highland freebooter was son of a servant maid who became pregnant by a married man. The man's wife, indignant at his unfaithfulness, got a bone from a witch, which, as long as it was kept, would delay the birth of the child; Allan being thus held in his mother's womb fifteen months beyond the proper time. But the husband made his Fool come home one night pretending intoxication. On being reproved by the lady of the house, he apologised by saying he had been at the servant maid's house, where a child had been born and where he had got a dram that 'went to his head.' The wife, naturally thinking that the witch had deceived her, in her anger threw the bone into the fire, where it disappeared in blue smoke and knocked down the chimney. Allan was thereafter born 'with large teeth.' Campbell also mentions that this 'infernal cantrip' could be played by means of a ball of black worsted thread in a black bag kept at the foot of the witch's weaving loom, where it might not be detected.

Amongst the folk in Scotland the hair during labour is usually undone from its fastenings and allowed to hang loose. Further, in some parts of the country,[2] there is a strong objection, during the puerperium and until the ninth day is past, to the mother raising her hands 'abune the breath' or 'redding' the hair, *i.e.*, combing it and dressing it by confining it in knots or pleats. Nine[3] is the popular

---

1. Campbell, *Witchcraft and Second Sight in the Scottish Highlands*.
2. Fife.
3. Salmon, in his *Dispensatory*, recommends 'nine rats' turds' to be swallowed as a cure for amenorrhoea. In Lincolnshire a cure for ague had as its chief ingredient 'nine worms from a churchyard and chopped up small'

mystic number in Britain, and danger is always apprehended in the puerperium until the ninth day is past.

If the mother during pregnancy has been much troubled with heart-burn it is believed the child will have a 'gude head of hair,' while if she has been 'lickin' oatmeal' or baking soda her offspring will be born with a copious coating of *vernix caseosa*. It is a prevalent belief, also, that the tastes (likes and dislikes) of the child are dependent on the mother's diet while pregnant, *e.g.*, a syrup-loving child will be born if the mother while 'carrying it' has eaten much syrup. Again, if the mother while pregnant has been 'greenin'' (longing for) any food which has been withheld from her, the child when born will keep shooting out its tongue until its lips have been touched with the article in question. Amongst the Gaelic portion of our population we find similar beliefs. In the Highlands[1] a pregnant woman was held in veneration and tenderness. Anything calculated to distress her mentally was withheld.[2] All coming in contact with her were expected to say, 'God bless you and that which is within you.' All she wanted had to be procured for her. If ungratified the child might have a sense wanting, or be 'aye yawnin'' or 'aye seekin'' during its life. Even birth-marks and deformities might be caused by ungratified pre-natal cravings. These marks[3] are by the Gaelic people called *miann*, literally 'a desire.' The mark is 'the concrete manifestation of the desire. It is all another person can know of it, and it is therefore called "the desire," *miann*.'

The popular belief in maternal impressions is in Scotland, as in all lands, fixed and certain; and how much or how little lies behind the belief is a moot point in scientific circles. 'If there is a vulgar credulity there is also a vulgar incredulity,' says Sir Walter Scott, and we can well bear in mind the *securus judicat orbis terrarum* of St. Augustine. Jacob's successful experiment with the peeled wands[4] shows that

---

(*Folk-lore of Lincolnshire*, p. 117). Red worsted wound nine times round the wrist is a cure for sprains. For hiccough drink nine times round a cup and the trouble leaves you (Worchestershire, *Folk-lore*, vol. xx, p. 346). A godmother's stay-lace knotted nine times round the neck for whooping-cough (Bristol).

1. Moodie, 'Highland Therapy,' *Caledonian Medical Journal*, vol, v, p. 332.
2. A pregnant woman should not see a corpse, otherwise her child will die (Aberdeenshire).
3. H. Cameron Gillies, M.D., 'Gaelic names of diseases and diseased states,' *Caledonian Medical Journal*, vol. iii, p. 242.
4. Certain black cattle breeders of the present day will not have any white objects about their steadings.

it prevailed in his day; and although he only used it in the shady paths of cattle-dealing it must have had its human application for him and his Babylonian forebears. And the folk of the present day, in their own rough way and in divers manners, are aware that the pregnant woman 'has her central nervous system so modified that the intellectual functions may be quickened or the reverse; habits, both religious and moral, intensified or otherwise,' and that 'a complete change in disposition or character is not infrequent.' And they know, too, although they cannot tell you in as many words, that 'morbid cravings and unnatural desires, as well as events of little importance, assume a disproportionate magnitude.'[1] But as examples of the more impossible type the following may be noted, sympathetic and mimetic magic ideas entering, of course, largely into them all:

(1) Case of a woman whose pregnancy was alleged to have continued for eleven months, because in the first month of it she saw a stallion cover a mare (who carries her young for eleven months).

(2) Man with mark of a frog on his side: mother when pregnant had a frog pitched at her in the harvest-field.

(3) Pregnant woman slapped on face with red handkerchief: child born with red mark on forehead.

(4) Child with mark like a red hand on belly: mother, when pregnant, set her nightdress on fire and slapped her hand on abdomen to extinguish flames.

It is always considered a most reprehensible thing amongst the folk to throw, even in jest—and more especially if it be done by the husband—any object at a pregnant woman on account of the danger of thereby causing a birth-mark ('rasp' or 'bramble mark') on, or even a deformity in, her coming child. Should something be thrown, however, and the part affected be an uncovered part of the body (face, neck, or hand), the probable birth-mark can be transferred to a part covered with clothing, if the mother touches the spot where she has been struck with her hand, and then touches a clothed part of her person. A young pregnant woman under such circumstances is always so advised by her wise elders; but the transference is only efficacious before the fourth month of pregnancy.[2] This power of the hand to carry evil is also seen in the folk-belief that if one grips

---

1. J.H. Martin, M.D.
2. *Cf. A Thousand Notable Things* (London, 1595). 'If a Rat, Mouse, or Weasel, or any other thing, suddenly leap or fall on the body of a Woman with child; or else any Cherries or a cluster of Grapes, or other things whatsoever,

a part of the body, *e.g.*, the breasts, while 'grewsin" (shivering: in a rigor), that part will 'beel' (suppurate).[1] Or again, if a mother while so shivering grips her child she may pass on the trouble from which she suffers to the child.[2]

The sex of the child is held by the wise 'howdie' to be indicated by its position in the womb of the mother. 'A laddie is carried mair to the front; a lassie to the back.' A variant is 'a laddie is carried high up; a lassie laigh doon,'[3] or tersely and metaphorically, 'The lassie bides nearest the door.'[4] Another version runs, 'a laddie is carried to the right; a lassie to the left.' 'Ye can tell whether the bairn will be a laddie or a lassie by the side she (the mother) lies on.' It is held, too, that a 'mishap' is more apt to occur with a male child than a female. A change in the woman's feelings is thought to foreshadow a change in the sex of the child. If a woman carrying twins notices one of her nipples to be getting smaller than the other it is a sign that one of her children will die before or at birth.[5]

---

chance to fall or hit any part of the body; by and by it haps that the Child is marked with some special note or mark on that part whereon they did fall or hit, except haply the Woman (on whose body the same did chance) wipe with her hand suddenly the part or member therewith touched, and lay her said hand on some other part further off. *Lemnius*. There are few women but know this to be true, and many have found it too true.' *Vide* also Anatole France, *The Elm Tree on the Mall* (John Lane's popular edition, p. 40, for interesting referenced to similar beliefs in France).

1. Fife.
2. Amongst the Nootka Indians, of Vancouver Island, a girl secluded at puberty may not touch her hair with her hands, but is allowed to scratch her head only with a comb or a piece of bone. To scratch the body is also forbidden, as it is believed that any scratch would leave a scar. Amongst the Chippeway Indians a menstrous woman had a fork-like bone provided for scratching her head, to prevent her using her hand, which would have caused injury to her health. The same uncleanness of, and danger in, the hand of sick, menstruous, or puerperal woman extends to homicides, murderers, and those touching the dead. Frazer, *G.B.*, vol, iii, p. 228.
3. *Vide Practitioner*, vol. lxxxiii, p. 848, for similar beliefs in Somerset (art, 'Ancient superstitions that still survive'). A form of divination is therein given: 'If towards the end of pregnancy a drop of breast secretion is squeezed into a glass of water and it sinks there will be boy; but if it spreads out and floats there will be a girl.'
4. A reference perhaps to the old 'forenichts,' when the men sat next the fire, with the women busy at the spinning wheel behind them (*vide* Gregor).
5. Hippocrates mentions this: 'If the Paps of a woman which is with child of two do wax little she shall lose one of them, and if it be the right Pap it is a man child that will be lost, and if the left a woman child.'

13
Labour

A woman on the verge of labour is said to be 'at the doon-lyin',' while labour itself is variously described as 'a cryin','[1] 'a cryin'-match,' or 'howdie-wark.' The mother is also said to be 'in the hole,' 'in the strae,'[2] or 'lyin'-in.' A husband summoning the doctor may employ the metaphor, 'The lum's on fire,' or say 'She's brakkin' in twa.'

During labour the 'kimmers' (French, *commères*) present console the patient with various stereotyped (and frequently Rabelaisian) remarks: 'Ye'll be waur afore ye're better'; 'Ye dinna ken ye're livin' yet'; 'Ye're greetin' ower what ye were lauchin' at afore'; 'Ye ocht to hae thocht o' this suner'; or 'Ye ken noo what your mither went through for ye.'[3] The child is spoken of as 'comin' hame' ('the bairn's near hame'), and 'the bairn's hame' means labour is completed and that the doctor is only in time to express regret and the placenta. The word 'lichter' means the same:

> Canny moment, lucky fit,
> Is the lady lichter yet?[4]

A curious slang term for an accoucheur in Fife was that of 'finger-smith.'

In West Fife, thirty years ago, in the smaller outlying mining hamlets, it was common for the mother to wish to be (and her previous custom to have been) delivered while on her knees before a chair.

Various things are held to influence the course of labour. Reference has already been made to the hindering power of knots and the spells of witches. In the North-East of Scotland[5] the locks of all doors (on the principle of everything being loosed and unconfined) were

---

1. *Cf.* Burns, 'O wha will tent me when I cry?'
2. *Vide* Brand, *Popular Antiquities*, on 'In the Straw.'
3. It was interesting to note in Northern France that consolation in similar terms was employed there during labour.
4. Scott's *Guy Mannering.*
5. *Vide* Gregor, *Folk-Lore of the North-East of Scotland*, p. 5.

opened during labour, and in Fife I have frequently seen the outer door quietly unlocked and left open by the older women while a tedious labour was in progress. At Newtonhill, a fishing village in Kincardineshire, the local 'canny man' was, within quite recent years, brought into and kept 'ben' the house until the labour had come to a successful issue. In one case of tedious labour the (unmarried) patient was told, 'Ye'll never get rid o' that bairn till ye curse the faither o't.'[1] The process of reasoning here is hard to follow, unless it was that the girl's keeping of her secret (for she declined to tell) constituted a 'knot' which had to be unravelled.

The 'turn o' the nicht' is supposed to have a definite influence, and if a parturient woman passes that she may 'gang the roond o' the clock' again. By the fisher folk the tide is held to exercise a similar effect, the child being born most easily when it is full.[2] So with the moon: children born at full moon being held to be 'lucky,' while those born at change of moon are sickly and small.[3] Chambers[4] mentions that Johnston of Warriston, who rose from the Bar to high office under the Estates and Commonwealth, had the misfortune to fall under the vengeance of the new government and was executed at Edinburgh in 1663. Lamont, a contemporary chronicler, says, 'Before and at his death there was a report noised abroad, said to be uttered by the midwife at his birth, thus:

> Full moon, high sea,
> Great man shalt thou be;
> But ill death shalt thou dee.'

Scott[5] gives us

> Full moon and high sea,
> Great man shalt thou be;

---

1. Perthshire
2. Gregor; *cf.* also Black, *Folk-Medicine*. Peggoty in *David Copperfield* goes out with the tide. Sir John Falstaff died 'at the turn o' the tide.'
3. *Cf.* Hardy, *The Trumpet Major*—'No moon, no man.' In the Isle of Man the best time for marrying or for engaging in any important undertaking is when the moon is full. In Worcestershire we find:
   Crop your hair in the moon's wax,
   Ne'er cut it in her wane,
   And then of a bald head
   You never shall complain.'
   Folk-lore, Vol. xx, p. 342.
4. *Popular Rhymes of Scotland*, p. 340, *cf.* Worship of Artemis, goddess of the moon, amongst the Greeks, as goddess of child-birth.
5. *Fortunes of Nigel.*

> Red dawning, stormy sky,
> Bloody death shalt thou die,

and makes David Ramsay say of the Duke of Buckingham: 'Long has it been said of him he was born at the very meeting of night and day, and under crossing and contending influences that may affect both us and him.'

It is unlucky for another pregnant woman to be in the room while labour is in progress. Gregor[1] mentions that if two women with child happened to be in the same house when one felt the pains of labour commence, 'they took a straw or a stalk of grass, or some such thing, and broke it, each repeating the words "Ye tak' yours and I tak' mine."' Nor was a woman giving suck allowed to sit on the edge of the accouchement bed; such would stop the lying-in woman's flow of milk. Here like hinders the progress of like (one interpretation of the Doctrine of Signatures, just as the red cloth hung at the foot of the bed in the Highlands checks post-partum haemorrhage, or as tying the navel-string with red thread, prevents bleeding of the cord, or as a coral necklace round a child's throat arrests nose-bleeding). If, however, such an unfortunate contretemps occurred, the child of the woman who had done the mischief was got secretly and passed under and over the lying-in woman's apron to get back the milk. Here we have a sham-birth rite of adoption, and the milk flows again in sympathy with the new connection between mother and child.

Brand[2] refers to girdles having been used in Scotland during labour to assist its progress. 'According to Henry, the ancient Britons, in the event of a labour being attended with any difficulty, put a girdle made for the purpose about the woman in labour, which they imagined gave immediate and effective relief. Girdles of this kind were till lately carefully preserved in many families in the Highlands of Scotland. They were impressed with numerous mystical figures, and the ceremony of binding them about the waist was accompanied with words and gestures indicating the great antiquity of the practice and its original derivation from the Druids.' Brand is here quoting from a note which 'Ossian' Macpherson put to the following passage in his 'Battle of Lora'[3]:

---

1. *Folk-lore of the North-East of Scotland.*
2. *Observations on Popular Antiquities.*
3. *The Poems of Ossian*, by James Macpherson, Edinburgh, 1805, vol. i, p. 283.

An hundred girdles shall also be thine, to bind high-bosomed maids. The friends of the births of heroes. The cure of the sons of toil.

Dr. W.J. Dilling[1] made a most thorough investigation into the whole question of girdles in all parts of the world, and says, as regards the Scottish ones: 'Laing believed that these girdles were in no way connected with Druids, but were merely belts consecrated by some of the Irish saints. This criticism I am inclined to homologate, although I have not seen a specimen of these belts. Fortunately, our evidence that such girdles were used by our Scottish forefathers does not rest solely on the somewhat questionable statements of Macpherson. Sir Walter Scott has also recorded an instance of the same practice in his *Demonology and Witchcraft*. Speaking of the trial of Bessie Dunlop for witchcraft, he mentions that "she lost a lace which Thome Reid (a spectre) gave her out of his own hand, which tied round women in childbirth had the power of helping their delivery."

'These girdles still exist; thus, in 1911, the late Mr. Henderson stated that they were sometimes worn by pious women "to sain the expected child as well as the mother from all harm, and to attach good spiritual powers to her side." They are, however, kept very secretly; this is evident from the fact that the writer has corresponded with several Highland medical men upon this matter and none of them had ever heard of one.'[2]

Dilling then goes on to quote the superstition that a pregnant woman who sees 'Macleod's Fairy Banner' is taken in premature labour, and adds that he 'has heard from a reliable source that the fisherwomen of Ferryden, Forfarshire,[3] are accustomed to tie their binders round them before delivery, but no reason was adduced for this practice.' He further mentions that in Dublin in 1906 he saw a belt applied in labour, 'a leather belt, old and greasy, about an inch and a half broad, and long enough to pass easily round the body; it possessed an iron buckle of ordinary design, and had from my recollection, no special marks on it.' It was bound loosely round the chest over the mammary glands 'to make the baby come more

---

1. 'Girdles: their origin and development, particularly with regard to their use as charms in medicine, marriage, and midwifery,' *Caledonian Medical Journal*, vol. ix, pp. 337 and 403.
2. Can any member of the Society in the Highlands or Islands help to trace and describe such a belt? Or has such a custom been heard of?
3. Can any local member elucidate this further?

quickly.' He learned subsequently that it was a belt worn by members of a society of St. Augustine, which helped them 'in times of sickness and childbirth.' As regards the use of obstetric girdles generally, he asks: 'Were they originally discovered to be helpful by exerting *vis a tergo*, or by supporting the abdomen, or were they merely religious emblems employed as amulets?'

14
The Child

In the Highlands when the child was born the mother and her offspring were, until comparatively recent years, secured by charms against the intrigues of the fairy folk. Campbell[1] narrates how at a confinement a house full of women gathered and watched for three days. 'A row of iron nails was driven into the front board of the bed; the smoothing-iron or a reaping-hook was placed under it and in the window; an old shoe was put in the fire;[2] the door posts were sprinkled with *maister* (urine kept for washing purposes—a liquid peculiarly offensive to the fairies); the Bible was opened and the breath blown across it in the face of the woman in child-bed; mystic words of threads were placed about the bed; and, when leaving at the end of the three days, the midwife left a little cake of oatmeal with a hole in it in the front of the bed.' The father's shirt[3] wrapped round the new-born babe was esteemed a preservative, and if the marriage gown was thrown over the wife she could be recovered if she were taken away.

In fact, until within comparatively quite recent times the belief in fairies, both in Highland and Lowland Scotland, was firm and widespread; and their power was especially to be feared in the case of women in child-bed and of unbaptised infants. The fairies had a great liking for human milk, which could only be obtained by carrying off unsained or unchurched mothers. The reason they wished possession of the infant was that every seven years they had to 'pay the teind to hell,' and this they endeavoured to do

---

1. *Superstitions of the Scottish Highlands, p. 36.*
2. To fill the chimney with offensive smoke.
3. The powerful influence of the father's clothing upon wife and child crops up in various ways in different countries. We have already seen in Scotland how it re-acts upon the sex of the child. In France, certain curious customs based on the idea that the male has influence on the foetus beyond the date on which he begot it still prevail amongst the peasantry. Dr. Marignan, of Marsillargues, attended a woman who put on her husband's hat to hasten

with a human being. In the North-East of Scotland the mother and offspring were sained in the following manner[1]: A lighted fir-candle was carried three times round the bed if that could be done, and, if not, it was whirled three times round the heads of mother and child; a bible[2] and bread and cheese, or a bible and a biscuit, were placed under the pillow, and the words were repeated—'May the Almichty debar a' ill frae this umman, an' be aboot ir, and bliss ir an' ir bairn.' A pair of trousers, or any other article of dress of the father, hung at the foot of the bed, had a strong effect in keeping off the fairies. I have never personally seen any of these precautions actually employed, except the bible and biscuit under the pillow, and another precaution against the changeling (to be mentioned later); but as an example of the persistence of superstitious observance, I have known a woman whose child had been dead-born weepingly attribute her disappointment to the fact that she had not, as her neighbours had, a lucky horse-shoe by her fireside. Regretting that she had previously scoffed at them for their belief in its efficacy, she took

---

labour, preferring it to ergot. Dr. Lalanne repeatedly observed a similar practice in the Landes, the parturient woman turning her husband's hat inside out and then putting it on her head. In Lorraine the husband's entire clothing is donned as an oxytocic. There, and in the Toulouse district, the husband's cotton night-cap is used as a pad tied against the vulva to prevent a threatened abortion. ('Les superstitions medicales,' *Journal d'Obstét. de Gynécol. et de Péd. Prat.*, 20th July, 1905.) In Spain if there is difficulty in getting the milk to flow the wife puts on her husband's shirt immediately after he has put it off. (*Gaceta Medica Catalana* 15 February and 15th March, 1910.) In the Border Country of Scotland the husband's 'homely blue bonnet' was left reposing on the bed of a lying-in woman. In Holland the wife's inflamed nipples are cured by the application of the newly-worn woollen night-cap of the husband. (*Janus*, 1910 volume.) A reference to the power of frightening away fairies and brownies is found in the poem of 'Aiken Drum':

> But a new made wife fu' o' frippish freaks,
> Fond o' a' thing feat for the first five weeks
> Laid a mouldy pair o' her gudeman's breeks
>   By the brose o' Aiken Drum.

The effect is to make the brownie leave at once.

1. Gregor, *Folk-Lore of the N.-E. of Scotland*, p. 5.
2. Similarly the Chinese scared away evil spirits by placing his classics under his pillow (M. Rolfe Cox, *Introduction to Folk-Lore*); while the Moslem has his talisman of verses of the Koran sewn in leather and worn slung round his neck.

the earliest opportunity of remedying this state of affairs by securing one.[1]

The precaution against the new-born babe being replaced by a fairy
changeling is a form of the fire-test which was applied with fatal
effects some thirty years ago to a sick woman in Ireland.[2] If, after
being dressed at birth, a child cries unnaturally and continuously,
the granny or other wise elder present, makes up a big fire and
then puts on 'the girdle,' the circular flat iron structure on which
scones and oatcakes are 'fired.' The idea is that if the child be 'a
witch or a warlock' (changeling) it would on being held near the
fire go forthwith up the chimney, while the girdle would prevent the
real child being injured by the flames on its return voyage home.[3]
Frequently at the present day when a child is so crying one will hear
the remark, 'If this gangs on we'll need to pit on the girdle,' although
not every one who says it can tell why she says it. Enquiries on being
pressed often drive the person interrogated to the usual last refuge
of—'That's what the auld folk used to say,' or 'I've heard my mither
say that; it's an auld frait.'

In the Highlands the charm repeated over a new-born child
ran thus:

> Hale fair washing to thee,
> Hale washing of the Fians be thine,
> Health to thee, health to him,
> But not to thy female enemy.[4]

At the time of birth when the cord is cut great care must be taken
not to cut it too short if the child be a male, as in such a case he will in
adult life run the risk of being childless.[5] If a good lengthy cord is left
the child will have a long penis, suggestive to the folk of procreative
power. If the child be a female, however, the cord should be cut short,

1. Fife
2. Case of Bridget Cleary of Clonmel. She was held over a fire by her husband
   and other relatives in the belief that she was a changeling and would thereby
   be forced back to her fairy folk, while the real Bridget would come back
   'riding on a grey horse.' She died of burns, and the perpetrators of the cure
   were tried for murder.
3. Fife. An eccentric and diminutive old 'character' in a Forfarshire village
   used, when chaffed about being a changeling, to reply: 'Na, Na! When
   I was a bairn I was held over a great big fire; noo, ye see, if I had been
   ane o' thae craturs I wad hae gane fluff up the lum.'
4. Campbell, *Witchcraft and Second Sight in the Scottish Highland*, p. 77.
5. One old 'handy-wife' (Kincardineshire, but born in the Highlands) laid
   down the rule, 'Fowre thooms' braidth for a lassie, five for a laddie.'

therefore securing for it in adult life a narrow vulva, suggestive to the popular mind of retention of the male element and consequently of fertility.[1] But this latter operation can be overdone. In *A Thousand Notable Things*, already drawn upon, we find it laid down that as soon as the child is born, 'especially a boy, there oughte to be great heed taken in the cutting of the Navel String; for the Member of Generation doth follow the proportion of the Navel String; and if it be tied too short in a Wench it may be a hindrance to her bringing forth her child. Therefore, it is meet that Midwives have a great regard therein.' Here, then, we have clearly pointed out to us the danger of overdoing what otherwise is a necessary precaution. In Scotland there is a further belief that if the umbilical cord be tied carelessly and allowed to bleed, the child will be a bed-wetter. The compiler of *A Thousand Notable Things* varies this somewhat, for he says: 'If the Navel String after it is cut do chance to touch the ground before it be burned, the same child will not be able to hold his or her water, whether night or day.' Elworthy,[2] speaking of Devonshire, bears testimony to this belief, and says: 'The piece of the *funis umbilicus* should be taken off at the proper time and burnt; if this is not done and it is allowed to drop off naturally, especially if it should drop on the floor, the child will grow to be a bed-wetter.' He then goes on to say: 'Much more might be said as to the reasons given for the careful attention to this operation, especially as to the different treatment of a boy and a girl.'

The number of 'knots' on the cord of a first-born child is held by many 'skeely-wives' to foretell how many of a family the mother is to have; divination and augury being thus added to the power of the navel string in addition to sympathetic effects.

In Lincolnshire[3] it is believed that the navel string should be (as in the case of a caul) carefully kept by the child's mother, otherwise harm will accrue to the child. And, to quote *A Thousand Notable Things* again, we find that 'a piece of a child's Navel String worn in a ring is good against the Falling Sickness, the pains of the Head, and of the Collick.' Later on we are told that this piece of 'Navel String must be borne so as to touch the skin' of the wearer. Salmon[4] tells us that 'a drop or two of the blood of the Navel String being first given to a new-born Child in a little Breast milk prevents

---

1. I found these beliefs existing in Picardy in 1915.
2. *The Evil Eye*, p. 75.
3. *Folk-lore concerning Lincolnshire*, p. 226.
4. *New London Dispensatory*, fourth edition, 1691, bk. ii, p. 190.

the Falling Sickness, Convulsions, and all other Fits; and very wonderfully revives if almost dead.' This last belief is also found in *The Several Declarations, together with the Several Depositions made in Council on Monday, the 22d of October, 1688, Concerning the Birth of the Prince of Wales.*[1] In her deposition, Elizabeth Lady Marchioness of Powis stated that she saw 'Sir Thomas Witherley sent for by the Midwife, who gave the Child Three Drops of Something which came into the world with him.' Dame Isabella Wentworth, one of the Gentlewomen of the Bedchamber to the Queen, deposed that she saw 'the Navel String of the Child cut, and three drops of the Blood, which came fresh out, given to him for the Convulsion Fits.' Mrs. Mary Ann Delabadie, Dry Nurse to the Prince, stated that she 'held the Spoon when the Midwife dropped the Blood into it, and stirr'd it with a little Black Cherry Water, and then it was given to the Prince.' Sir Thomas Witherley, second physician to the King, safe-guarded himself for taking part in superstitious usages by explaining in his deposition that he had 'a Command from the Queen' so to do, and that the blood was given 'as the Queen commanded.'

Another reference to this belief is found in the ballad of 'Leesome Brand':

> Put in your hand at my bed head,
>   There ye'll find a gude grey horn,
> In it three draps o' Saint Paul's ain blude
>   That hae been there sin' he was born.
> Drap twa o' them o' your ladye
>   And ane upo your little young son;
> Then as lively they will be
>   As the first night ye brought them hame.

Whereupon the dead wife and child are miraculously restored to life.

But the belief that the navel string has a sympathetic connection with the child, and that what is done to it produces a corresponding effect for good or ill on the child, is common in various parts of the world. Hartland[2] shows how barren women drink water containing blood from the navel string of a new-born infant, or water in which an umbilical cord has been soaked; suck blood from a child's navel; eat the dried remains of a navel string, &c. For example, a Kamtchadal woman who after delivery desires to

---

1. London: Printed and Sold by the Booksellers of London and Westminster (N.D.).
2. *Primitive Paternity.*

become pregnant again soon will eat her infant's navel string. The placenta is used in the same way, eaten or taken dried in pill form. In Mandeling[1] the midwife cuts the cord with a piece of a flute on which she has first blown so that the child may have a good voice. Amongst some tribes in Western Australia it is held that a man swims well or evil according as his mother put his navel string in water or not. In Rhenish Bavaria the cord is kept for a while wrapped in old linen, and then cut or picked to pieces according as the child is a boy or a girl, in order that he or she may be a good workman or a skilful seamstress. The navel string of a boy in ancient Mexico was given to soldiers for burial on a battlefield in order that the boy might acquire a passion for war. So amongst the Indian tribes of British Columbia the cord fastened to the dancing mask of a famous dancer will make the child a good dancer; attached to the knife of a skilful carver a good craftsman in woodwork; attached to the baton of a singing master a good singer. And the navel string of the King of Uganda is kept with the utmost care throughout his life. Wrapt in cloth, the number of wrappers is increased with the years of the king until it ultimately assumes the form of a human figure swathed in cloth. The custodian ranks as an important Minister of State, the bundle being from time to time presented to the king.

Should the new-born child have enlarged mammae, the common and dangerous practice of 'milking the breasts' used too frequently to be indulged in, more especially if the infant was a female. Boys were frequently saved this mal-treatment through the belief that such 'milking' would disadvantageously affect their chance of having progeny when they came to enter the marriage state.

The child at birth, should, if a male, be wrapped in a woman's petticoat; if a female, in a man's shirt. If this is not done the child is held to run the risk of either not being married at all, or, if married, of being childless. Kelly[2] quotes the proverb, 'He was wrap'd in his Mother's Sark Tail,' with the explanatory text of 'The Scots have a Superstitious Custom of receiving a Child when it comes into the World, in its Mother's Shift if a male, believing that this Usage will make him well-beloved among Women. And when a Man proves unfortunate that way they will say, "He was kep'd [caught, received] in a Board-cloth: he has some hap to his Meat, but none to his Wives."'

A similar idea is seen amongst the Galelareese[3] in connection with

---

1. Frazer, G.B., vol. i, pp. 54, 55.
2. *A Complete Collection of Scottish Proverbs*, London, 1721.
3. Frazer, G.B., vol. i, p. 39.

trees. When a tree bears no fruit they hold it to be a male, and to remedy affairs, they tie a woman's petticoat round it. Frazer explains this by saying that the tree 'being then converted into a female will naturally prove prolific.' May it not rather be, as it apparently is in the Scottish custom to secure offspring by the association of male and female attributes? But there are some curious 'male and female' beliefs, as, *e.g.*, in Lincolnshire, where a boy afflicted with whooping-cough is advised to ride for a quarter of a mile on a female donkey, a jackass being substituted when the patient is a girl.[1] In Malta[2] the blood of a tortoise is held to be an excellent remedy for jaundice caused by fright. If the patient be a man he bleeds a female tortoise in the leg, and makes the sign of the cross on the joints of his arms and legs; while if the patient be a woman she bleeds a male tortoise.

At the child's birth the midwife (*howdie, canny-wife, skeely-wife*) if of the old school moulds and presses (*straiks*) the child's head 'to pit it in shape.' She then takes a mouthful of whisky and spits it carefully over the scalp[3] to 'strengthen the heid.' In rural Scotland not so long ago two caps (*mutches*) were then put on the child's head, the *under-mutchie* (a plain tight-fitting cap) going on first, and the *ower-mutchie* (a more ornamental piece of head-gear) going on above. All this was done as the child was supposed to be very ready to take cold on 'the brain' through the 'openin's o' the heid' (the fontanelles), and these caps were accordingly worn until the fontanelles closed.

If at birth the child cries lustily the by-standers make a point of saying 'Weel, it's got a gude brain ony way!'[4] It is curious to note

---

1. *Folk-lore concerning Lincolnshire*, p. 106.
2. *Folk-lore*, vol. xiv, p. 85.
3. Spittle amongst the ancients was esteemed a charm against all kinds of fascination. Persius adverts to the custom of nurses spitting upon children. Seward, in his *Conformity between Popery and Paganism*, states that the practice of nurses lustrating their charges with spittle was one of the ceremonies used on the Dies Nominalis, the day the child was named, 'so that there can be no doubt of the Papists deriving this custom from the Heathen nurses and grandmothers.' The eighth day for girls and the ninth day for boys were the days of lustration. The old grandmother or aunt moved around in a circle, and rubbed the child's forehead with spittle, and that with her middle finger, to preserve it from witchcraft (Brand's *Popular Antiquities*. Chapter on 'Saliva or Spitting.')

   Rubbing a child's nose with spittle is a common folk-cure for a cold in the head.
4. Aberdeenshire, Kincardineshire, Banffshire.

how many, even of the older women, have lost the meaning of the word 'brain' as here used, and look upon the crying as evidence of future intellectual power. 'Brain' here means a voice, and the word is also used as a verb = to cry out, to shout. Lung-power does not necessarily imply brain-power (*pace* the proletariat) but it does help to make a noise in the world.

If the child micturates freely at birth it is held to be a sign of good luck, especially for those who may be wet by it.[1]

At birth the child is carefully examined to see if it be 'wice an' warl'-like' (strong, mentally and physically), and have no signs of being an 'objeck' (physically deformed), or a 'natural' (mental deficient). A 'bramble-mark' or a 'rasp' (naevus) is not objected to unless on the face, as it is considered a sign of good-luck. Such marks are held to increase in size and darken in colour as the fruit they resemble ripens. They are also held to be more prominent as each birthday comes round; and, it may be noted, they can be removed by being stroked with the dead hand of a blood relative.

For a child to be born with a caul (*coolie, hallie-hoo, happy-hoo, silly-hoo*)[2] is considered very lucky, and for this reason the dried caul is almost invariably preserved. Twenty years ago in Aberdeen a midwife laid one carefully aside, and gave as her reason that it 'was to assist her in her business.' In the Highlands a child born with a caul (and also a child born feet first) is held to have the gift of second sight; a belief that probably arose through its being born looking 'through a veil.' Such a caul prevents the child from being drowned, or the fairies and evil spirits taking it away. The second sight belief is shared by the Boers, who also hold that strange properties are possessed by the *man met die helm*. As long as the caul is preserved those born with it are able to look into the future. In Scotland the caul is always looked on as worthy of respect. Some years ago a tradesman told me that all his four children had been born with cauls; that he had had all the cauls dried and preserved, and that he would not part with them for a hundred pounds, as he had prospered every day since the

---

1. In reference to such 'luck,' Mungo Park, in his *Travels into the interior of Africa*, describes how, after a Moorish wedding, he was wakened by an old woman discharging a bowlful of the bride's urine in his face. By young unmarried Moors this is held to be an auspicious compliment, and accepting it as such, Park sent his acknowledgements to the lady.

2. *Coolie* = night-cap; *hallie-hoo* = holy hood; *happy-hoo* = lucky hood, or perhaps, wrapping hood (*cf.* to hap, to wrap up); *silly-hoo* = fairy hood (*cf.* numerous *silly* or *seely* hillocks and howes in Scotland).

first child arrived. The caul has also the power of giving the gift of eloquence. Thirty years ago I saw such a dried caul which had been kept by its possessor for sixty-five years.[1] If given to another person the caul acts as an indicator of its real owner's health. If it keeps dry he or she is in good health; if it becomes moist, in bad health. Henderson[2] mentions the necessity of keeping the caul carefully, for should it be lost or thrown away the child will pine or even die. This superstition, however, 'is world-wide, and of such antiquity as to be reproved by Saint Chrysostom in several of his homilies. Its universality in France is attended by a proverbial expression— *être né coiffé*, means to be prosperous and fortunate in everything.' Brand[3] deals comprehensively with the subject in a chapter on 'The Silly Hood.'

I have already stated that a child born feet first is held to have the gift of second sight; alternatively, it is believed to be born to be a wanderer. The same fate hangs over a child born with two hair-whorls on its head, while another interpretation of this phenomenon is that the child will live to see two ruling monarchs crowned.[4] The child born feet first is also looked on as a 'healer,' and to have the power of healing complaints, such as lumbago and sciatica, by treading on the parts affected.[5]

It is considered unlucky to weigh a new-born child, and I have seen, twenty to thirty years ago, very genuine opposition offered to such a proposal.[6] The reason is probably the same as that of the objection among fisher-folk to count the number of their catch, or the number of the fishing fleet, or to have themselves counted.[7] Undue praise of the child ('fore-speaking') is also deprecated.

To wash the child's 'loof' (palm) thoroughly is considered unlucky, as thereby destroying its chances of acquiring and retaining this world's gear. By some it is also considered wrong to wash the child's back for the first two or three weeks or so, as it is thereby weakened. This is also the belief of the old Fifeshire miner regarding

---

1. Fife: the owner was a woman.
2. *Folk-lore of the Northern Counties*, p. 22.
3. *Popular Antiquities*.
4. Aberdeenshire, Fife.
5. Highlands; *vide* also *Northumberland Folk-lore*, p. 48.
6. Fife.
7. Is this the idea of not looking a gift-horse in the mouth? What has been given should be accepted as a gift and no attempt made to examine critically its exact proportions.

himself: to wash his back or his knees too often weakens them. The weakening effect of water, too, is seen in the belief that decay of the teeth results from living too close to running water.

The new-born child used frequently to be held up by the heels and shaken to prevent it taking 'a sair weim' (colic).[1] This old cure of inversion for colic is quite common in rural districts, more especially amongst farm-lads and schoolboys, and is held in esteem as a means of getting rid of 'a sair inside.'[2] A teething ring of aspen wood[3] was used in the Highlands to ensure safe teething, this tree being sacred owing to the belief that the Cross was made from it.

When dressing the child for the first time the 'witch-brooch' was within quite recent times[4] always pinned on the child's dress as a safeguard against witches, fairies, and the evil-eye. The brooch is of silver and is heart-shaped, and was never taken off until the child was a considerable age. The shape was probably derived from that of the flint arrow-heads—the 'elf-shots' of the folk. Mounted in silver, these arrow-heads are still in use by the Irish peasantry[5] and others, and within recent years in Scotland the flint arrow-head was esteemed—so long as it was not allowed to touch the ground—as a safeguard against witch and warlock.[6] To prevent fairy interference, too, the soiled 'hippins' (napkins) were not allowed to be left out after sunset, as with these articles in their possession the fairies could work evil on their owner. It was for the same reason that the nails of the child were not to be cut, but bitten off and swallowed by the mother, and that hair and teeth were burnt or otherwise carefully preserved from falling into possibly hostile hands.

If the child 'neezes' (sneezes) the act is always greeted by 'Bless the bairn!' In Florida, Zululand, West Africa, France, Germany, and many other places, this old and widespread custom of acknowledging the act of sneezing prevails, as it did in Ancient Rome and Homeric Greece.[7] The exclamation originated in the belief that a spirit could take possession of a man, and that the act of sneezing cast the spirit out with 'monstrous potency,' while the Zulus believe that the ancestral

---

1. 'Old Highland Therapy,' in *Caledonian Medical Journal*, vol. v, No. 2.
2. Aberdeenshire, Fife
3. Juniper wood (Sutherlandshire).
4. Aberdeenshire, Banff, Kincardineshire.
5. *Cf.* also *Folk-lore of the Northern Counties.* Specimens are to be seen in the British Museum.
6. Aberdeenshire, Kincardineshire, Banff.
7. *Introduction to Folk-lore*, p. 203.

spirit was there as a beneficent visitant. In Scotland, the sneeze is held 'to clear the brain,' but of what is not stated.

On its first visit to another house the child's mouth is frequently filled with sugar 'for luck.' Unless this were done the infant would always be licking its lips, shooting out its tongue, or be generally discontented. Such a first visit brings luck to a house unless the child is carried by its mother. Gregor mentions that a child entering a house for the first time had to have something given it, otherwise 'hunger was left in the house.' If in spite of sugar being put in its mouth the child persisted in shooting out its tongue and licking its lips, these actions were attributed to an unsatisfied craving of the mother when pregnant. She was therefore asked what she had been 'greenin' for and hadna gotten,' and if the article was procurable it was got and rubbed on the child's lips.

Various beliefs centre round the cradle as a power to affect the child's health. The first child should not be rocked in a new cradle, but in a borrowed old one, nor should the cradle be brought into the house before the child is born.[1] In sending the borrowed cradle it should never be sent empty, but with a blanket or some other object lying in it, nor should it touch the ground on its journey. Even after the child is older and the mother wishes to take the cradle into a neighbour's house it is held to be unlucky to carry the cradle there empty. In some districts[2] if the cradle was borrowed for a boy the object put into it was a live hen; if for a girl a live cock.[3]

An empty cradle should never be rocked. I have frequently tested this idea by deliberately rocking an empty cradle. I was either openly checked for doing it, or the cradle was unostentatiously pushed out of my reach. In Fife it is held that rocking the 'toom' cradle gives the child a 'sair wame.' Henderson,[4] quoting the Wilkie MS., gives the old rhyme:

> O rock not the cradle when the baby's not in,
> For this by old women is counted a sin,
> It's a crime so inhuman, it may na be forgi'en,
> And they that will do it hae lost sight of Heaven.

In some parts of England to rock an empty cradle is held to

---

1. Amongst the Thonga (S. Africa) it is taboo before the birth of a child to prepare the 'ntehe,' the skin in which the baby is to be carried on the shoulder of its mother.
2. Gregor, *Folk-Lore of the North-East of Scotland*.
3. *Vide ante*, pp. 88–89.
4. *Folk-lore of the Northern Counties*.

rock a new baby into it, while in New England the settlers have an adage:

> Rock a cradle empty,
> Babies will be plenty.

The belief against rocking the empty cradle holds also in Holland and Sweden.

Many popular beliefs also exist about the teeth and teething: augury, divination, and incantation all occurring. A child born with teeth has to have them 'howked oot' by the howdie, to avoid disheartening the mother, for 'sune teeth, sune sorrow.' The person who first discovers that a child has cut a tooth has to get a present from the mother. Gums through which the teeth are shining are described as 'breedin' gums,' and such teeth are usually brought through the gum by rubbing with a silver thimble or a shilling. It is very unlucky to cut the upper teeth before the lower. Hence the proverb

> He that cuts teeth abune
> Will never wear his marriage shoon.

'Sune teeth, sune mair,' 'sune teeth, sune anither,' or 'sune teeth, sune taes,' all express the belief that quick teething means an early successor to the child.

When teeth come out or are extracted, each tooth should be put in the fire with a little salt, and either

> Fire, Fire, burn bane
> God gie me my teeth again,

or

> Burn, burn, blue tooth,
> Come again a new tooth,

repeated. In Northumberland the lines are added,

> Not a crooked but a strite ane,
> Not a black ane but a white ane.

Here we have the careful destruction of the teeth, as of hair and nails, lest they fall into unfriendly hands and be used for working evil against the owner.

A child which learns to speak before it walks will turn out 'an awfu' leear.' A child which speaks before it is six months old will, if a boy, not live to 'comb a grey heid.' A child should not be allowed to see itself in the looking-glass before it gets its teeth, otherwise it will not live to be five years old.

On the first occasion that a mother after her confinement goes to draw water from the well she must take care not to spill any on the ground. If she does, her child will become a drunkard.

[94]

The Child

The first time a child creeps, if it makes for the door it will creep through life and be a 'slow coach,' and never make a name for itself. Similarly, if a child on first walking is inclined to run it will have more failures than successes in life. If a child's bowels move while it is sucking it is held 'to have a bad breath.' Any person seeing an infant for the first time should give it a present, otherwise the visitor will 'gang awa' wi' the child's beauty.' In the same way any person not 'drinkin' oot the dram' offered after the child's birth will 'tak awa' the bairn's luck.' Such dram-drinking is called 'wettin' the bairn's heid,' and is probably a test for a well-wisher or ill-wisher to the child, in case of possible evil-eye influence.

If a child on being given a piece of money holds it tight, it will turn out 'awfu' grippy' (greedy, miserly); but if, on the other hand, it lets it slip through its fingers it will be open-handed and generous.

The first time a mother takes her child out she should not carry it into another house herself, but should get someone else to do it, otherwise evil will speedily befall the child. A newly-born child should be carried upstairs before it is carried down, so as to secure that it will 'rise in life.' If no stair be available the nurse may secure this end by mounting a chair or a box with the child in her arms.

If the child's first cry sounds like 'Dey' (father)[1] the next child will be a male.

A child with differently coloured eyes (*e.g.*, one blue, one brown) will never live to grow up; while a male child whose second toe is longer than his first will grow up to be 'bad to his wife.'

---

1. Fife.

15

Vernacular Anatomical and Medical Terms

Before dealing with 'cures' we may consider some of the popular terms used in Scotland for various parts of the human body and the troubles that affect them.

A skeleton is called an *atomy*, an emaciated person being described as 'reduced to a fair atomy.' The cranium is the *harn-pan*; the brain the *harns*. The *openin'* (or *open*) *o' the heid* is in the infant the anterior fontanelle, but in the adult it is used loosely for the top of the head, the crown. The *haffits* are the temples; the *chafts*, the jaws; the *chowks*, the cheeks. The eyelids are the *winkers*; the pupil of the eye, the *sicht o' the e'e*—e.g., a foreign body in the eye may be described as 'a fire fair on the sicht o' the e'e.' The *neb* is the nose, a person with a keen sense of smell being described as *neb-wice* or *nose-wice*. The *mou'* or *gab* is the mouth; a prognathous person is *gash-gabbit*. The *lug* is the ear; *hawse, hass, craig*, and *thrapple* are used for the throat. The *pap, clap,* or *clapper o' the hawse* is the uvula. It is also frequently called the *wee tongue*. The *breist* is the thorax; the *slot o' the breist* or the *spoon o' the breist*, the line of the sternum. *Wame* or *weim, kyte* or *baggie* (in children) are used for the abdomen; the *puddens* are the intestines. The *birth* signifies the external female genitals. *Fore-birth* for vulva, and *hind-* (or *back-*)*birth* for the anus are sometimes differentiated, but the commonest name for the latter is the *back-passage*.

The axilla is the *oxter*, a crutch being called an *oxter-staff* or a *hiltie*. The elbow is the *elbuck*; the 'funny-bone,' the *dirly-bane*. The *shackle-bane* is the wrist; the *loof*, the palm of the hand; the *nieve*, the clenched fist. *Curnie, crannie, pinkie* and *pearlie* are all used for the little finger, while the terminal phalanges are the *nebs o' the fingers*. A *lucken-handed* person is one with web fingers, while *lucken-taed* means web-toed.

The nates are the *arse, doup, hurdies, backside* or, in children, the *dock*—to 'pay the dock' being to bestow chastisement in that appropriate situation. The sacro-iliac synchondrosis is the *couplins o' the back*. The *hainch* is the haunch; the *hunker* or *rumple-banes*, the ischial tuberosities; the *herkle* or *hurkle-bane*, the ilium. The *clatter-bane* or *whistle-bane o' the arse* is the coccyx. The *lisk* is the groin. The *lid* or *knap o' the knee* is the patella; the *yield* or *bught o' the knee*, the popliteal space; the *bran o' the leg*, the calf; and the *cuit* or *queet*, the ankle.

A tendon is a *leader* or a *sinon*. Ganglion is correctly enough described as a *luppen sinon*, but the term is often loosely applied to varicose veins. The *fell* is the skin, a deep-seated pain being described as 'betwixt the fell and the flesh.'

A new-born child is, if healthy in body and mind, described as *wice an' warl'-like*—the opposite being a *natural* (imbecile) or *objeck* (physically deformed). *Sharger* (with the saying, 'Hair and horn grow weel on shargers'), *weirdie*, *drauchle*, *tittlin'*, *worral* or *messan* are all applied to an under-sized dwarfish person, these terms being also used for the smallest pig in the litter. *Sharger-baned* is applied to a woman with a narrow pelvis. The word *reglan* is also employed for an undersized person, but *reglan* is properly either a hermaphrodite or an imperfectly castrated animal.

Of the slighter deviations from the normal we have *lamiter*, cripple; *hirple*, to limp; to *gang cheeky-on*, walk in a lop-sided manner, *e.g.*, as in scoliosis; *glee, gley* or *skell*, to squint, with the adjectives *gleed, gleyed* or *skelly-e'ed*; *mant*, to stammer (*stammer* in Scottish dialect means to stumble); *boolie-backit*, round-shouldered; *humphie-backit*, hump-backed; *boo-houghed*, out-kneed; *shauchly*, walking in a shuffling manner. To *isk* is to hiccup (with the adages 'ilka time ye isk a drap o' blude leaves the heart,' and 'as the bairn isks the heart grows'); to *neeze*, to sneeze. *Silly* is used for bodily not mental weakness; while *stoot* means robust and *unstoot* weakly. The expression *not strong* is almost always used to signify phthisical, and a medical man may convey a totally wrong impression by saying this, and even cause grave offence; for phthisis is considered to be a matter of *heirskep* (heredity) and consequently a slur on the 'constitution' of the family.

An albino is described as *blin'-fair*; a left-handed person as *car-, cur-, curry-, kerry-, derry-, pawly-, kippie-handit* or *doakie*. *Deafy* or *taebetless* means benumbed, partially or totally devoid of sensation. A *pawly* or *poalie* finger is a 'sair' finger; *whittle* is a whitlow; a *wrat* is a wart. A *plook* is a pimple; a *fleein'-oot, hive* or *oot-strikkin'* is a rash; *fern-tickles* mean freckles. The *carry* or *scaw* (scab) is used both for impetigo and ring-worm.

A *scart* is a scratch; a *chack* is a nip; an *income, gatherin'* or *beelin'* is an abscess. *Rin, render, beel, sype* or *seep* are all used for discharge; while a *dottle* or *melt* signifies any stringy tenacious substance, such as the detritus of a boil or the membrane in diphtheria.

The *lily* is thrush; *crewels* or *waxen* (swollen) *kernels* are enlarged glands, especially cervical, a *naar* is the scar left after suppuration in such glands; a *scurl* is a scab. Necrosed bone coming away from a wound in small particles is described as *marled, murled,* or *mirled* (crumbled) bone.

To *bok* is to vomit, to belch. A *dry bok* is a retching. *Cowk* is also so used. To *scunner* is to disgust, to nauseate. To *gar the heart rise* is to make sick—*e.g.*, 'it fairly gart my heart rise.' To *gar the heart fill* is to affect almost to tears; *the heart is gey near the mooth* means the same. *Great-heartit* means emotional. To *get roond the heart*—*e.g.*, 'it fair got roond my heart'—is to cause to feel faint. To *gang wi' the heart* is to go with one's inclinations—*e.g.*, of food it is said, 'He'll tak' that; it'll gang wi' his heart.' Any injury on the left side of the chest is considered dangerous, as being *near the heart*. An injury complained of, say, on the leg, will be referred to contemptuously by an onlooker as *far frae the heart*—'Ye'll no' dee o' that: that's far frae the heart.'

A *hoast* is a cough; *kink-hoast*, whooping-cough, a person so afflicted being a *kinker*. A *kittlin'* (tickling) *hoast* is an irritable cough, as is a *clocher*. *Glut, glit,* or *corruption* (Fife) is expectoration. Noisy breathing is described as a *hirslin' at the breist*, a *whauzlin'* or a *rothie*; to *fob* is to pant—*e.g.*, 'Fobbin like a fat kitlin' (kitten); to *thratch*, to breathe heavily with a rattle as in the *deid-thraw* (death-agony).

Staved means jammed; a *scob* is a splint; a *batter*, a plaster.

Pain is variously described as a *yawin'* or *yarkin'* (gnawing) pain; a *beelin'* (throbbing) pain; a *stoondin', loupin'* or *gowpin'* pain, shooting pain such as that of acute toothache or neuralgia.

The *perfervi [dum] ingenium Scotorum* is proved to a certain degree by the various words we have to describe mental conditions. *Thocht* means worry, care. *Vogie* means excited—almost fey; *dowf, feckless, thowless*, spiritless; *moithered*, confused; *doited, donnert, dottrified, dottled*, stupid through age, senile; *skeery, camsteery, rampageous*, highly excited; *carried*, delirious; *deed to the warl'*, unconscious. *Sair felled* or *sair made*, much prostrated.

A *grewsin'*, rigor; *tongue-tackit*, tongue-tied; *lust*, seborrhoea; *mirls*, measles; *watery-pox* or *crystal-pox*, chicken-pox; *netteral-* (natural) *pox*, small-pox; *branks, buffets*, mumps; *hare-shaw*, hare-lip; *whummle-bore*, cleft palate; *bramble-mark* or *rasp*, naevus, are all in common use.

16
Disease and its Cure

In dealing with this section of our subject, it may be better at this stage merely to mention the universal cures (applicable to all diseases) which are found in (1) the power of 'the healer' (the seventh son, or, better still, the seventh son of the seventh son); (2) healing wells; and (3) charms and incantations. These may be better dealt with later on.

It will be, I am afraid, almost impossible to deal systematically with diseases and their folk-cures; the only way will be to consider these diseases as they most commonly occur; for the more common the trouble the more numerous are the cures for it.

It is a common and unfortunate popular belief—although much less common within the last thirty years—both as regards phthisis and other infectious disease that an older person is not liable to take infection from a younger. The clothes in an infectious case may thus, according to this belief, be quite safely washed by an older person—'She's auld be's (compared to) him'—without any special precautions being taken, and the older person may safely sleep with the younger. Fortunately, this belief is to some extent antagonised by another, viz., that if there is a marked difference of age—or of strength—in persons sleeping together the older (or stronger) will 'draw the strength oot o'' the younger (or weaker). It was on this former understanding that the young woman was put into the bed of the aged Psalmist. And here, perhaps, we may also note the belief in the existence of a 'white liver' in a man who has several times been a widower. Along with this curious popular pathological condition it is held there goes 'a bad breath' which is fatal to the spouse. Over-laying is explained away on similar lines by the suggestion that the child may have been killed by the 'foul breath' or the 'strength o' the breath' of the parents.

The old belief of ridding oneself of disease by transference is always cropping up. 'When disease was recognised, though tardily, to have positive existence, and the fact realised that, despite prayer and offerings, it might mysteriously be communicated by the sick person to another person who suffered in much the same way, complaining of similar pains and exhibiting the same general symptoms, a step had been taken in folk-medicine. If a man could, without conscious act on his part, infect his neighbour, why might he not, of purpose, transfer his complaint to something of a lower order, which would suffer the disease in his place?'[1] And the history of witch-craft in Scotland shows that many suffered the extreme penalty for putting this idea into practice, and professing to transfer disease to cats, dogs, calves, and other animals.[2] Within recent years in Fife, on the advice of a 'tinkler-wife' (for, as an old woman once said to me, 'Ye'd won'er what gaun'-about folk kens') a litter of black puppies was killed, split up, disembowelled and applied warm to the poisoned arm of a man, the 'tribble' being thus transferred from the human body to the canine. A black cat was killed and similarly treated and applied to a sore in the latter half of last century in Strathdon, Aberdeenshire, while a sufferer from venereal disease—a laird who was a notorious evil liver—was about the same time in Fife laid inside the carcase of a freshly killed and disembowelled ox. (Such a sufferer is always described in popular parlance as 'rotten,' the term usually used in the old books of popular medicine.) In Lockhart's *Life of Scott*, Sir Walter himself, in the autobiographical part, relates how he was in his early years, while visiting his grandfather at his farm, placed inside the warm newly-flayed skin of every sheep killed, in the hope of his weak leg being thereby improved. In Yorkshire at the beginning of this century a calf's brain was removed and applied to the head of a sufferer from neuralgia, and afterwards replaced in the calf's skull and buried. As the brain decayed the pain left the sick man's head. So with all the common cures for *wrats* (warts) in Scotland and elsewhere: the rubbing of a slug on the wart, and sticking the slug on a thorn to decay: the rubbing of the wart with a piece of stolen beef which was then buried: the burying of a string on which knots to the number of the warts had been tied, or straws corresponding in number to the warts: the placing of the warty hand into the throat of a newly-killed pig: the stroking of the wart with the dead hand of a relative.

And the popular faith in the efficacy of a poultice lies not so much in its heat and moisture as in its power to 'draw the tribble.' The disease is an entity which is 'in' until it is brought 'oot.' Some poultices, *e.g.*, carrot, turnip, 'apple-ringie,' cow-dung,[3] soap and

---

1. Black, *Folk-Medicine*, p. 34.
2. Dalzell, *Darker Superstitions of Scotland*, pp, 104–5.
3. A specially good remedy for 'foul shave' (Fife).

sugar are held to be 'awfu' drawing things,' and 'is it no' drawin' it owre sair?' is a common query. A blister which fails to rise shows that the trouble is 'dour to draw,' 'ill to move,' and that it is 'deep in.'

The commonest cause, of course, of criminal assaults on young children is the wish to get rid by transference of venereal disease, while I have come across a case where a nurse-maid acknowledged having deliberately 'smittit' her charge with *impetigo contagiosa* to rid herself of the complaint.

When a patient is ill, too, there is always the fear of taking any food that may 'feed the tribble.' 'For ony favour,' said a woman to me on one occasion, 'dinna gie me ony drogues that'll gar me eat; for a' I tak' just gangs to the hoast and strengthens it.' Behind it all, unknown to the speaker, lay the old idea of demoniacal possession, just as Zoroaster believed that a woman suffering from the menstrual flow was to be kept on low diet, for the strength she acquired from food would go to the fiends.

Hence comes, perhaps, the idea that those who 'arena feared at a tribble winna tak' it,' on the principle of resisting the Devil and he will flee from you. It is an idea that has even yet to be combated in dealing with infectious disease; plenty of people, otherwise intelligent, believing that a disease 'isna catchin',' provided 'they arena feared at it.' In one old medical book we find that 'Feare corrupts the Juices of the Braine (through the Force of Imagination) and makes them fall doune and disperse themselves into all the parts of the bodie filled with a sicklie qualitie, and soe contrarie to Nature. This is the reason why fearfull men are apt to die of slight wounds: Whereas a valiant spirit has always flesh apt to be healed.'[1] An echo here of Ecclesiastes with 'a merry heart doeth good like a medicine, but a broken spirit drieth the bones.'

An infectious disease is described as a *catchin'* complaint, while for contagious the word *smittle* (v. to *smit*) is used. Often, however, the word *smittle* is used for both infectious and contagious. The belief as regards measles, scarlatina, whooping-cough, &c., that they are merely 'bairn's tribbles,' and therefore as inevitable as teething, is responsible for much infantile mortality; for 'pit them a' thegither an' hae dune wi't' is often enough quietly practised. In the case of measles it is not so long since it was believed that an attack of measles made a child less liable to contract other diseases, and the mother of a sufferer would confer a favour on the child of a

---

1. *Helps for Suddain Accidents*, London, 1633.

neighbour by permitting it to become a contact.[1] 'Measles manna be wet' is a popular saw, and is too often the authority for leaving the patient in a lamentable state of dirt.

Cold water is still frequently regarded in popular belief as a most dangerous drink in acute illness, and the attendant will narrate with pride how she has refused this natural craving of the patient. 'A rash drink o' water' will either 'foonder' the sufferer or cause a 'burst.' The alarming statement 'he's burst himsel',' or 'he's gien himsel' a burst,' will satisfactorily explain any skin condition from *plooks* (pimples) to pemphigus, and the 'burst' is usually caused by a drink of cold water taken when the patient is heated by over-exertion. Cold water is an especially forbidden drink in the puerperium, and the medical attendant who permits its use must assume responsibility for any illness that follows, from *chackit paps* upwards or downwards. I have referred already to the weakening effect of water when used externally to the infant's or the miner's back, and the consequent objections to over-much washing.

Change of water is assumed to do as much harm as change of air does good. People coming to a new district often blame this for causing illness, especially boils, pimples, constipation, or diarrhoea; often, of course, correctly enough in the last two conditions should the water be abnormally hard or not above suspicion of pollution. Running water in the vicinity is held to be a cause of decay in teeth, and there is a common belief that water which has run 'owre three stanes' is safe to drink.[2]

As regards boils, the general idea is that these are a sign of rude health, or, at any rate, only apt to appear in those who are exceptionally well. Another belief of the same nature is that *pediculi capitis* only appear on strong children, and are 'a sign o' life.' And a curious instance of muddled reasoning is found in the action of an old woman who deliberately collected these undesirables from the head of a healthy child and transferred them to the head of a sickly one, under the belief that 'life gives life' and that the invalid would thereby acquire strength.[3]

As another instance of sympathetic magic we can take the application of the eel's skin in sprains. Other popular cures for sprains, the use of *oil o' saut, fore-shot* from a distillery, or *swine's seam* have the merit of either counter-irritation or massage. But the eel's skin

---

1. Crathie, Aberdeenshire.
2. Aberdeenshire, Kincardineshire, Dumfriesshire.
3. Kirkcaldy, Fife.

is not even applied as a bandage or a support: it is merely loosely twisted round the ankle, wrist, or other part affected. The reasoning is obvious, for the sprained part is stiff, and the eel being one of the most supple of living creatures the virtue of the latter goes to the former. A miner whom I knew in Fife kept such a skin, which was regularly lent out for this purpose. A salmon skin is used in the same way for the same purpose,[1] while a hare's skin[2] is applied to the chest in asthma. Here we have the skin of one of the most long-winded animals applied to the chest of a short-winded sufferer in the hope of a transference of attributes. In Dr. John Brown's *Letters* we find this recommended in asthma[3] by Dr. Martin (an Annandale man) to whom he was assistant. It is on the same principle that some Bechuanas wear the skin of a ferret as a charm, because being very tenacious of life it will make them, in turn, difficult to kill. Other Bechuanas wear the hair of a hornless ox amongst their own hair, and the skin of a frog in their mantle, because the ox having no horns is hard to catch, and the frog being slippery is the same. Perhaps, too, from the idea of movement as well as of nourishment hare's flesh and hare-soup were administered in the Highlands in menostasis.[4]

An example either of transference of disease or of sacrifice—perhaps of both—is seen in the Highland cure for epilepsy by burying an entirely black cock[5] alive on the spot where the patient had the first fit. A modified form of this is the cure used for giddiness,[6] when a hole was dug and the black cock put in it alive. The patient was made to lie face downwards over the hole, after a handful of earth had been thrown over the unfortunate fowl, and inhale the 'smell o' the earth' stirred up by the fluttering of the bird's wings. Whether the old man who recommended this cure suspected that the giddiness was due to *petit mal* is hard to say; but here we have the transference of disease idea associated with the earth cure to be mentioned later as in use for whooping-cough, 'bad air,' and phthisis. Other cures for epilepsy are burning (or burying) the patient's clothes where he had the first fit;

---

1. Strathdon, Aberdeenshire.
2. Aberdeenshire.
3. Other cures for asthma are cob-web (*moose-wab*), pills, and wearing a string of *lammer* (amber) beads round the neck. These are also worn for eye trouble, as are ear-rings. In the National Museum of Antiquities, Edinburgh, there are some amber beads which were so used in Argyllshire.
4. 'Old Highland Therapy,' *Caledonian Medical Journal*, vol. v, p. 400.
5. 'With yellow beak and yellow legs' ('Sutherland and the Reay Country').
6. Inverurie, Aberdeenshire, within the last thirty years.

drinking water out of the skull of a suicide,[1] or of one who has met with a violent death, preferably a young man who has been cut off 'in his strength;'[2] while Salmon, in his *Dispensatory*, and Moncrieff, in his *Poor Man's Physician*, mentions the power of 'powdered skull of dead man' in all diseases of the head.

And now let us look at some of the commoner complaints and their cures. In the case of *kink-hoast* (whooping-cough) the sufferer may be taken to a lime-kiln, a gas-work, down a pit, or made to 'breathe the air off' a hole freshly dug in the ground. This earth cure[3] is also held to be of value in phthisis (as is the smell of stable manure) and it used to be considered specially efficacious by the Fifeshire miner of a bye-gone generation in treating those who had suffered from bad air or gas in the pit.[4] A hole was dug in the earth, and the patient made to lie face downwards over it. Even after he had somewhat recovered and had been put to bed, a 'divot' or turf was cut and laid on the sufferer's pillow, so that the gentle breath of Mother Earth might play about him as he slept.

The child ill with whooping-cough may also for his cure be passed under the belly of a donkey, sacred for its association with Christ, wherefore it carried the mark of the Cross on its back. Children riding on a donkey to school remained free from whooping-cough during a local epidemic, until the steed unfortunately died, when the riders were thereupon attacked by the disease.[5] Another cure is to carry the patient until a man on a white—some say a piebald—horse is met with. He is then asked what is 'good for' whooping-cough,

---

1. Such a cranium was recently in use in the Lewis, being kept buried when not required at the spot where the suicide occurred.
2. In the *Progrès Medical*, of 26th December, 1908, Dr. Cornet mentions that, before the Roman Conquest, the Gauls, like the Scythians, Scandinavians, and other savage peoples, drank out of human skulls. Such skulls would be those of enemies killed in battle, men in the prime of life and the fulness of their strength.
3. The health-giving power of earth frequently crops up in folk-medicine. 'It should be remembered that touching and lifting the earth was in many countries considered a remedy for diseases, especially those of the eye. Earth taken from the spot where a man was slain was prescribed in Scotland for a hurt or an ulcer' (*Folk-Lore of the Isle of Man*).
4. Some twenty-five years ago an old miner expressed to me great surprise that this 'cure' had not been tried in a pit accident where several men died from the effects of after-damp.
5. Crimond, Aberdeenshire.

and what he says must be given.[1] After the acute stage of the disease is over, a 'cheenge o' air' is always considered essential to complete the cure, the change being, if possible, 'across water.'[2] A curious variant of the idea is that the sufferer need not have the change of air if he be treated with some food which has undergone it. I have frequently known cases where the Fife miner took more bread than he required down the pit for his 'pit-piece,' and this surplus food—which had received the necessary change of air—was then administered to the sick child. Efficacy also lies in bread and milk administered by a woman whose maiden surname is the same as her married one.[3] Gregor[4] mentions this, with the addition that if the patient is taken to and from the woman's house through a wood the cure will be more sure. (Variants of this are to take the patient over running water—south running water is best—or through three lairds' lands.) He also mentions that a decoction of sheep's excrement was esteemed as a cure both for kink-hoast and jaundice. (This was used by the Boer women in the concentration camps during the last South African war.) Eating the food with a 'quick-horn' spoon (*i.e.*, a spoon made from a horn cast by a living animal) or a draught of water which had gathered on a 'yird-fast stane' or a tomb stone[5] were also recommended. Taking the patient to another laird's land, drinking asses milk or riding on an ass were both held to be good treatment, while Black[6] mentions that in Scotland and Devonshire alike a hair from the sufferer's head put between slices of bread and butter and given to a dog transferred the disease to that animal, more surely if, on eating, the dog (as was natural) coughed while consuming the hair. Another transference cure was to make the 'kinker' cough into the mouth of a live fish or a frog which was then replaced in the water. Similarly, a live spider placed in a bag and slung round the patient's neck was held to be helpful: the disease went to the

---

1. Jamieson says the enquirers for information would shout, 'Man on the piety (piebald) horse, what's gude for the kink-hoast?'
2. *Cf.* the belief that witches cannot cross running water. *Vide* 'Tam o' Shanter.'
3. An old woman, still alive and in her ninetieth year, had this qualification. On my saying to her that she must have been useful when kink-hoast was about, she replied. 'Ach! the year I was mairrit it was a fair scunner! A' the bairns in the parish had the kink-hoast, and they were a' sent to me for breid an' milk' (Portlethen, Kincardineshire).
4. *Folk-Lore of the North-East of Scotland*, p. 48.
5. Aberdeenshire.
6. *Folk-Medicine*, p. 35.

spider and on its death the cure was complete. But perhaps the most extraordinary remedy of all is that which may be seen in the Antiquarian Museum, Edinburgh, viz., a goose's thrapple filled with lead drops which was used as a charm against kink-hoast in Galloway. Certain healing wells were specially curative for the disease, *e.g.*, St. Fillan's, and 'The Kinker's Stone' in the woods at Elphinstone, near Pitcaple, Aberdeenshire.

The Pains

The Pains (rheumatism) being like kink-hoast, a common complaint, has also many cures. A potato carried in the pocket is held by many—even 'educated'—persons to effect a cure. The maximum effect is obtained when the potato shrivels up. It is considered to 'draw the iron oot o' the blude.' A hare's foot—the left fore-foot for preference—is also valuable when carried in the pocket. It is interesting to note that Pliny mentions the use of the foot of the hare for gout in the feet. Black slugs 'masked' (infused) in a teapot[1] supply an oil which is good for 'rubbing in.' The marrow of bullocks' bones twice boiled is used as an inunction, while 'swine's seam' (pig fat) is a very common application. The inflamed and swollen joints may also be switched with freshly-gathered nettles. This was the favourite application twenty-five years ago of an old man, eighty years of age, in Fife, a sufferer from rheumatism of many years' standing. A poultice of boiled 'sleek'—a species of seaweed—was in common use there amongst the coast-dwellers of 'the Kingdom.' Flowers of sulphur rubbed over the joint or dusted inside the 'flyped' stocking is often used, and, spread on blue flannel (itself held to be a 'rale healin' thing') is used for the treatment of lumbago. A rather risky (although common) 'cure' is the supping of turpentine mixed with sugar.

Cramp

This is also treated with sulphur. A piece of sulphur under the pillow is held to ward off cramp from all occupants of the bed, however numerous. I have seen a sulphur candle (served out by a sanitary inspector to disinfect a room after scarlet fever) devoted to this higher use. A 'sulphur-band' is made by tying or sewing a piece of sulphur firmly into the garter, and sulphur worn in the 'oxter' also works a cure, as does sulphur rubbed into the affected part or into the

---

1. Fifeshire.

palm of the hand. For under the pillow use, cork[1] is sometimes used. Rubbing the fingers between the toes and 'smelling the sweat' is also curative: in view of the rare foot-washing of some of the folk, this, at least, provides something possibly more disagreeable to think about.

Worms

It is a popular belief in Scotland that medicine for worms is best administered when the 'moon is at its heicht,' as the worms are then held 'to come oot.'[2] One common cure is to make the child chew dry bread. The worms are supposed to 'come oot' at the noise of the chewing, and on whisky being given the worms are killed. A cure of a similar kind was, on the advice of an old woman,[3] carried out (in 1904) in the case of a child who was supposed to have 'the drinkin' diabetes.'[4] The sufferer was given a salt herring to eat, her arms were tied behind her back, and she was made to lean over south-running water. 'A beast cam' up her throat,' and she was then held to be cured. Here 'the beast' that caused the disease was so tormented by the salted food that it 'cam' up' to drink at the sound of the running water, and the cure was complete. The reasoning, at any rate, is simple.

The 'heicht o' the moon' brings up again the effect of season and time of day and night on disease. Leap year is held to be 'unlucky for beasts and bodies; there's a heap o' witchcraft gaun aboot in leap year.'[5] May is a bad month for marriage, for

> O' marriages in May
> Bairns die in decay,

and of children born in May it is said, 'May birds are aye cheepin.'

There is 'a cheenge in the system'[6] every seven years.[7] In spring there is a necessity to 'clear the blude,' and of old this was done by bleeding. Short of that (or in addition to it), 'spring medicine' was

---

1. Also in Lincolnshire.
2. In the *B.M.J.*, 29th May, 1926, Dr. J.W. Lindsay, of Balen, Paraguay, writing on the effects of the tropical full moon, says: 'Children with intestinal parasites, especially *ascaris*, suffer more from convulsions then than at other periods. Europeans are unwilling to believe what the natives tell them about the moon and many other things, but they find later that the natives are often right.'
3. Fife.
4. In popular phraseology diabetes is either 'the eatin' diabetes' or 'the drinkin' diabetes.'
5. Fife.
6. The fairies pay teind to Hell every seven years.
7. Cf. Black, *Folk-Medicine*, p. 135.

taken, usually sulphur and cream of tartar. 'A purge and a vomit' were the objects formerly aimed at. Sibbald in his *History of Fife* mentions a well in the parish of Auchterderran which was much resorted to for this purpose, and all over the country were numerous 'medicine wellies,' the word 'medicine' (like 'physic') having (as it still has amongst the folk) the meaning of a purgative.[1] Eruptions on the skin, boils, &c., are all explained as 'bein' just the time o' year,' if occurring in spring.

Animal cures

A few notes may be given on animal cures. Years ago I came across a boy[2] who was having given to him, thrice daily, for enuresis, a tablespoonful of the liquor in which a mouse had been boiled. The cure was, I found, well known and esteemed in the district by the older women, although some preferred to roast the mouse (on a shovel over the fire) to a cinder, powder it down, and so give it to the invalid. This mouse cure was also given in whooping-cough. Zola, in *l'Assommoir*, mentions it is an anthelmintic, and Salmon, in his *Dispensatory*, so recommends it. Bulleyn (Elizabethan), in his *Book of Simples*, recommends for enuresis 'a small yong mouse roasted.'[3] Other popular cures for this were giving porridge boiled with the child's own urine, and making it drink its own urine; while a napkin wet with urine was used for swabbing out the child's mouth in thrush.

'Skate-bree,' *i.e.*, the liquor in which skate has been boiled, is popularly recognised as an aphrodisiac.[4] A barren woman, too free

---

1. A fairly comprehensive list of curative wells is got in Mackinlay's *Folk-lore of the Scottish Lochs and Springs*.
2. Fife.
3. *Vide* also articles, 'The Mouse,' in the *American Druggist*, of February, 1926, and 'The Mouse in Fable and Folk-lore' (*Folk-Lore*, vol. xxxvi, p. 227), by Warren R. Dawson.
4. Hence probably the saying, 'Gang to Banff and bottle skate.' A variant is 'and beetle (*i.e.*, pound) skate.' Another reference is in the old Scottish song:
   I'll catch the white fish
      To please my lassie's e'e,
   But the bonnie black-backit fish
      Has aye the sweetest bree.
   Robert Fergusson sings:
   Then neist, when Sammy's heart was faintin',
   He'd longed for skate to mak' him wanton.

with her tongue, will be checked with the contemptuous rejoinder, 'Awa' an' sup skate-bree!' Gregor[1] mentions skate-bree only as a liniment for sprains and rheumatism. Sweat is also believed to have an aphrodisiac action. Kraft-Ebbing[2] mentions the belief as existing in Germany, and Gregor states that when two lozenges, covered with sweat and stuck together, were given to the one whose love was sought, strong affection was excited by the eating of them. Peter Buchan, writing (1828) in a note to the ballad of 'Geordie Downie,' says: 'It has long been proverbial, and even to this day believed by many, that the itinerant tinkers, *alias* wandering gypsies, possess a charm by which they can make any woman they please submit to their embraces. I have seen receipts for such, but had no faith in them, even although given by the celebrated Reginal Scott, in his *Discovery of Witch-craft.*' And not unassociated with the idea of sweat is the verse of the ballad, 'Fause Sir John and May Colvin,' where we find:

> Frae below his arm, he's pull'd a charm,
>   And stuck it in her sleeve,
> And he has made her gang wi' him
>   Without her parents' leave.

Another popular aphrodisiac was an infusion of *deutzia gracilis*, whole plant.

Pig's blood has already been referred to as a cure for warts. The gall of the pig is used as an application for chilblains. The rind of a piece of ham with the fat attached, applied externally round the neck, was within recent years held in high estimation in Fife as a cure for sore throat. *Swine's seam* (pig fat) was an universal inunction for rheumatism, sprains, swollen glands, &c. It was also the common basis of many home-made ointments, being often combined with gunpowder, sulphur, 'chappit leeks,' &c., to make a 'healin' sau','

Trout, shellfish, and salt are also held to be aphrodisiac; 'Fond o' saut, fond o' the lasses,' being a common saying. Thomas Jordan, a seventeenth century poet (*vide Oxford Book of Verse*), writes:

> We'll sport and be free with Moll, Betty and Dolly,
> Have oysters and lobsters to cure melancholy,
> Fish dinners will make a man spring like a flea,
>   Dame Venus, love's lady,
>   Was born of the sea;
> With her and with Bacchus we'll tickle the sense,
> For we shall be past it a hundred years hence.

1. *Folk-lore of the North-East of Scotland.*
2. *Psychopathia Sexualis.*

another common 'sau'' being made by burying fresh butter (wrapped in a cloth) in the earth for some days.

As regards sore throat, it was usual to consider it due to 'the pap o' the hawse' (uvula) being 'doon'; and it was believed that there was one hair in the head[1] which, if found and pulled, would bring it 'up' again—the difficulty, obviously, being to find the hair.

Hives

One of the commonest of all children's complaints met with in Scotland is that which in popular parlance is termed *Hives*. The word is constantly in use,[2] and it is difficult to say how much or how little it connotes. Jamieson[3] gives it as meaning 'any eruption on the skin when the disorder is supposed to proceed from an internal cause. Thus, bowel-hive is the name given to a disease in children in which the groin is said to swell. Hives is used to denote both the red and yellow gum (Lothians), A.S. *Heafian*, to swell.' Campbell[4] says '*Breac-shith* (Gaelic), 'elfin-pox,' Hives, are spots that appear on the skin in certain diseases, as hooping-cough, and indicate a highly malignant form of the disease. They are not ascribed to the Fairies, but are named *sith* because they appear, and again disappear, 'silently,' without obvious cause, and more mysteriously than other symptoms.' From my own observation I should say that, generally speaking, if an infant is at all out of sorts it is said to be 'hivie'; diarrhoea, vomiting, thrush—all these conditions come under the adjective; while a frequent cause of sudden death in children is held to be 'the hives gaun roond the heart.' The commonest varieties of the disease, so far as we can classify them, are:

1. *Bowel-hives*; the green, slimy diarrhoea associated with malnutrition, dentition, and malfeeding.
2. *Oot-fleein' hives*; a rash of any sort, short of the exanthemata. For example, eczema capitis is often described as starting from a 'hive' on the brow, and the sudamina so common on neck and nose in the first few days of infant life are looked on as a good sign and called 'the thrivin' hives.'
3. *In-fleein' hives*; more difficult to define, and usually spelling sudden death for the patient; or, at any rate, sudden death is

---

1. Fife. Probably derived from a confused interpretation of the Scriptural statement regarding the hairs of the head being numbered.
2. Fife and the Lowlands of Scotland.
3. *Dictionary of the Scottish Language.*
4. *Superstitions of the Scottish Highlands.*

quite satisfactorily explained by the statement that the 'hives have gane inwan' (inwards), or 'gotten roond the heart,' the usual goal being this organ. 'Dumb fits' is another term used.

4. *The bannock-hive*; a term applied, usually humorously and contemptuously, to the sufferer from gastric derangement due to overeating. When doubt is thrown in the family circle on a member's claim to be an invalid we hear the phrase, 'Weel, if ye're hivie, it's the bannock-hive,' similar to 'Ye're meat-hale, ony wey,' or Galt's famous 'Ony sma' haud o' health he has is aye at meal times.'

Hives, either with 'The Mayflower' or at some subsequent date, went over to America. It crops up in many of those trans-Atlantic medical advertisements with which we are so abundantly favoured, and in the fiction of the United States, and apparently means urticaria.

As regards, 'the hives gettin' roond the heart,' there is also an idea that severe fright or shock will 'ca' the heart aff its stalk,' and so cause sudden death. Sudden death in pregnancy is often held to be due to 'the bairn pittin' up its hand an' grippin' the (mother's) heart.'[1] In the case of a child dying from shock after a severe scalding the reason given was that 'the heart had been ca'd aff its stalk.' Whether this idea of the heart possessing a stalk is due to its pear shape or not is hard to say; but more likely the aorta was looked on as the stalk upon which the heart hung; and, as a large amount of popular anatomy must have spread to the multitude through pig-killing (for has not man 'got a' the puddens o' a soo but ane'?) and other butchery, we cannot expect it to be very exact. 'It flittit my heart,' *i.e.*, made my heart move from its place, is another expression used. Burns in his 'Hallowe'en,' when the vision of an 'outlier quey' came

---

1. The intimate relation of the infant to the mother's heart crops up frequently in ballad literature. In 'Burd Helen' we have:

> And the bairn that lay beneath her heart
> For cauld began to quake.

And again in 'Mary Hamilton':

> The King is to the Abbey gane
> To pu' the Abbey tree,
> To scale the babe frae Marie's heart,
> But the thing it wadna be.

A variant of the second line is

> To pu' o' the savin tree.

The royal would-be abortionist of the ballad was Darnley.

between the widow Leezie and the moon, says her heart 'maist lap the hool,'[1] while the Orcadian says, 'My heart is oot o' hule.' In the Highlands,[2] in connection with insanity, there is a belief that the cause is the heart getting displaced ('jumping out of its husk') owing to a sudden shock.[3] Hence the attempt to make it jump back again by administering another shock, *e.g.*, attaching the sufferer to a rope and towing him behind a boat until he was exhausted.

Toothache

Toothache was held to be caused by a worm in the tooth, and could be cured (1) by snuffing salt up the nose (a fisher cure), (2) by smoking tobacco until sick, (3) by carrying a worm in the mouth from one laird's land to another's.

Cancer

Cancer, even yet, is almost always spoken of by the folk as 'eatin' cancer,' and is popularly supposed to 'eat' all applications put to it. It is not uncommon at the present day to hear weird tales of 'it ate a loaf o' breid and a bottle o' whisky a day.'

---

1. Hool, the covering of a bean; the husk.
2. Moodie, 'Highland Therapy,' *C.M.J.*, vol. iv.
3. This idea was exploited in asylum treatment of the eighteenth and early nineteenth centuries in the shape of 'the surprise bath,' when the floor was made to give way and the patient to fall into cold water, and 'the whirling chair,' a revolving seat into which the sufferer was strapped and then spun rapidly round.

17

Scottish Proverbs Bearing on Medicine

On doctors

First of all there is the general declaration of fact—with which we will all agree—contained in the statement 'There's a cure for a' thing save stark deid,' or in its rhyming form:

> There's nae remeid
> For stark deid.

'Deid,' as most know, is the old Scots word for 'Death.' It is further driven home by 'Death defies the doctors,' while a gentle libel on our profession is 'Leeches kill wi' licence,' amplified in another:

> When the doctor cures,
> The sun sees it.
> But when he kills,
> The earth hides it.

'Diet cures mair than doctors' conveys an idea carried on with 'Eat in measure and defy the doctor,' or its variant 'Live in measure and laugh at the mediciners.' A man refusing to take the advice of a friend still gets out of it by saying 'That's but ae doctor's opinion'; while we all know 'The cure may be waur than the disease.' There is considerable wisdom, too, in 'Doctors differ, and sae do diseases,' but none in 'A drucken doctor's clever.'

> Tak the fee
> When the tear's in the ee'

still holds good, however.

On personal characteristics

Everyone knows:

> A hairy man's a geary man,
> A hairy wife's a witch.

'A hasty man never wantit wae' and 'A hasty man is never lasty' are old sayings. ('Lasty' = capable of prolonged effort.)

[113]

As regards personal appearance, we have the well-known sneer, 'He's waur than daft, he's reid-heidit,' and the common school-boy taunt:

Reid heid,
Curly pow,
Pish on the gress
An' gar it grow.

Fair people—there may be old racial reasons and hatreds behind it—generally come in for criticism; for we have 'Fair folk are aye fushionless,' and 'Fair hair may have foul roots,' the latter, however, due to a popular belief that head lice are more commonly got in fair hair than in dark. We have also the rhyme (applicable to women):

Fair and foolish,
Black and proud
Lang and lazy,
Little and loud.

Another is:

Lang and sma'
Gude for naethin' ava'.

('Sma" = slender.)

Small people and big people are dealt with indiscriminately. 'Short fowk is soon angry,' and 'Short fowk's he'rts is soon at their mou" are balanced by 'Muckledom is nae virtue,' 'Muckledom is nae manliness' (or 'Muckle but nae manfu"), where of a long, loosely-built man it is said, 'There's owre muckle o'm to be a' weel at ae time.'

Of corpulent people we get 'Fat flesh freezes soon.' 'Fat paunches bode (indicate) lean pows,' and 'He that has a wide wame never had a lang arm,' *i.e.*, obese and apathetic.

Dealing with eyes, folk-wisdom gives us,

Grey-eyed greedy,
Broon-eyed needy,
Black-eyed never blin'
Till it shames a' its kin.

It is noteworthy that blue eyes are not mentioned.

A saying of general application is, 'Him that's no' handsome at twenty, strong at thirty, wise at forty, rich at fifty, will never be handsome, strong, wise or rich.'

Big heid, little wit,
Has an arse and canna sit

demonstrates by its second line the truth of its first.

A curious saying is, 'It's a' oots an' ins, like Willie Wood's wife's wame.' (Note the alliteration, common in many folk-sayings.) One would like to have known more about Mrs. Wood's case: there is probably a history attached to the proverb, as there is to many where a proper name is brought in.

'Wide lugs and a short tongue is best' contains sense; while a good description of a careless fellow is, 'He wad tyne his lugs if they werena tackit till 'im.'

'Tak tent o' the man that God has set his mark on' refers to an old Scottish belief that any man deformed by birth, illness, or accident should be watched with care in what dealings one has with him.

An old rhyme is:

> The gravest fish is an oyster,
> The gravest bird is an owl,
> The gravest beast is an ass,
> And the gravest man's a fool.

'He's like's bannock, he's like's bit,' is applied to any one in a thriving condition of health. 'Hair and horn grow weel on shargers' (undersized, weakly folk) expresses an old belief.

'Ye wad mak a gude howdie: ye haud the grip ye get,' is an old reference to the art of obstetrics.

Drink, diet and the stomach

We find a large amount of material here, mostly, but not always, on the side of moderation and plain living. For example, we have 'Surfeits slay more than swords,' 'Suppers kill mair than doctors cure,' and 'A crammed kyte maks a crazy carcase,' emphasised again in more metaphorical diction by 'Double charges rive cannons.'

'Hunger is gude kitchen,' or 'Sliver and sharp teeth 's the best kitchen,' gives the Scots version of 'Hunger is the best sauce'; and it is enlarged in the saying 'Hunger is gude kitchen to a cauld potato, but a wet divot to the lowe o' love,' that is, hunger acts as an anaphrodisiac.

Temperance in diet is further preached in 'Licht suppers mak lang days,' 'Drink little that ye may drink lang,' 'Never lat the nose blush for the sins o' the mou',' 'Muckle meat, mony maladies,' and 'After cheese, naething.'

But other proverbs urge us in the other direction, such as, 'A fu' wame maks a straucht back,' 'Fill fou and hand fou maks a stark man,' 'Beef steaks and porter mak gude belly mortar,' 'Better belly rive than gude meat spoil,' 'Double drinks are gude for drooth,' 'Drunk folk seldom tak harm,' 'A fou man's a true man,' 'Fair fa' gude drink, for it gars folk speak as they think,' 'When the wine sinks words soom,' 'When the wame's fu' the tongue wags,' and various others of the same kidney.

As regards the preparation of food we have, 'God sends meat and the Deil sends cooks,' and 'Owre muckle cookery spiles the brochan.' Still, *per contra*, we have 'Better wait on cooks than leeches.'

A rather rash proverb is 'Quick at meat, quick at work.' We as a profession practise it against our wills, and suffer accordingly; but this other has much truth in it, namely, 'Poor folk seek meat for their stamacks, and rich folk seek stamacks for their meat.'

Folk-wisdom tells us that 'Lang fastin' hains nae meat,' and, further, that 'Lang fastin' gathers wind.' We are told, too, that 'A hungry man has aye a lazy cook,' 'A hungry man's an angry man,' "A hungry man smells meat far,' 'A hungry wame is aye cravin',' and, best of all for vigour and terseness, 'A hungry wame has nae lugs.'

Decrease of appetite as hunger gets satisfied is described well in 'As the soo fills the draff soors.' In praise of plain living we find, 'What fizzes in the mou' winna fill the wame': *i.e.*, delicacies are not satisfying.

There are two proverbial references to butter as an article of diet. One is 'Butter is gold in the morning, silver at noon, and lead at night.' Another is 'Butter and burn trouts are kittle meat for maidens,' a reference to the aphrodisiac action that trout (along with skate, shell-fish, etc.) is supposed to have. A variant of the latter is 'Butter and burn trout gar maidens force wind.' 'Butter was her first meat' is said of a gossiping woman.

Of a greedy person we have the terse saying, 'His ee's bigger than his belly,' or 'His ee's greedier than his guts.'

After dinner sit a while,
After supper run a mile

has its prose variant, 'When the wame's fu' the banes wad be at rest.'

Diseases, injuries and old age

In dealing with diseases, injuries and old age, we again find much folk-philosophy. For example, take 'It may come in an hoor what winna gang in seven years,' 'Every wight has his weird and we maun a' dee when oor day comes,' 'A man is no sae soon healed as hurt,' 'The langer ye live ye see the mair ferlies,' 'Though auld and wice, still tak advice,' 'Young folk *may* dee, auld folk *maun* dee,' 'When ye get auld ye get nirled,' 'Auld folks are twice bairns,' 'There's nae fules like auld fules,' 'Auld wives and bairns mak fools o' physicians.'

The bearing of youth on age is shown in 'While ae gab's teethin' anither's growin' teethless,' 'Lazy youth maks lousy age,' 'Reckless youth maks ruefu' eild' (old age), 'Young men's knocks auld men feel,' 'Young saints, auld sinners,' 'Royt (wild) lads mak sober men,' where again we find the inevitable contradictions of all proverbial literature.

Wounds and injuries

'A green wound is half hale.' 'A bad wound may heal, but a bad name will kill,' 'Sairs shouldna be sair han'lt,' 'A scabbit heid loesna the kame,' 'A scabbit heid is aye in the way,' 'A scabbit heid is eith to bleed,' 'The sair place aye gets the lick,' 'A scarred heid is soon broken,' 'An elbuck dirl will lang play thirl,' 'Better a finger aff as aye waggin.'

General health axioms

'If ye wish to be soon weel be lang sick' is a proverb, naturally, not beloved of friendly societies or Board of Health functionaries. It is, however, most generally (and appropriately) applied to women in child-bed. Another sound axiom is, 'No weel is waur nor sick in bed,' *i.e.*, to go about feeling unwell without knowing what is wrong is often more dangerous than being laid up with a definite illness. 'Better wear shoon than sheets' is also sound, and may be extended to speak in favour of walking exercise. 'Feed a cold but hunger a colic' is a variant of the more common 'Feed a cold and starve a fever.' To hunger a colic is good treatment, and the hero of the following proverb had probably not acted on it: 'Like the man wi the sair guts—there's no gettin' quat o't.'

> Rise when the day daws,
> Bed when the nicht fa's,

is good enough advice for those who can manage it. A variant is 'Bed wi' the lamb and rise wi' the laverock.'

'Gude health is better than wealth' and 'It's gude sleepin' in a hale skin' both ring true.

> Keep the heid and feet warm,
> And a' the rest will tak nae harm,

has as a companion,

> When wind blaws on ye through a hole,
> Mak your bed and mind your soul.

The

> *Mingere cum bombis*
> *Res est salvissima lumbis*

of the *Schola Salernitana* is declared with equal frankness in the Scottish version:

> Fart dry and pish clear,
> And ye shall live for mony a year.

A variant is

> Pish and fart,
> Soond at the heart,

while an old expression of popular goodwill lays the same stress on the health value of free passing of wind and water in 'Lang may ye pish and fart and never need the doctor.'

'The clartier the cosier' puts you in touch with another: '"A clean thing's kindly," as the wife said when she turned her sark after a month's wear.'

Mental attributes, imagination and fancy

There are many wise saws. Of the advantages of cheerfulness we have—'A blythe heart maks a bonny look,' 'As lang lives the merry man as the sad, and a nicht langer.' 'It's the life o' an auld hat to be weel cockit' means that one should make the best of things and put a good face on them.

Fools, properly enough, come in for plenteous condemnation, hence:

> A fool at forty will never be wise.
> Fools are fond o' flittin'
> And wise men o' sittin'.

'Fools are aye fortunate'—an envious remark of the unfortunate— 'Fools are aye seein' ferlies' (wonders), 'Fools are fond o' flattery,' 'Fools are fond o' a' they forgaither wi',' 'Fools ravel and wise men redd,' 'Fools shouldna hae chappin'-sticks,' 'Forbid a fool a thing and that he'll do,' while the proverb-maker, like Silas Wegg, drops into poetry when he says:

> Ill's the gout, and waur's the graivel,
> But want o' wit mak's mony a traivel.

A prose variant is, 'Little wit in the heid maks muckle traivel to the feet.'

All of us will agree that 'A liar should hae a gude memory' and that 'A safe conscience maks a soond sleep,' while 'A tricky man is easiest trickit' and 'A thochtless body is aye thrang' cannot well be denied. And so with 'A wise heid maks a close mou'' and 'A wise man wavers, a fool is fixed,' which last supports the individual who talks about the 'damnable monotony of consistency.'

'Glum folks is no easy guidit' must appeal to the alienist and to all of us, as does 'He that looks to fraits, fraits will follow him.'

'He that speaks to himsel' speaks to a fool' bears its own uncomplimentary explanation.

> He that speaks wi' a drant (drawl)
> An' sells wi' a cant (whine)
> Is richt like a snake in the skin o' a saunt

dates back to Puritan or Covenanting times.

Hypochondriacs

'It's lang or like-to-dee fills the kirkyaird,' 'Dinna hae the saw waitin' on the sair,' 'Ye're feared o' the death ye'll never dee,' and 'Fancy may kill or cure'; while of malingerers we have 'Ye may be sick but ye're no sair-handled,' that is, exhausted with work. And to both these classes is given the hardy advice, 'Keep up your heid tho' your tripes is trailin'.'

A very true saying is 'Nae wonder ye're auld-like: ilka thing fashes ye,' which drives home that it is worry and not work that knocks one out; while 'Naething maks a man sae auld-like as sittin' ill to his meat' (that is, being ill fed) carries conviction with it.

Yawning

> Gantin' bodes (indicates) wantin'
> Ane o' three,
> Meat, sleep,
> Or gude companie,

or, as a prose variant,

> They never gantit but wantit
> Meat, sleep, or makkin' o' (caressing).

Women

On *women* much proverbial lore has, naturally, been expended, and generally follows the lines exploited by Solomon and all other sages who have given the subject practical attention.

Modern feminine fashion tends to reverse the values in 'Wit is worth mair than a weel-turn'd leg'; and even 'Maidens should be mild and meek, quick to hear and slow to speak,' sounds a little out of date. But the next is perhaps more in touch with the times, as it sounds an universal truth—'Maidens want naethin' but a man, and syne they want a'thing.' Still,

> A gude wife and health
> Is a man's best wealth,

but if a man draws a bad wife in the lottery he can get consolation from 'An ill coo may hae a gude calf.'

'Bad legs and ill wives should baith bide at hame' seems plausible enough, as does 'Wae's the wife that wants the tongue, but weel's the man that gets her.'

A curious old proverb is 'Ae year a nurse and seven years a daw (slut).' One commentator[1] says, 'because feeding well and doing little she becomes liquorish and gets a habit of idleness.' Another old one is 'Lang-tongued wives gae lang wi' bairn,' as is 'Greenin' wives are aye greedy.' The senseless, giggling, hyper-aesthetic type which contributes so frequently to the illegitimate birth-rate is well hit off by 'Easy kittled (tickled), easy coortit, easy made a fule o'.'

A quaint saying is 'What's gude for sick John is gude for hale Janet'—possibly starting from some tale about a wife annexing her invalid husband's special diet.

Children

On children much folk-wisdom has also been expended. A curious one is 'A daft nurse maks a wise bairn.' It seems, in view of present-day knowledge, to be a dangerous experiment, and not worth the risk involved.

> Gie a bairn his will
> And a whalp his fill,
> And nane o' the twa will thrive

is sound advice; while 'Silly (weakly) bairns are eith (easy) to lear (teach)' is a fact that is often noticed. 'A tarrowing bairn is never fat'—'tarrowing' = our present-day vernacular word 'touty,' particular, easily put off food. Such weakly children are often supposed to trace their weakness to being born in May: hence, 'May birds are aye cheepin',' and

> Of marriages in May,
> Bairns die in a decay.

The last one to be given will genuinely appeal to the modern type of parent. It is in rhyme:

> Waly, waly, bairns are bonny,
> Ane's eneuch an' twa's owre mony,

and might be suitably inscribed in gold—or preferably in brass—over the doorways of the present-day Birth-Control Clinics.

---

1. Kelly, *A Complete Collection of Scottish Proverbs*, London, 1721.

18

The Galar Mor:
How our Forefathers Dealt
with the Plague

[From *Scots Magazine* 22 (1934–35), 118–22]

Plague, that dread scourge of our Scottish past, first visited the country, if we accept the somewhat doubtful authority of Hector Boece, in the year 1282 A.D. According to John of Fordun, the true date was 1349-50, when one third of the whole population is said to have perished. It returned in 1361; and in 1380 a raid by the Douglas across the Border, to exploit plague-stricken England, brought back the Black Death once more to Scotland. The direst results followed. We have record of it again in 1456, when a Parliament was summoned by King James II to decide, *inter alia*, what measures should be taken to combat the prevalent epidemic. The main public health measure agreed upon, and put in force, was the isolation of the victims; and, during the numerous later outbreaks of the plague between then and 1645—its last epidemic appearance in Scotland—this policy held the field. It was, in fact, the only practical one, as the medical treatment of the day was of little or no value in dealing with plague.

These early sanitary attempts to control the disease were not entirely without merit. Dr. Maxwell Wood tells us that, in the case of Edinburgh, such sufferers as had not the means to support themselves were compelled to leave the town, while their wealthier fellow-citizens were equally bound to supply them with both food and a dwelling, 'lest by wandering about they should be a further source of infection. Contaminated houses, in the interests of public health, were allowed to be destroyed; but as fire, in those days of inflammable house-structure, was a daily peril, a condition was added that no house was to be burned unless it could be done without injuring those of the neighbours. The better-off classes were allowed to remain in their own houses, but only on condition that they consented to be immured.'

Heavy penalties were inflicted on those who concealed the disease;

one woman, convicted of this in 1530, was drowned. Similar penalties were inflicted on others who, without authority, left infected areas. A definite attempt at local hospitalisation of the sick was made in 1568, when great havoc was wrought by the disease in Edinburgh. Temporary huts for the sufferers were erected on the Burgh Muir, and there, 'as soon as a household was declared stricken, the whole family, with their goods and belongings, were removed.' Any attempt at concealment involved, as before, the death penalty.

But still the plague, when it came, remained unconquered. The epidemic of 1645—fortunately, as has been said, the last—'was as virulent and disastrous as any of its predecessors. Parliament hastily removed to Stirling. Even the prisoners in the Tolbooth were set free. Grass grew round the City-Cross, and only the bier-bearers went about the streets.' It was said that there were only sixty men left who were capable of defending the town in case of attack.

One curious method of treatment, based on the folk-idea of disease being transferable to another habitant and so giving relief to the original sufferers, was tried as a sanitary measure. It must have proved but a frail help. Large pieces of raw flesh, or bunches of peeled onions were hung up on poles in the streets, 'under the impression that whatever infection was present in the air would be drawn to, and absorbed by, such agents. After hanging for some time they were taken down, and, with much ceremony, enclosed between two large pewter plates and burned.' More efficacious, perhaps, were 'the open fires on the streets, emitting plenty of smoke.'

Small wonder, then, that fear entered and gripped the hearts of a stricken people, and that, even to our day, tales and legends of the plague, inspired by the deep-rooted horror of our forebears, still persist. We have seen that in the Scottish capital the destruction of the houses of the sick and the isolation of their inhabitants were enforced as a safeguard of the public health; but in various parts of the country we have some additional and curious evidence that the popular dread of the disease led to the taking of a further and more ruthless step—the slaying of the sufferers themselves by burying them alive in the ruins of their houses. The people, century after century, had been 'weel learned' in the hardest of schools that the plague was 'smittle.' Now, that honest Scots word conveys to the folk the idea of both infection and contagion, with, perhaps, a faint comprehension of 'germs' and their activities; then, it carried a definite meaning to them of disease as an entity that could be 'cribbed, cabined and confined' by being driven into and held captive in some inanimate object. The same, and ancient, belief was wide-spread on the Continent. Dr. John Ritchie notes that 'according to popular tradition St. Carlo Barromeo conjured the plague of 1576 into one of the pillars of Milan Cathedral, as duly witnessed by the mark of a "boil" on the marble! And Ammianus Marcellianus is credited with the statement that certain Chaldean priests shut the plague into the temple of Apollo. This was later broken open by some soldiers, and the famous Antoninian plague began.'

But this conception of disease as an entity contained the first glimmer of a great sanitary fact, namely, the value of isolation—even if 'for good and all' —in preventing the spread of infectious disease. It might, on occasion, result in harsh treatment of the individual; for one variant of the belief was that a person might be looked upon as himself the incarnation of the disease. This was done not so many years ago in Russia, where, during an epidemic of variola, a stranger entering a hitherto uninfected village was slain at sight, and in quite good faith, as 'The Smallpox.'

Throughout the entire period in which plague was rife in Scotland the dwellings of the poorer folk in the wilder and more isolated parts of the land were but primitive structures; either mere huts, or, if more substantial, rough buildings walled with undressed stones, earth, grass, and 'fog' being packed into the gaps, and roofed with coarse baulks thatched with heather. This type of house still survives in the Highlands and Islands, while their ruins can be found by the score in any depopulated glen. It would thus be no hard task to do as Grant describes in his *Legends of the Braes of Mar*, when he says that the only preventive there when the plague broke out was 'to knock down the houses on all the inhabitants, infected or not, and bury it with them in the ruins.' He makes no specific mention of these ruins being subsequently covered with earth, which is part of the detail in other such tales. On the banks of the Feugh in Kincardineshire, for example, are two mounds popularly believed to have been made by heaping earth and stones on plague-stricken houses. It is said that, on a daring adventurer opening one of them, the laird interfered and bade him cease, as 'trouble' might ensue. They are, in reality, natural formations. The Murlingden mound, near Brechin, carries no such legend of an immolated dwelling; it is merely stated to be the burial place of the victims of the 1645 outbreak. Attached to it, however, is the usual story of grave danger to the community should it ever be opened.

In *North and South of the Tweed*, by Jean Lang, the tale is again told of how the plague was buried. Here the local legend has much greater wealth of detail. A grassy mound in a wild part of Teviotdale is held by the folk there to have been at one time a shepherd's cottage. To it, during the outbreak of 1645, the much-feared pest was brought by a packman who was trafficking, amongst other things, in clothing taken from those who had died of the Black Death. The day after his visit the wife fell ill; soon afterwards, the children. Stricken with grief and fear, the shepherd hastened to the nearest farmhouse and begged frantically for help. But the verdict of his neighbours was swift and unanimous—the plague, in the interests of the community, must be buried. Going with every available hand to the cottage, they shut and firmly fixed the door; and then, with terror as a spur, they hastily shovelled earth on the dwelling, burying it five feet deep, in spite of the frenzied cries and supplications of the wretched inmates. The last scene in the drama was the laying of a large 'divot' on the chimney—and the wailings of the mother and her bairns were stilled for ever. The shepherd, doubtless fearing for his own life, rushed wildly, 'like a mad thing,' over the heather, and none saw him again. So runs the tragic old story; and a persistent local legend can never be held as entirely negligible.

But the Black Death

     . . . with equal foot, knocked at the door
      Of castles of the rich and hovels of the poor,

and high and low, if all tales be true, shared the same harsh treatment. Amongst the many 'redes' of Thomas the Rymour, is that dealing with the Bass at Inverurie, in Aberdeenshire:

     When Dee and Don shall rin in one
      And Tweed shall rin in Tay,
    The bonny Water o' Urie
      Shall bear the Bass away.

The Bass is a green mound which, to the archaeologist, is all that now remains of a 12th century 'peel,' or 'motte.' But the folk of the past 'knew better,' or at least endowed the tumulus with a weirder history; for they held, with characteristic tenacity, to the belief that in it lay the ruins of an old castle long ago destroyed and covered with earth because the inhabitants were infected with plague. It was, therefore, with understandable dread that, at their ingles, they reverently repeated the rhyme of True Thomas; firmly believing that should the Urie wash away the Bass the plague would be at once set free to work its evil will and spread, as of yore, dule and woe throughout the countryside. To guard against this fearful happening, barriers were raised and carefully maintained to resist the encroachments of the river. These, happily, have up to now proved effectual.

[124]

An even more elaborate story is told of the Castle of Kindrochit in Braemar, now well known to many as a mere 'rickle o' stanes.' When the Galar Mor, the Great Disease, was, on one of its numerous visits, ravaging Scotland, it reached Mar, and the inmates of the castle were attacked by it. As it was beyond the power of local effort to raze it to the ground, a company of artillery was ordered up all the way from Blair Castle. (If one engages in the unprofitable task of trying to date the legend, it may be noted that the first use made of artillery in Scotland, on any large scale, was at the siege of Roxburgh Castle in 1460). Grant gives a detail of the gunners' route. 'They came up through Athole. The road cut to allow the cannon to pass is yet pointed out by the old people in Glenfernat. On they came over the Cairnwall, and their way is again visible from the cuttings above the Coldrach—on over to Corriemulzie. Then they turned down Cor-nam-muc, and the cannon were put into position at Dalvrechachy.' And then the legend tells us how 'the queen stood in the castle door, combing her hair. The first round brought the walls down about her. None of those within escaped, and the noble towers were levelled to the ground.'

Long years after, 'when the red-coats were stationed here,' one of them was bribed to enter a hole, 'open like a flue,' leading to steps going down to a vault. To ensure his safe return he was tied to a rope, and when, 'pale and trembling,' he was pulled up above, 'he vowed he had seen queer things, dreadful things, and that nothing should induce him to go back again. For in one room or vault he had come on a ghastly company, sitting around as if living, in strange garb, with glittering ivory faces, motionless, breathless, and dead.'

'The queen' gives cause for doubt: the legend is evidently at fault here. And yet, as Grant says, she may have been the mistress of one of the Kings, or of one of the Earls of Mar, or even a Countess of Mar. One fears that 'what the soldier said,' when once again above-ground, is, as Justice Stareleigh remarked on another occasion, 'not evidence,' or at least not acceptable to the stricter historian. But, later still, 'a wealthy family living in Castletown, began to clear out the ruins, and found numbers of old coins, broken vessels, iron doors, smashed grating, immense quantities of deer horns, and bones of various animals.' The reader is not surprised, then, that at this stage 'a little old man with a red cap appeared to them, and bade them desist if they valued their own welfare.' For this ancient and undersized prototype of the military police well knew, if the explorers did not, the danger of once again setting free the Galar Mor to play havoc with the good folk of Mar.

19
Urine as a Remedy

[From *British Medical Journal* (1936), I: 142]

Forty years ago, in the 'Kingdom' of Fife, urine was frequently employed as a remedial application for the cure of 'rose' (erysipelas), and a child's wet napkin was used often to wipe out the mouth and fauces of a sufferer from 'thrush.' Dan McKenzie, in *The Infancy of Medicine* mentions that one of the stock drugs of the ancient Hindus was decomposing urine, and, although it has never come under my own observation, I have been told by patients of cases where the sufferer's own urine was taken as a remedy for 'bladder trouble' and gonorrhoea.

20

The Healing of the Circle

[From *Scots Magazine* 25 (1936), 61–4]

The underlying idea in passing the sick through circles, whether these be garlands, hoops, iron rims, bands, skeins of yarn, or, as in some cases, holes or clefts in rocks, trees, walls, &c., is probably that of regeneration, of securing a new birth; of making a fresh start with all the old physical frailties left behind.

In days bygone, one can find many instances, both in this country of ours and elsewhere, of a belief in the protective and curative power of the circle. Dalyell, in his *Darker Superstitions of Scotland*, reminds us that it has always borne an important share in occult purposes, and that it protected those within its precincts from the 'invasion of Satan.' Hence it is that 'transmission through a cleft, or through such an opening as could be resolved into a circular form, has been recognised as productive of the most beneficial consequences.'

In eighteenth century Moray, children who were suffering from 'hectic fever,' as well as consumptive patients, were passed thrice through a circular wreath of wood-bine, which was cut during the increase of the March moon and let down over the body from the head to the feet. In 1597, a certain Janet Stewart stood her trial for witch-craft; one charge laid against her being that she had healed sundry women 'By taking ane garland of green wood-bynd, and causing the patient pas thryis throw it, quhilk thereafter scho cut in nyne pieces and cast in the fire.'

One notes here the use of 'the mystic nine' which crops up so frequently in folk-belief, as, for example, in the healing-power of the ninth wave. In another case the operator passed the sufferer 'throw ane girth of wood-bind thryis thre times saying: "I do this in the name of the Father, the Sone, and the Halie Ghaist"'; while in yet a third instance of the 'cure' the patient was put through a 'hesp of green yarn' which was afterwards cut in nine pieces and buried in the lands of three owners. Besides the recurrence of the magical 'nine,' we here get introduced to the supposed virtue of 'three lairds' lands,' which also figures in many folk-cures; as, for instance, that—and it is only one of many—for 'kink-hoast,' where the child, when taken to get bread and milk from a woman whose married name was the same as her maiden name, had the efficacy of the 'treatment' enhanced by passing over the lands of three lairds on the way to the house of the healer.

In an old and well-phrased Gaelic love song we find the lover say of his lady:

> Beautiful maiden of smoothest hair,
> Delightful to me thy every movement,
> Even if I were sick unto death
> Thy love would be as the healing of the circle to me.

What, then, was this ceremony as carried out in our Highlands? For there was a more elaborate rite in use than the wreath of wood-bine as in Moray; and faith in the power of the circle had existed long before and continued long after the days of the unfortunate Janet and her colleagues. Writing in the 'eighties of last century, that well-known Celtic scholar and historian, the Rev. Dr. Alexander Stewart of Nether Lochaber, relates an instance of it (told to him by one in whose veracity he had every confidence) which had been carried out in the district.

This man, having occasion to go up a glen (unnamed) to see a shepherd, found the door of the cottage closed and the occupant from home; but as smoke was rising from a wooded hollow nearby, the visitor thought some women might be washing clothes there, and that he could leave his message with them. On reaching some bushes commanding a view of the hollow he saw, on a plot of grass beside the burn, five women engaged in a way that excited his curiosity. Two of them, standing opposite to each other, held a hoop vertically between them, round which was bound, except where their hands gripped it, something that was burning briskly and emitting small jets of flame and a good deal of smoke. Other two, also opposite each other, stood on either side of the hoop, handing a child of some eighteen months backwards and forwards to each other through the flaming circle. The fifth, the child's mother, stood a little aside, looking earnestly on. After the child had been several times passed and repassed, it was handed to the mother, and the burning hoop was carried by its bearers to a pool in the burn and there thrown in.

Without revealing his presence the spectator went silently away, knowing well that any inquiries as to the why and wherefore of the ritual would not only be unwelcome but also lead to his receiving a garbled account of the affair. Some little time after, however, he got his wife to call on the child's mother who, after a certain amount of cajoling, told the meaning of the proceedings. The child had for some time been a weakling, fractious, fretful, and not thriving; and matters not having been bettered by orthodox medical advice a 'wise woman' of the glen had been asked for aid. Her diagnosis was that the child was obviously under the influence of 'an evil eye of great power,' and that the sole way of 'lifting' it was the rite of the *Beannachd na Cuairte*, the Blessing of the Round, or Circle. It was only then that the mother recalled having, a few months back, offered bread to a wandering beggar-woman who had refused it and demanded money instead. This not being granted, the beggar had peered into the infant's face, saying: 'Oh, what a beautiful child!' before, 'with a chuckling laugh,' she had gone her way. Here, then, was the cause of the illness.

The detail of the rite of the Circle as related by the mother was both definite and simple. The iron rim of a big disused washing-tub was wrapped with a straw rope, and some oil dropped on it here and there to make it burn more brightly when set alight. The child had been passed and repassed eighteen times through the hoop, one for each of the eighteen moons that represented its age. So far as the mother knew, no incantation had been used, although she agreed that something of that nature might have been uttered at a moment when she was not present; but after the patient had been taken home and put to bed the old crone had drawn from her bosom a sprig of bog-myrtle which was hung at the head of the bed and left there undisturbed until she came to take it down at the time of the next crescent moon.

And what was the result? That, after all, is the main test of every 'cure.' By the time the aged priestess of the cult came to reclaim her sprig of bog-myrtle the child had 'already very visibly improved both in health and temper'; while six months later there 'was not a healthier two-year-old in the country.' But whether this was merely *post hoc* or genuinely *propter hoc* must, of course, remain a matter of opinion.

In any case we cannot dismiss the story of the 'Healing of the Circle' as one that appeals only to the mentality of the Gael, for in Scotland it holds good outside that debatable frontier, the Highland Line. The settings of the ceremony may not be so picturesque there—no wreaths of wood-bine, no three times three; no burn wimpling amidst the hills, nor guiding hand of white witch. But we find the circle, duly associated with iron and fire as in Nether Lochaber, exerting its healing power in Wigtonshire during the 'thirties of last century. For, when the rim to be fitted to a cartwheel was brought white-hot from the smiddy and laid on the flat circular stone outside so that it might be hammered to gauge, it was customary for any sick person who might wish the 'cure' to stand in the central hole of the slab. Then, bending down, he had the tire lowered into position over his head, remaining in the fiery ring until the work was completed. This done, the rim was raised over his head from the side opposite to that on which it was laid down. The patient then stepped out of the hole to receive the congratulations of his friends.

Another method of circle-healing, although unassociated with iron and fire, was prevalent in many parts of the country, and applicable to 'beasts' as well as to 'bodies.' In the glen of Cushnie, Aberdeenshire, over eighty years ago, a farmer, having lost several of his calves through sickness, bethought himself of a certain old woman called Nannie, who had a local reputation as a 'canny wifie,' and with whom he fortunately was on good terms. To her he stated that another of his calves was ill, and she at once said: 'We'll pit it throw the Muckle Wheel Ban', Sanners.' The 'muckle wheel' was the driving-wheel of the old-fashioned spinning-wheel, and was driven by placing the hand on the top of it and giving a strong, smart, backward turn. It was connected by a band with the spindle, and was at least three times the circumference of the latter treadle-driven wheel. Having now only one calf left, the farmer readily agreed, and the sick animal was brought into the house. Setting her wheel in motion, Nannie passed the calf through the band, and, bestowing a sound smack on its back, said: 'Ye'll live to be a gey ox yet and gang i' the ploo.' And then, having effected the cure, Nannie, as in the Highland case, sought to trace the origin of the mischief. 'They're nae far awa' that's interferin' wi' your caur (calves), Sanners. They'll be comin' in whiles to see ye; but jist meal doon some bread in a sup milk, and gi'e them that to drink. They'll nae be for takkin't at first; but press them to tak' it, an' try an' spull some o' the milk on them, an' they'll sup it quick eneuch efter that.' The amount of pressure that had to be exercised, or the readiness with which the proffered refreshment was accepted, was the test of guilty or not guilty in the matter of evil eye influence having been used. But the tale as told to me ended there: whether the 'ill-willer' was detected or not history does not record.

The underlying idea in passing the sick through circles, whether these be garlands, hoops, iron rims, bands, skeins of yarn, or, as in some cases, holes or clefts in rocks, trees, walls, &c., is probably that of regeneration, of securing a new birth; of making a fresh start with all the old physical frailities left behind. Like many if not most folk-beliefs, the custom is world-wide, of unfathomable antiquity, and certain to survive in some form or other so long as sickness afflicts the scattered races of mankind.

II
FOLK TRADITION

21

Folk-Medicine in Scots Ballad and Rhyme: I. Gynaecology and Obstetrics

[From *Caledonian Medical Journal* 10 (1914–17), 62–71]

When love, lawful and unlawful, is so largely the theme of the old ballads, one looks for and finds references to the natural results. And, as would be expected in orally transmitted popular traditional song, these references are very straightforward and very definite.

1. Love-charms and aphrodisiacs

Although perhaps not strictly admissible, one may be allowed to give a few notes under this heading as leading up to the title proper of the paper. In the ballad of 'Fause Sir John and May Colvin,' we find the hero making use of a love-charm:

> Frae below his arm, he's pulled a charm,
>> And stuck it in her sleeve,
> And he has made her gang wi' him,
>> Without her parents' leave.

In a note to the similar ballad of 'Geordy Downie,' Buchan[1] says—'It has long been proverbial, and even to this day believed by some, that the itinerant tinkers, *alias* wandering gypsies, possess a charm by which they can make any woman they please follow them and submit to their embraces. I have seen receipts for such, but had not faith in them, even though given by the celebrated Reginal Scot in his *Discovery of Witchcraft*. In the ballad of "Jonny Faa, the Gypsy Laddie," we are informed that the Countess of Cassillis made a *faux pas* in her husband's absence, and went away with a tinker. It is said he "kiest the glamour o'er her." What this glamour is I cannot rightly define.'

To return to 'Fause Sir John,' it is probable that, as he 'pulled the charm frae below his arm,' the charm would be wet with

---

1. *Ancient Ballads of the North.*

sweat, and sweat is recognised among the vulgar as having an aphrodisiac action. Krafft-Ebbing[1] mentions it in this connection, while Gregor[2] tells that amongst the Scottish peasantry of his day in Aberdeenshire two sweets stuck together with sweat were held to exercise a compelling action over the woman sought after.

Skate is held by the folk to have a similar action, as, to a minor extent, have trout and shell-fish. 'Skate-bree' (the liquor in which skate has been boiled) is especially potent in this direction, and in an old Scots song the lines

> I'll catch the white fish
>> To please my lassie's ee,
> But the bonny black-backit fish
>> Has aye the sweetest bree

probably refer to this. Fergusson,[3] too, has a reference to skate:

> Then neist, when Samy's heart was faintin',
> He'd longed for skate to mak' him wanton.

In 'Donald M'Queen's Flight wi' Lizie Menzie,' we find cheese figuring as an agent of temptation:

> O wae mat worth ye, Donald M'Queen,
>> Alas! that ever I saw thee;
> The first love token ye gae me,
>> Was the tempting cheese o' Fyvie.

> O wae be to the tempting cheese,
>> The tempting cheese o' Fyvie,
> Gart me forsake my ain gudeman
>> And follow a footman laddie.

Fyvie is still a famous dairying district, but its cheese is not specially vaunted for sale on the lines of the ballad. In any case the ballad is a local variant of another in which the amorously stimulating food-stuff figures as 'The tempting cheese o' Faery.'

Low fare and high thinking—'to cultivate the muses on a little oatmeal'—is recognised Scots procedure. But the reverse can also be found in our ballad literature; for in 'Marie Hamilton,' of which Child[4] refers to twenty-eight versions, we have a reference to the evil effects of luxury:

---

1. *Psychopathia Sexualis.*
2. *Folklore of the North-East of Scotland.*
3. *Poetical Works of Robert Fergusson.*
4. *English and Scottish Popular Ballads.*

But the queen's meat it was sae sweet,
　　And her clothing was sae rare,
It made me long for a young man's bed,
　　And I rued it evermair.

2. Pregnancy

The signs of pregnancy are usually dealt with very frankly in ballad literature, and the discovery is frequently not made until the lady has been duly married to a man other than the father of the prospective infant. In 'Burd Ellen,' where the lady has followed her lover as a page, the feminine eye of the knight's mother detects her condition through her disguise:

Sometimes his cheek is rosy red,
　　And sometimes deadly wan,
He's liker a woman big wi' bairn,
　　Than a young lord's serving man.

In 'Willie o'Winsbury' we have:

Her apron was short, and her haunches were round,
　　Her face it was pale and wan.

And in a variant:

Her petticoats they were so short
　　She was full nine months' gone.

In 'Tam Lin' we find:

Four-and-twenty ladies fair
　　Were playing at the chess,
And out there came the fair Janet,
　　As green as ony gress.

In one variant we have:

As green as ony glass.

In 'The Sleepy Merchant' we get:

O my dear, how may this be,
　　That ye're sae blae aneath the ee?

In a note Kinloch[1] says—'It is considered among the vulgar a sure sign of the unchastity of a young woman to have the under eyelid of a blackish or dark-blue colour.' Tytler, in 'The Bonnie Brucket Lassie,' takes notice of this characteristic:

The bonnie brucket lassie
　　She's blue aneath the ee.

---

1. *The Ballad Book.*

And in the old song, 'The shearing is no' for you,' we observe the proverbial expression:

> You're blue below the ee
> Where a maiden shouldna be.

Physicians, however, do not recognise this as a sign of unchastity; but all the howdies declare that it is a breeding sign. 'If under the lower eyelid the veins be swelled and appear clearly and the eyes be somewhat discoloured, it is a certain sign she is with child' (*Aristotle's Masterpiece*). Green was also a sign of conception.

3. Labour

The actual descriptions of labour are brief and to the point. For example, to take one out of many, in 'Leesome Brand' we have:

> But when nine months were come and gane,
> This lady's face turned pale and wane, . . .
> 'O wae's me,' said that gay ladye,
> 'I fear my back will gang in three.'

It is interesting to note that most of the children begotten and born beneath greenwood tree are of the male sex. In 'Young Akin' we have:

> He's kept her there in Elmond's wood,
>   For six lang years and one,
> Till six pretty sons to him she bare,
>   And the seventh she's brought home.

This is, of course, the expression of a very prevalent idea. In the Isle of Man,[1] for example, on May Day, branches of trees, especially of the mountain ash (the Scots 'rowan tree'), were strewn on the thresholds of the houses, probably a method of invoking the reproductive powers of nature, as trees were supposed to exercise a fertilising effect on both women and cattle. It is held in Scotland that conception may be effected in a sterile woman by coitus carried out on the ground out of doors. I have heard on several occasions the saying as regards a newly-born illegitimate male child, 'It couldna but be a boy, as it was gotten under a green-tree,' or 'among the green girse (grass).' Robin Hood, a typical specimen of sturdy virility, was 'gotten under greenwood tree.'

References are frequently found to labour retarded by what may be called natural (as distinguished from supernatural) causes, with

---

1. *Folklore of the Isle of Man.*

the necessity of instrumental interference. In 'The Bonny Earl o'
Livingston' we have one sister saying to the other:

> O we were sisters seven, Maisry,
>> And five are dead wi' child;
> There is nane but you and I, Maisry,
>> And we'll go maidens mild.

She is married, however, later, in spite of what is apparently a family
history of contracted pelvis, to the Earl of Livingston, and in time
shows the pendulous belly indicative of future mischief:

> She had not been at Livingston,
>> A twelvemonth and a day,
> Until she was as big wi' bairn,
>> As only ladie could gae.

Her mother was sent for in all haste, but

> Ere she wan to Livingston,
>> As fast as she could ride,
> The gaggs they were in Maisry's mouth,
>> And the sharp sheers in her side.

This ballad does not say whether the child 'from its mother's
womb untimely ripped' survived or not; but her mother, in spite
of her six daughters' death in childbed, says to the survivor, who is
appalled at what she has seen:

> O hold your tongue, my ae daughter,
>> Let a' your folly be,
> For ye shall be married ere this day week,
>> Though the same death you should die.

A similar history is given in the ballad of 'the death of Queen
Jane'—Jane Seymour—one of Henry VIII's numerous spouses. Child
tells us that the true story was that the birth was a natural one, but
in consequence of imprudent management she died twelve days
afterwards. There was a persistent popular belief, however, that she
had received severe surgical treatment, and on this belief the ballad
was founded. It is different from all the others in that male aid is
demanded by the sufferer, and not only male aid, but ultimately the
aid of the husband:

> Queen Jeanie, Queen Jeanie, travel'ed six weeks and more,
> Till women and midwives had quite gi'en her o'er;
> 'O if ye were women as women should be,
> Ye would send for a doctor, a doctor to me!'

> The doctor was called for and set by her bedside.
> 'What aileth thee, my ladie, thine eyes seem so red?'

'O doctor, O doctor, will ye do this for me?
To rip up my two sides and save my babie!'

'Queen Jeanie, Queen Jeanie, that's the thing I'll ne'er do,
To rip up your two sides to save your babie.'
Queen Jeanie, Queen Jeanie, travel'd six weeks and more,
Till midwives and doctors had quite gi'en her o'er.

It was no matter for wonderment, considering the charming uncer-
tainty of Henry VIII's temper, that the doctor hesitated to interfere.
The Queen next appeals to Henry himself, who, not having yet
become an adept in wife-slaughter, likewise refuses. In the long run,
however, the deed is done, by whom is not stated:

But with sighing and sobbing she's fallen in a swoon,
Her side it was ripped up and her babie was found;
At this bonnie babe's christening there was mickle joy and mirth,
But bonnie Queen Jeanie lies cold in the earth.

Of labour retarded by supernatural causes there are several
instances to be found in ballad literature, and the case of 'Willie's
Lady' may be taken as a typical one. Willie marries contrary to
the wishes of his witch-mother, and, when his wife comes to be
confined, no progress is made in her labour:

He's woo'd her for her yellow hair,
But his mother wrought her mickle care,
And mickle dolour garred her dree,
For lichter she can never be;
But in her bower she sits wi' pain,
And Willie mourns o'er her in vain.

All pleading with, and offering of gifts to the mother are in
vain, but she is at last circumvented through the sage advice of
the household sprite, 'the Belly Blind,' who advises the making
of a wax infant and inviting the witch-mother to the christening.
She, thinking that the real child has been born in spite of all her
machinations, says:

O wha has loosed the nine witch knots
That was amo' that lady's locks?
And wha has taen out the kaims o' care
That hangs amo' that lady's hair?
And wha's ta'en down the bush o' woodbine
That hang atween her bower and mine?
And wha has killed the master kid
That ran beneath that lady's bed?

All this being noted by the anxious husband, he hurries back to his wife; and the knots and other obstacles being removed, the labour progresses favourably.

'The master kid' has long been a difficulty for commentators, but the late Gavin Greig, our greatest authority on Scots folk-song, secured from the recitation of an old woman a hitherto unpublished variant, of which he sent me a note shortly before his death. In it the spells go thus:

> Wae worth the han's that brak the ban's
> That I had on his lady's arms!
> Wae worth the key that opened the lock
> That I had on his lady's bed stock!
> Wae worth the knife that killed the tead
> That I'd aneath his lady's bed!

The kid here becomes the toad, the well-known friend and ally of the witch. We all know the popular objection to the toad as 'a poisonous creature.' In Fife the ploughman believes to this day that the blood of a toad sprinkled across the road will prevent a horse from passing over it, and that rubbed inside a horse-collar it will make any horse refuse to let the collar be put over its head.

A prose variant of this story of obstructed labour is given by Campbell[1] in the Highland legend of Allan of the Faggots. This celebrated West Highland freebooter was son of a servant maid who became pregnant by a married man. The man's wife, indignant at his unfaithfulness, got a bone from a witch, which, as long as it was kept, would delay the birth of the child. Allan was by these means kept in his mother's womb fifteen months beyond the proper time. But the husband made his Fool come home one night pretending intoxication; and, on being reproved by the wife, the Fool said he had been at the servant maid's house where a child had been born, and where he had got a dram 'which went to his head.' Thinking the witch had deceived her, the wife, in high dudgeon, threw the bone into the fire, where it disappeared in blue smoke and knocked down the chimney. Allan was then born 'with large teeth.' Campbell also mentions that this 'infernal cantrip' could be played by means of a ball of black worsted thread in a black bag, kept at the foot of the witch's weaving loom, where it might not be detected. Black[2] also mentions the power of witches in Scotland over labour. 'Owing to a supposed connection which the witches knew between the relation of husband and wife and the mysterious

---

1. *Witchcraft and Second Sight in the Scottish Highlands.*
2. *Folk Medicine.*

knot, the bridegroom, formerly in Scotland, and to the present day in Ireland, presents himself occasionally, and in rural districts, before the clergyman with all knots and fastenings on his dress loosened; and the bride, immediately after the ceremony is performed, retires to be undressed, and so rid of the knots.' Gordon[1] also tells the same story of the Keith district, saying that in the eighteenth century before entering the kirk for a marriage every knot and string of the clothing of the bride and bridegroom were unloosened at the back of the kirk. 'When the wedlock knot was tied there were many willing allies to sort petticoats, garters, mutches, neckerchiefs, and shoe-latches.' It is a common belief, also, that when a boot-lace or an apron-string comes untied the person's lover is thinking of him or her. For as knots are kept tight by those thinking evil of, or wishing evil to you, so are they unloosed by the kindly thought of the well-wisher. Another common Scots belief is that a pregnant woman should not sit cross-legged, nor with folded arms, as she may thereby cause a cross-birth, and Brand[2] quotes Sir Thomas Browne to this effect, while Juno is depicted in this posture to hinder the delivery of Alcmoena.

4. Abortion

Attempted abortion is referred to in several instances in ballad literature. In 'Tam Lin' the pregnant lady goes to greenwood:

> She hadna pu'd a double rose,
>   A rose but only twa,
> Till up then started young Tam Lin,
>   Says 'Lady, thou pu's nae mae.
>
> Why pu's thou the rose, Janet,
>   Amang the groves sea green,
> And a' to kill the bonie babe,
>   That we gat us between?'

In 'Marie Hamilton,' also, we have:

> She's gane to the garden gay
>   To pu' of the savin tree,
> But for a' that she could say or do,
>   The babie it would not die.

In one variant the royal lover goes himself to procure the abortifacient:

---

1. *The Chronicles of Keith.*
2. *Observations on Popular Antiquities.*

> The King is to the Abbey gane,
>> To pu' the Abbey-tree,
> To scale the babe frae Marie's heart,
>> But the thing it wadna be.

In the Abbotsford MS. we find Marie's lover described as one of the medical profession, an apothecary, and his efforts, as one would expect, were more prolonged and more complicated:

> My love he was a pottinger,
>> Mony drink he gae me,
> And a' to put back that bonnie babe,
>> But alas! it wadna do!

22

The Romance of Mélusine, and Absence of Men During Childbed

[From *Folklore* 25 (1914), 383–5]

In *Folk-Lore* (vol. xxiv, p. 194), Mr. E.S. Hartland, in mentioning how Pressine stipulated that her husband should not intrude upon her childbed, touches on the general seclusion of women from men at such times, both amongst savage peoples and generally throughout Europe.

It is of interest, perhaps, to note how this is insisted upon in ballad literature. Taking a few cases at random we find in 'Leesome Brand' that the lady says:

> O gin I had but a gude midwife
> Here this day to save my life,
> And ease me o' my misery
> O dear, how happy I would be!

To which her lover replies:

> My love, we're far frae ony town
> There is nae midwife to be foun'.
> But if ye'll be content wi' me,
> I'll do for you what man can dee.

But the lady insists:

> 'For no, for no, this maunna be,'
> Wi' a sigh, replied this gay ladye.
> 'When I endure my grief and pain,
> My company ye maun refrain.'

The lover is sent to hunt while she is in labour, with the proviso:

> Be sure ye touch not the white hynde,
> For she is of the woman kynde.

In 'Bonnie Annie' the lady refuses her lover's help at a similar time, but apparently more on the ground of his inexperience:

> She hadna sailed far till the young thing cried 'Women!'
> 'What women can do, my dear, I'll do for you.'
> 'O haud your tongue, foolish man, dinna talk vainly,
> For ye never kent what a woman driet for you.'

[144]

Again in 'Willie and Earl Richard's Daughter' we have, under like circumstances:

> O for a few of yon junipers
>   To cheer my heart again,
> And likewise for a gude midwife,
>   To ease me of my pain.

When the lover proffers his services the lady replies:

> Had far away frae me, Archibald,
>   For this will never dee,
> That's nae the fashion o' our land
>   And it's nae be used by me.

In 'Rose the Red and White Lily' the lady refuses [male] help thus:

> 'Twas never my mither's fashion,' she says,
>   'Nor sall it ever be mine,
> That belted knights should e'er remain,
>   Where ladies dreed their pine.'

In 'Prince Heathen' the coarseness of the lover in outraging the woman's feelings is shewn by the fact that he refuses female aid to her:

> He's taen her out upon the green,
>   When she saw women never ane,
> But only him and's merry young men
>   Till she brought hame a bonny young son.

The reverse of this is shewn in 'Burd Isabel and Earl Patrick' when the proper course is carried out:

> It fell ance upon a day
>   She fell in travail pain,
> He has gane to the stair-head,
>   Some ladies to call in.

But while the man himself is banished at such times, it is curious to note how his clothing may exercise a protective and beneficial influence. Gregor (*Folklore of North-East Scotland*, p. 5) mentions how a pair of trousers was hung at the foot of the bed to protect mother, and child when it arrived, from the fairies. Henderson (*Folklore of the Northern Counties*, p. 14) relates how at Selkirk, Scotland, a mother saved her child from the fairies by seizing her husband's waistcoat and placing it over herself and the child. Similarly we have the custom in Scotland and elsewhere of the newly-born female child being received in the father's shirt. This is not so much, however, with the idea of protection, as of securing future fertility for the child, as the male child is placed in the mother's petticoat.

In Spain[1], if there is difficulty in getting the milk to flow, it may be induced by the mother putting on her husband's shirt immediately after he has taken it off. In Holland[2], for inflamed nipples, the newly-worn woollen night-cap of the husband is applied to the affected part. In France[3] the husband's hat is frequently, amongst the peasantry, put on to hasten labour, the hat being in some cases first turned inside out (Lorraine and Tours). In the same districts, and in parts of the country round Toulouse, the husband's entire clothing is donned as an assistance to rapid labour.

---

1. *British Medical Journal*, Oct. 15, 1910, quoting articles by Dr. Martin Carrera y Dellunder in *Gaceta Medica Catalena* of Feb. 15 and March 15, 1910.
2. *Ibid*, Nov. 19, 1910, quoting article by Dr. A. Van A[m]del of Govinchen in July, Sept. and Oct. numbers of *Janus*.
3. *Ibid*, Aug. 12, 1905, quoting Dr. Isambert of Tours in *Journal de Obstét. de Gynec.*, etc., July 20, 1905.

23

Folk Medicine in Scottish Ballad Literature[1]

[From *Caledonian Medical Journal* 14 (1929–31), 259–70, 291–7]

It is only fitting that I should first acknowledge my high sense of the honour you have done me in asking me to deliver this Memorial Lecture. I make that acknowledgment with pleasure; although it is a pleasure tinged with no small misgiving when I realize that I stand here in direct succession to that past master of the apt and happy phrase, my old friend, Dr. Charles E. Douglas.

He in whose memory we meet to-day was a well-known figure in the Edinburgh medical life of the last generation. Deafness, one of the most trying of physical disabilities, ultimately laid him aside from the active practice of his profession, and even from much social intercourse with his fellows. But he had the great compensation of being a book-lover; and it was in his library that, like Montaigne, he found consolation for the discourtesies of Fate. And I like to think that he must, of necessity, both as a Scot and as a lover of letters, have taken an interest in these Scottish Ballads to which I have gone for the subject-matter of what I am now going to lay before you.

I take it that it is also safe to assume there are very few—if any—here to-day who have not a genuine affection for our ballad literature. In fact, one could quite justly apply the acid stimulus of Sir Walter Scott's 'breathes there a man with soul so dead' to this improbable minority, and follow it up with Robert Burns' charitable advice to 'Auld Nickie Ben' to 'tak' a thocht and men'.' For in all our heritage as Scots, in all that our strenuous forebears have left us, there is nothing of higher price than the ballads. They weld Scotland together in one harmonious whole from the Borders to the Highland Line, beyond which there is further treasure in another tongue; and sometimes tragically and sadly, but always musically, they vividly recall to our minds the varied and stormy story of our country's past.

---

1. The Dr. Alexander Black Memorial Lecture of the Royal College of Physicians, Edinburgh, 1930.

And remember, too, that for hundreds of years, the ballads were the main mental relaxation, perhaps even the main mental pabulum, of the folk: as one writer says, 'the ballad was the novel of the common people.' They were orally transmitted long before they found their way into print; and even long after that, until the people generally became what we now loosely call 'literate.' The result of this oral transmission was the training and development of extraordinarily tenacious memories: when four or five variants of one ballad are compared it is astonishing how little difference there is, after all, in these variants. The main theme usually stands fast: lines, or even whole stanzas, may differ: an attempt may be made now and then to shift the locality of the incidents described with the object of increasing the interest of the hearers; but as a rule there is a close family resemblance throughout all versions of the rhymed tale. How tenacious the folk-memory was—it is now, in this direction, at least, atrophied through disuse—is shown by the case of Bell Robertson, a peasant woman in Buchan, who, while the late Gavin Greig was collecting the material which after his death was published as *Last Leaves of Traditional Ballads and Ballad Airs*, contributed no fewer than 383 items to his list, both ballads and folk-songs. Most of this knowledge was gained from her mother, and as Bell was born in 1841 and lived to the age of 81, she formed an invaluable link with the ballad reciters of the past.

This is neither the place nor the time to enter into the many debatable points about ballad literature: the question of their communal or individual origin: the question of whether any or many of our popular ballads were composed or even largely transmitted by professional minstrels: the question as to which ballads are primarily English or Scottish, and the many other matters which still form a wordy battle-ground for the pundits. But we may bear in mind two things—firstly, that the various racial strains in our blood result in linking up our ballads with the ballad lore of many other nations: and secondly, that the ballads to get first into print and to rank as 'texts' were not necessarily the oldest nor the best versions.

The mention of minstrels, however, might, legitimately enough, tempt one to stroll away from the beaten track for a minute or two, in order to look at the Scottish Court of King James IV at Falkland Palace. There is an old Fifeshire saying which runs: 'They're queer folk no to be Falkland folk,' and this saying almost certainly took its rise at the time when, in the retinue of the Scottish monarchs, there were to be found foreigners of various nationalities: ambassadors, cooks, minstrels and musicians. Probably these two last (with the inevitable artistic temperament added to their 'fremit' tongue and garb) would alone have been sufficient to lay the foundation of the proverb. For amongst those who tackled and tickled the ear of James's Court—and we can take his Court as typical of the rest—were men of many countries, all of whom duly received, as his Lord High Treasurer's books detail, the royal largess; men who played the harp, the fiddle, the lute, the tabor, the pipes, the organ, the monocord; men such as the 'four Italian menstrales and the More Taubroner,' or 'Annsshle Guilliam and the Taubroner that passit in Denmerk.' To the simple folk beyond the palace gates those foreign 'landloupers' as they took the air must have been queer folk indeed. But of their own Scots countrymen there were even queerer, for the Falklanders must have seen many with what the folk of those days mistakenly called 'the mark of God' upon them; such as 'Johnne, harper with the ane hand,' 'the broken-bakkit fitular in Sanet Andris,' and 'the crukit vicar of Drumfries that sang to the King.' And then we have 'Widderspoune, the foular, that tauld talis and brocht foulis to the King,' 'Wilyeam sangstar of Lythgowe,' who 'brocht a sang buke to the King,' 'Wallass, that tells the geistis to the King,' and many others of the same kidney. James had evidently been a generous, if indiscriminate, patron of the Muses; and the beards of his court, duly dashed with wine, must have wagged merrily in the hall to many a highly mixed and probably indecorous programme. But it shows the value set in olden days, even by royalty, on popular song: and the harpers must have struck their 'trembling strings' to many an old ballad for ever lost to us.

But to-day I go to the ballads for one purpose alone; and that is to find such medical and surgical references as may be of interest to you; and I earnestly crave your indulgence if you should think that I make my title embrace more than strict accuracy warrants.

Leeches

How did our profession fare in the ballads? Much as it fares now: there was, evidently, a sub-acid popular pleasure in pointing out, as is still so often done by 'In Memoriam' notices, that 'physicians were in vain.' Take first, for example, the somewhat slighting reference in the ballad of 'Lord Thomas Stuart' to the physicians of this, our Scottish metropolis. Lord Thomas is setting out from

Edinburgh with his lady to go to Aboyne, in Aberdeenshire, but suddenly falls ill.

> When steeds were saddled and weel bridled,
>   An' ready for to ride,
> There came a pain on that gude lord,
>   His back, likewise his side.
>
> He said, 'Ride on, my lady fair,
>   May goodness be your guide,
> For I'm sae sick an' weary that
>   No farther can I ride.'
>
> Now ben did come his father dear
>   Wearing a golden band,
> Says, 'Is there nae leech in Edinburgh
>   Can cure my son from wrang?'
>
> 'O leech is come an' leech is gane,
>   Yet, father, I'm aye waur,
> There's not a leech in Edinbro'
>   Can death from me debar.'

In 'Young Johnstone,' where the husband is wakened from sleep by his wife's unexpected entrance and stabs her to the heart in the belief that his foes are upon him, we get the remorseful cry,

> Now live, now live, my fair lady,
>   O live but half an hour,
> There's ne'er a leech in fair Scotland
>   But shall be in thy bower.

Truly a poetic licence! Impossible then, equally impossible now, even with the aid of wireless and aeroplanes.

These references are to professional leeches, but the amateur leech was also given due credit. In the ballad of 'Tom Potts,' which runs to ninety-six stanzas, we have an account of some surgical skill in the field. Lord Phenix makes love to a fair lady, but she abruptly informs him that her affections are irrevocably fixed on Tom Potts, the serving-man. Unused to be foiled by a mere footman, the high-handed Lord Phenix, naturally enough, decides on the early slaughter of his rival. They meet on horseback, and in the preliminary bout the knight, more skilled in such encounters, has the best of it and draws first blood. But, says the ballad,

Tho' Thomas Potts was a serving-man
  He was also a phisityan good,
He clapt his hand upon his wound,
  With some kind of words he staunched the blood.

Here Thomas Potts—most unromantic of names—did well from a
first-aid point of view: he apparently attempted to put his finger on
the bleeding point. The 'some kind of words' he uttered, were, if not
of a profane nature, probably a spell or charm. In bout number two,
Lord Phenix is, in turn, unhorsed and wounded, but his rival proves
magnanimous:

'Why then, be of good cheer,' saies Thomas Potts,
  'Indeed your bucher I'll never be,
For I will come and staunch your bloode,
  Giff any thanks you'll give to me.'

And in the long run the lady becomes the wife of the good-
hearted Thomas Potts, with the blessing of the grateful Lord
Phenix; the happy result being largely due to a knowledge of
leech-craft.

Combats, casualties, and wounds

In all the many fights which the ballads record, the numbers
engaged are usually grossly exaggerated—in 'The Battle of Harlaw,'
'The Battle of Otterburn,' 'The Battle of Philiphaugh,' and other
sanguinary combats, big or little, the singer of the winning side
magnifies the glory of the victory by increasing the number of the
enemy. At Harlaw, for example, fought in 1411 near Inverurie, the
loser, Donald of the Isles, had a force of Islesmen and men of Ross
estimated at 10,000; but the ballad says,

As I cam' in by Dunidier
  An' doon by Netherha',
There was fifty thousand Hielan men
  A' marching to Harlaw.

And although the battle was over in one day, we are calmly
told,

On Monanday, at mornin',
  The battle it began,
On Saturday at gloamin'
  Ye'd scarce kent wha had wan.

For in the artistic temperament a certain amount of exaggeration
is a necessary part of the make-up; and, besides, the hearer likes
to think that he is drinking in the story of really big things; he
prefers twopence coloured to penny plain. The street-corner political

orator is in direct and legitimate descent from the street-corner ballad-singer; in the matter, at least, of his slack adherence to facts.

In all the combats chronicled in the ballads the fighting was good, honest, hand-to-hand and face-to-face fighting; hot blood and cold steel were natural allies; and the wounds, got from sword, spear, and battle-axe, were plenteous and grievous. In the ballad of 'Earl Brand,' where the father with the help of his seven sons—a favourite number—endeavours to overtake his eloping daughter, her lover, Lord William, calmly slays all the brothers without any expostulation from their sister; but when she sees her father getting the worst of it, she at once interferes:

> 'O hold your hand, Lord William,' she said,
>   'For your strokes they are wondrous sair,
> True lovers I can get money an ane,
>   But a father I can never get mair.'

This, as a plain statement of an undeniable fact, impresses Lord William, who duly holds his hand. She then renders first-aid to her parent,

> O she's ta'en oot her handkerchief,
>   It was o' the holland sae fine,
> An' aye she dighted her father's bloody wounds
>   That were redder than the wine.

Then, having done all she knew in that way, she leaves him lying on the green-sward and goes off with her lover. But he also had been needing surgical help, for when

> They lighted doon to tak' a drink
>   O' the spring that ran sae clear,
> Then doon the stream ran his gude heart's blood
>   An' sair she gan to fear.

> 'Hold up, hold up, Lord William,' she says,
>   'For I fear that you are slain';
> 'Tis naething but the shadow of my scarlet cloak
>   That shines in the water sae plain.'

But it was his good heart's blood, after all; and Lord William dies later of unarrested haemorrhage.

In the ballad of 'The Twa Brothers,' we have the history of an accidental and fatal wound sustained, not in fight, but during a wrestling match on the way to school.

> They wrestled up, they wrestled doon,
>   Till Sir John fell to the ground,

And there was a knife in Sir William's pouch
　　Gied him a deadly wound.

'O brither dear, tak' me on your back,
　　Carry me to yon burn clear,
And wash the blood from off my wound
　　And it will bleed nae mair.'

He took him up upon his back,
　　Carried him to yon burn clear,
And washed the blood from off his wound
　　But aye it bled the mair.

And then more appropriate treatment is tried by his grief-stricken brother, for

He took the holland sark off his back,
　　He tore it frae back to gare,
He laid it on the bloody wound
　　That still bled mair and mair.

Here, too, the unfortunate sufferer dies; again of exhaustion following on loss of blood.

In 'Young Riedan' we have the assassination of the hero by a lady whose love he has slighted. Although he had unfeelingly and rashly told her that he was going off to keep tryst with another and a fairer maiden,

He leant him owre his saddle-bow
　　To gi'e her a kiss sae sweet,
She keppit him on a little pen-knife
　　An' gae him a wound sae deep.

(It is interesting to note, incidentally, how often the 'little pen-knife' is used as a lethal weapon in the ballads.) He is then led off, dead or dying, on his horse's back, and her accomplices fling him into 'the deepest linn in Clyde.' His friends search for him in vain, until 'the wily bird that sat on a tree'—a sooth-sayer who constantly appears in ballad literature, sometimes as a dove, sometimes as a gay goshawk, sometimes as a parrot—says,

Leave off, leave off your day seekin',
　　An' ye maun seek by nicht,
Aboon the place young Riedan lies
　　The cannels burn bricht.

And then when the body was recovered,

White, white were his wounds washen
　　As white as any lawn,

[153]

> But soon as the traitor stood before
> Then oot the red blood sprang.

Here, of course, we have two interesting old folk beliefs—one that the corpse-lights burn by night above any pool where a dead body lies; the other, that the approach of the murderer causes the wounds of his victim to bleed freely. We all remember how this test by ordeal was applied in *The Fair Maid of Perth*, when the poor little braggart bonnetmaker, Oliver Proudfute, was killed. And Sir Walter Scott tells us that, as late as 1688, it was seriously urged, as an evidence of guilt in the High Court of Justiciary in Edinburgh, when a certain Philip Standsfield was accused of the murder of his father, Sir James Standsfield, witnesses stating that the wounds of the corpse had bled when the son touched the body.

No man's name is more deserving of honour amongst Scotsmen than that of Sir William Wallace; and in the ballad of 'Gude Wallace' we have a fine description of one of his many exploits against the Southron invader. Entering an inn with a comrade, he found twenty Englishmen there—twenty: note the number. Wallace greeted them with a pleasant 'Benedicite'; and their captain rashly and rudely replied, 'Thou art a Scot: the devil take thy nation!' Naturally annoyed, Wallace acted promptly; for

> He struck the captain owre the chafts
> Till that he never chewed mair;
> He stickit the rest aboot the board,
> An' left them all sprawling there.

The innkeeper and his wife were horrified at this deed of derring-do, and

> The wife ran but, the gude man ran ben,
> It put them all in a fever,
> Then five he stickit where they stood,
> An' five he tramped in the gutter.

There is a fine touch of national contempt expressed in that last line—the treating of the enemy as if he were a rat: the mailed foot instead of the mailed fist—although it can hardly claim the true literary flavour. But in the military history of Wallace there was always evidence of more need for chaplains to bury the dead than for leeches to tend the wounded.

But let us note another fight when the English scored in their turn. It is found in the ballad of 'Durham Field,' the battle following the invasion of England by the young King of Scotland, David Bruce, who was taken prisoner there. As the fight progressed,

> The King of Scots in a study stood
>   Among his companye,
> An arrow struck him through the nose
>   And through his armorye.
>
> The King went to a marsh-syde,
>   And light beside his steed,
> He leaned him down on his sword hilt
>   To let his nose bleed.

This last line is, again, a non-literary line, nor is the injury of the romantic kind suited either to a king, or to minstrel-craft.

In the ballad of 'Chevy Chase'—and the same fight is recorded in 'Otterbourne,' and 'The Hunting of Cheviot'—we find Sir Hugh Montgomery charging Earl Percy so fiercely that

> With such a vehement force and might
>   His body he did gore,
> The staff ran through the other side
>   A good cloth-yard and more.

An English archer immediately retaliates:

> Against Sir Hugh Montgomery
>   His shaft full right he set
> The grey goose-wing that was thereon
>   In his heart's blood was wet.

But the finest and fiercest warrior of them all was the immortal Witherington, of whom the ballad writer sympathetically sings,

> For Witherington needs must I wayle
>   As one in doleful dumps,
> For when his legs were smitten off
>   He fought upon his stumps.

And Witherington, mark you, does all this without any mention of surgical attention to his injuries. Truly those were hardier days.

Take another example in proof of this, and let us leave the Army for the Navy. In the ballad of 'Sir Andrew Barton,' an account is given of how this famous admiral of James IV fought his last sea-fight against the English, when he was slain by an archer. Sir Andrew had on his 'armour of proof,' and defied his assailants until a skilled enemy archer picked out two vulnerable spots.

> But at Sir Andrew he shot then,
>   He made sure to hit his mark,

Under the spole of his right arm
   He smote Sir Andrew quite throu' the heart.
Now you must note that Sir Andrew was directing operations from
the topcastle of his ship,
   Yet from the tree he would not start
     But he clinged to it with might and main,
   Under the collar then of his jack
     He stroke Sir Andrew throu' the brain.

  Mark well that the gallant sailor was shot through the heart and the
brain—wounds now counted as severe—but the Scots were always a
dour race, and in spite of his injuries, the indomitable mariner makes
a speech to his crew,

   'Fight on, my men,' says Sir Andrew Barton,
    'I am hurt, but I am not slain,
  I'll lay me down and bleed a while,
    And then I'll rise and fight again.'

   'Fight on, my men,' says Sir Andrew Barton,
    'These English dogs they bite so low,
  Fight on for Scotland and Saint Andrew
    Till you hear my whistle blow.'

But the shrilling of his whistle was never to rouse the decks again;
and James's anger at Barton's death was one of the causes that led
to Flodden of evil memory.

Poisoning

As might be expected, references to poisoning occur in several of
the ballads. In the ballad of 'Lord Randal' the youth returns to his
mother, after visiting his true love, evidently ill and 'like to dee.' She
inquires anxiously:

   'O where ha'e ye been, Lord Randal, my son?
   O where ha'e ye been, my handsome young man?'
   'I ha'e been at the greenwood, mother, mak' my bed soon,
  For I'm wearied wi' hunting and fain wad lie doon.'

   'And wha met you there, Lord Randal, my son?
   And wha met you there, my handsome young man?'
   'O I met wi' my true-love: mother, mak' my bed soon,
  For I'm wearied wi' hunting, and fain wad lie doon.'

   'And what did she give you, Lord Randal, my son?
   And what did she give you, my handsome young man?'

'Eels,[1] fried in a pan: mother, mak' my bed soon,
For I'm wearied wi' hunting, and fain wad lie doon.'

And now come the verses that confirm the mother's fears:

'And wha got your leavin's, Lord Randal, my son?
And wha got your leavin's, my handsome young man?'
'My hawks and my hounds: mother, mak' my bed soon,
For I'm wearied wi' hunting, and fain wad lie doon.'

'And what becam' o' them, Lord Randal, my son?
And what becam' o' them, my handsome young man?'
'They stretched their legs oot an' died: mother,
   mak' my bed soon,
For I'm wearied wi' hunting an' fain wad lie doon.'

And he lay down, only to share the fate of his hawks and his hounds.

In the ballad of 'Giles Collin and Lady Alice' we have the story of two lovers, whose affection for each other was not approved of by the respective mothers. The mother of Giles Collin poisons her son with some water-gruel, and the mother of Lady Alice, in turn, also poisons her daughter. There was evidently a medical man present in the latter case, although the only mention of him is in the fatal stanza,

Her mother she made her some plum-pudding,
   With spices all of the best,
Lady Alice she ate but one spoonful,
   And the doctor he ate up the rest.

Why? And how came it about that he survived? It looks as if he had either been in the pay of Lady Alice's mother, or that he had some antidote which he refused to share with the victim: a questionable fellow, I am afraid, at best.

Care-bed

As regards nervous diseases there is, I think, only one, apart from insomnia, mentioned in the ballads, and that is care-bed. To it there are many references. Child defines it rather curiously in his glossary as 'almost, or quite, sick-bed.' But care-bed obviously means what it says—a bed of care, the restlessness, sleeplessness and depression caused by worry and anxiety. In rural Scotland in the days gone by, the word 'thocht' was used as synonymous with 'worry,' as

---

1. The eel is not a popular food amongst the folk in Scotland, and by many it is still looked on as unwholesome or poisonous.

for example: 'He's better o' himsel'' (i.e., physically better), 'but sair hauden doon wi' thocht'. Too much thinking was held, and rightly, to produce lack of sleep. And what most of the sufferers from care-bed thought about was unrequited love; although in one case the mother of a hunter, hearing that his enemies were in wait for him and fearing he was going out to his death, takes to care-bed in her anxiety for her son's safety. It is in the old Border ballad of 'Johnie Cock':

> Johnie's mother has gotten word o' that,
> And care-bed she has ta'en:
> 'O Johnie for my benison,
> I beg you'll stay at hame;
> For the wine so red and the well-baken bread
> My Johnie shall want nane.'

Note the feminine and traditional gastronomic temptation of the male: the 'feed the brute' tradition. Her fears, of course, are well founded, and the reckless son, defying all restraint, goes to his death.

But in all the other examples of care-bed it is a case of the wooer and the hard-hearted fair; or, less often, the fair and the fickle wooer. And in two cases, one male and the other female, the condition of care-bed results in insanity. Take 'Sir Cawline,' for example, the gentle knight who unavailingly loved the King's daughter,

> Till it befell upon a day
> Great dule to him was dight,
> The maiden's love removed his mind,
> To care-bed went the knight.

The King, ignorant of the cause of his absence, asks why he is not present at court,

> But then answered a courteous knight,
> Fast his hands wringing,
> 'Sir Cawline's sick and like to be dead
> Without and a good leeching.'

Whereupon the King cries out,

> Fetch ye down my daughter dear
> She is a leech full fine;
> Ay, and take ye doe and the baken bread,
> And drink he on the wine so red,
> And look no dainty is for him too dear,
> For full loth I would him tine.

Like the hearty old warrior that he is, the King evidently believes in an invalid diet containing plenty of what is popularly called 'support':

with generous rations he aims at curing him by the strait and narrow way of his stomach: we all know the type, for it survives. But the fair leech—for the woman in old tale and ballad was often the expert healer of wounds in those hardier days when man meddled only with the making of them—refuses to give what the sufferer alone desires, namely, her hand. And yet at long last—at the forty-sixth stanza, to be exact—she yields, and

> Then did he marry this king's daughter,
>> With gold and silver bright,
> And fifteen sons this lady bore
>> To Sir Cawline the Knight.

Soporifics

It is interesting to note, too, how in care-bed, and in other illnesses and emergencies, sleep was induced. Sometimes a charm is used, as in the ballad of 'Lady Isabel and the Elf-Knight.' Here the lady comes under the influence of fairy glamour and goes off to greenwood with her demon lover, there to be told, with dire directness,

> Seven King's daughters here hae I slain,
> And ye shall be the eight of them.

But the Lady Isabel, with nimble wit, replies, although somewhat inconsequently,

> 'O sit down a while, lay your head on my knee,
> That we may hae some rest before that I dee,'
> She strok'd him sae fast, the nearer he did creep,
> Wi' a sma' charm she lull'd him fast asleep.

Then, binding him fast with his sword-belt, she stabbed him with his own 'dag-durk,' saying,

> If seven King's daughters here ye hae slain,
> Lye ye here, a husband to them a'.

In 'The Broomfield Hill' a witchwoman advises a 'lady bright' how to secure the sleep of a gallant knight,

> Take ye the blossom of the broom,
>> The blossom it smells sweet,
> And strew it at your true-love's head,
>> And likewise at his feet.

Again, in 'The Twa Knights,' a witch-like woman, the 'fause carline,' with evil intent, uses other means to make a lady

> sleep as soun a sleep
> As the night that she was born.

[159]

> She row'd that lady in the silk,
>   Laid her on holland sheets;
> Wi' fine enchanting melodie,
>   She lull'd her fast asleep.

Three methods—the 'sma' charm,' broom blossom, and a 'fine enchanting melodie,' not found nowadays in our official list of hypnotics, but all fitting and romantic, and all apparently efficacious in the gallant and gay practice of ballad literature at least.

Dreams

From sleep we pass naturally to dreams, the happy hunting-ground of Freud and his apostles. In 'Fair Margaret and Sweet William' the latter says to his lady,

> I dreamd a dream, my dear lady,
>   Such dreams are never good,
> I dreamd my bower was full of red swine,
>   And my bride-bed full of blood.

And she makes echoing answer, curiously suggestive of habitual and soothing agreement with the views of her spouse,

> Such dreams, such dreams, my honoured lord,
>   They never do prove good,
> To dream thy bower was full of swine,
>   And thy bride-bed full of blood.

This is the usual evil dream of the ballads: we find it also in 'Lord Thomas Stuart,' and in 'Lord Livingston,' although in the last-named the red swine become 'milk-white swans'—a much less terrifying apparition; personally, I should much prefer white swans to red swine on going a-dreaming. Everyone knows the unluckiness of swine in popular Scottish thought and belief, especially amongst the fisher population; the milk-white swans, unless they were indulging in swan-song and so indicating a last farewell, are not so obviously of evil omen. But the Freudian school would doubtless, linking up the swan with Leda, expound it all to our edification, or at least to their own satisfaction.

Leprosy and plague

In the ballads we find references to both leprosy and plague. The former occurs in 'Sir Aldingar,' which gives a story of the 'eternal triangle' (and the ballads rival Euclid in the number of their triangles), in which a baffled and evil lover creates a smoke-screen of compromising circumstances by intoxicating a 'leper man' in the lady's bower, where later he is found by the King, her husband. The clinical description given by the horrified monarch is neither romantic nor exact, for he exclaims,

> Plooky, plooky are your cheeks,
>   And plooky is your chin,
> And plooky are your armis twa,
>   My bonny queen's layne in.

But one may surmise that in bygone days, under the general heading of leprosy, many other skin diseases were included either by crass ignorance or slack diagnosis.

Plague comes on the scene in the well-known ballad of 'Bessy Bell and Mary Gray.'

> O Bessy Bell and Mary Gray
>   They were twa bonny lasses,
> They biggit a bower on yon burn-brae
>   And theekit it owre wi' rashes.

> They theekit it owre wi' rashes green,
>   They theekit it o'er wi' heather,
> But the pest cam' frae the burrows-toon
>   And slew them baith the-gither.

Child says that in the 'Transactions of the Society of Antiquaries of Scotland' for the year 1822 there is a letter written in 1781, from Major Barry, then proprietor of the estate of Lednock, in which he states:

'When I first came to Lednock I was shewn in a part of my ground (called Dranoch-haugh) an heap of stones almost covered with briers, thorns and fern, which they assured me was the burial place of Bessy Bell and Mary Gray. The tradition of the country relating to these ladies is that Mary Gray's father was laird of Lednock and Bessie Bell's of Kinraid, a place in this neighbourhood; that they were both very handsome and an intimate friendship subsisted between them; that while Miss Bell was on a visit to Miss Gray the plague broke out, in the year 1666; in order to avoid which they built themselves a bower about three quarters of a mile west from Lednock House, in a very retired and romantic place called Burn Braes, on the side of Beauchieburn. Here they lived for some time, but the plague raging with great fury they caught the infection, it is said, from a young gentleman who was in love with them both. He used to bring them their provision. They died in this bower, and were buried in the Dranoch-haugh, at the foot of a brae of the same name, and near to the bank of the river Almond.' Child considers that the date 1666, given by Major Barry, should be put back twenty years. Lednock is seven miles from Perth, which was fearfully ravaged by the plague in 1645 and a year or two following. Three thousand people are said to have perished. Scotland escaped the pestilence of 1665–66. By this old ballad—and more, perhaps, by the better-known song Allan Ramsay made out of it—a romantic tragedy is for ever commemorated. For if love laughs at lock-smiths, plague sneers at both, while, as the old proverb says,

> For stark deid
> There is nae remeid.

Blood-letting

In the ballad of 'The Death of Robin Hood' (of which there are enough Scottish variants to allow of its inclusion here) we have an account of how that noble outlaw was done to death by his cousin, the lady prioress of the nunnery of Churchlees, to whom he went for blood-letting. Here, again, we have a demonstration of the fact that medical treatment was largely in the hands of the fair sex, although in this case it was used in a most unfair manner.

> 'I will never eate nor drinke,' Robin Hood said,
> 'Nor meate will do me noe goode,
> Till I have been at merry Churchlees
> My vaines for to let bloode.'

So he goes there, in spite of the expostulations of his hench-man, Will Scarlett, and gives the prioress a fee of twenty pounds in gold—prepaid: a healthy custom that has largely fallen into desuetude.

> And down then came dame prioresse,
> Downe she came in that ilke,
> With a pair of blood-irons in her hands
> Were wrapped all in silke.

> 'Set a chaffing dish to the fyer,' said dame prioresse,
> And strip thou up thy sleeve,
> (I hold him but an unwise man
> That will noe warning lieve).

> She laid the blood-irons to Robin Hood's vaine,
> Alack! the more pitye!
> And pearst the vaine and let out the bloode,
> That full red was to see.

[162]

> And first it bled the thicke, thicke bloode,
> And afterwards the thinne,
> And well then wiss good Robin Hoode,
> Treason there was withinne.

Having by these means brought him to great weakness, the traitress shut him up in the room to die. Little John breaks in to his rescue, and, being a man of action and soldierly habit, asks leave to burn down the nunnery. But Robin Hood, like-minded in such matters to William Wallace, refuses, saying,

> I never hurt woman in all my life
> Nor men in woman's company.

All he asks is:

> Lay me a green sod under my head,
> And another at my feet,
> And lay my bent bow by my side,
> Which was my music sweet,
> And make my grave of gravel and green,
> Which is most right and meet.

And so they buried him, to sleep in death, as he had done in life, under the greenwood tree, an outlaw and a gentleman.

Gigantism

I think that what I shall quote to you from the Aberdeenshire ballad of 'Lang Johnnie More' will justify the inclusion of its hero and his two allies under the head of gigantism, if we hold solely by the medical dictionary's definition of 'excessive or monstrous size and stature.'

Adopting the characteristically cautious and Scottish qualification of two lines of the ballad,

> If a' be true that they do say,
> An' if a' be true we hear,

we can then certainly affirm that there were giants in those days, and none bigger than those bred in Aberdeenshire. The story plunges off gaily and boldly,

> There lives a lad in Rhynie's lands,
> An' anither in Auchindore,
> But the bonniest lad amang them a'
> Was lang Johnnie More.
>
> Young Johnnie was an airy blade,
> Fu' sturdy, stoot, an' strang,

> An' the sword that hung by Johnnie's side
>   Was fully ten feet lang.

> Young Johnnie was a clever youth,
>   Fu' sturdy, stoot an' wight,
> Just full three yards aboot the waist,
>   An' fourteen feet in height.

In like manner as our big northern men still go south to join the Metropolitan Police Force, so did Lang Johnnie More fare to London to be standard-bearer to the King. And, when there, it was small wonder, if any at all, that the King's daughter should fall in love with such a prodigy, and that the King, when he heard of it, should say,
>   That wighty Scot shall strait the rope
>   An' hangit he shall be.
Johnnie at first defies those who would arrest him; but, says the narrative,

> The English dogs is cunnin' rogues
>   An' roon' him they did creep,
> They've gi'en him drams o' lodomy
>   Till he fell fast asleep.

> Fan Johnnie wauken'd frae his sleep,
>   A sorry man was he,
> Wi' his jaws an' hands in iron bands,
>   His feet in fetters three.

In spite of this the stout-hearted youth contrives to send a messenger to his uncle, Auld Johnnie, at Bennachie, bidding him come south at once with his friend Jock o' Noth. To summon the latter, Auld Johnnie simply shouts from the hill of Bennachie to that of Tap o' Noth; and if you glance at the map you will easily gauge the wondrous carrying power of the old man's voice. But Jock o' Noth hears him with ease, and

> Upon the plains the chieftains met,
>   Twa grisly ghaists to see,
> There were three fit atween each brow
>   An' their shoulders broad yards three.

> These men they ran owre hills an' dales,
>   An' over mountains high,
> Till they came on to London town
>   At the dawn o' the third day.

[164]

On their arrival they find the gates of the metropolis locked, with much beating of drums and ringing of bells going on in the town to celebrate the approaching execution of Lang Johnnie More. His uncle angrily demands admittance, but the trembling gatekeeper says he has no key. That matter, however, is quickly settled,

> Ye'll open the gate, ye proud keeper,
>   Ye'll open withoot delay,
> Or there's a body at my back
>   Frae Scotland's brocht the key.

And then out speaks his gallant ally,

>   'Ye'll open the gates,' said Jock o' Noth,
>   'Ye'll open them at my call,'
>   An' wi' his fit he has dung in
>   Three yard-breadths o' the wall.

Entering by the breach thus easily made, the two mighty rescuers march, amidst a terrified populace, defiantly through London; free young Johnnie, and on his behalf imperiously demand from the king the hand of his daughter. The amazed monarch hastily consents,

>   'O tak' the lady,' the King he says,
>   'Ye're welcome to her for me,
>   For I never thocht to see sic men
>   Frae the fit o' Bennachie.'

And then, by a casual mention of his reserves, Auld Johnnie firmly and definitely settles once and for all the question of Scotland's superior physique.

> 'If I had kent,' said Jock o' Noth,
>   'Ye'd wondert sae muckle at me,
> I would ha'e brought ane larger far
>   By sizes three times three.
>
> Likewise if I had thocht I'd been
>   Sic a great fricht to thee,
> I'd brocht Sir John o' Echt and Park,
>   He's thirty feet an' three.'

And then we have the triumphant conclusion:

>   They've ta'en the lady by the hand,
>   An' set her prison-free,
>   Wi' drums beatin' an' pipes playin',
>   They're on to Bennachie.

Is it not, perhaps, in fearful memory of Auld Johnnie and Jock o' Noth that the effigies of Gog and Magog are still preserved in the civic heart of London? Other explanatory legends there may be—but who can ever say at the bottom of which particular well the truth lies?

And now that we have, somewhat breathlessly, perhaps, scaled the furthest heights of hyperbole and national vaunting, let us take our rest there, and, at our leisure, 'praise famous men and the forefathers that begat us.'

24
Going, Going—Gone?[1]

[From *The Aberdeen Book-Lover* 6 (1928–31), 150–3]

For forty years I have had a familiar knowledge of the interiors of bothies, and of the doings of the hardy race who, of nights, seek (or should seek) a well-earned repose therein. Many changes have occurred in these dwellings during that period; and, from the point of view of sanitation and comfort, at least, these changes have been definitely for the better. The 'chaumer,' immediately above the stable, and reached by a ladder from it, is now practically a thing of the past. Such an apartment was warmed chiefly from the heat of the horses below; there was an all-pervading smell of manure; but this, fortunately, according to popular and comforting belief, was healthy, especially for those whose lungs were weak. Nevertheless, to one not in need of such therapy, it was close and stuffy to a degree, even when the atmosphere had been judiciously toned down by the added odours of harness composition and bogie-roll; while the information gained by the use of a stethoscope was materially lessened in accuracy by the steady munching of the animals underneath, the rattle of the halter-chains, an occasional 'nicher,' or the stamp of a heavy hoof.

That unromantic affliction, the itch, was common in such places: an acute illness such as pneumonia had often to run its course there: a case of typhoid, even, had often to lie in such surroundings for some days before it could be 'hospitalised.' Yes, a bothy was not a bed of roses for a sick man in the days gone bye.

Fifty years ago the ploughman was more unsophisticated than now, and his sphere of influence more limited. True, he was better off in one way than his immediate predecessors; for the 'velocipede,' soon followed by the 'high' bicycle, had swum into his ken, and amorous youth had thus a wider choice of Delilahs. Later came

---

1. The *Bothy Songs and Ballads of Aberdeen, Banff and Moray, Angus and the Mearns.* Collected and edited by John Ord, F.S.A. (Scot.), with a Foreword by Robert S. Rait, C.B.E., M.A., LL.D., Principal and Vice-Chancellor, University of Glasgow.

the 'safety,' to reign undisturbed for many years; until the motor 'bike' and the motor bus removed all desire from the restless spirit to remain at home and be dependent on the more peaceful pleasures of his immediate environment.

And in the home environment of those past days what was there to fill the place of the present gramophones and wireless sets? The concertina—for the melodeon had not arrived—the penny-whistle, and the Jew's harp (who, nowadays, ever sees or hears a 'trump'?) each had its able exponents; but they are all now gone beyond recall as media of musical expression. And going, too, if not yet altogether gone, are the cheery old bothy songs and ballads, whose choruses were duly emphasised by the rhythmical beat of tacketty boots.

There is much sadness in the thought that, like Gavin Greig, Superintendent Ord did not live to see the final result of his work as a collector. The introduction he wrote for his book is a very interesting one, and a really able *précis* of the subject. Possibly here and there he claims a little too much. While one can agree with him that there 'is no comparison between the folk-songs and ballads of our country and the modern music-hall songs, which are simply a string of pure nonsense highly seasoned with indelicate double meaning, and sometimes grossly indecent and obscene,' I am afraid that, had Mr. Ord printed in his collection all the material which fell into his hands, some of it at least would have come under the second-hand book-catalogue's useful heading of 'Facetiae,' which affords the same wide cover as Charity. Take, for example, that bothy classic (not, of course, in this collection), 'The Ball at Kirriemuir,' a high-kilted and undeniable favourite, which frequently burst forth on the high roads and in the dug-outs of France and Flanders. *Double entendre*, certainly, the bothy singer never troubled about: it was beyond his comprehension. But much of his singing might have been, out of politeness, called Rabelaisian or naïve, and, in honest truth, 'gey roch'. For, when you are dealing with folk-song, you must take the folk as you find them, for better or worse; and, all things considered, it is wonderful how much of it can now be 'safely' reproduced in a collection such as this. Let another fifty years be past and the material which Mr. Ord has brought together will be solely a reference volume for the student of things bye-gone; while the sophisticated and highly paid mechanic who then handles the machinery for milking cows or for ploughing or reaping will either spend his leisure time enjoying, with the aid of television, the latest metropolitan vaudeville, or taking a trip by 'plane to the nearest city to wallow in it at first-hand. But meanwhile, every honest man who cares for his country's song should certainly add this book to the contents of his Scottish bookshelf.

25

Some Old Scottish
Rhyming Riddles

[From *Scots Magazine* 23 (1935), 148–54]

Riddles come down to us from the far past as one of the oldest
forms of humour. 'They spring,' says Dr. Henry Bradley, 'from
man's earliest perception that there are such things as analogies in
nature. Man observes an example of analogy, puts his observations
in the form of a question and there is the riddle ready made.' And,
to quote Miss C.S. Burne, 'making and guessing riddles becomes
a trial of wits, a dialectic combat; and riddles are in fact used by
various peoples not only as a form of amusement, but as a means
of education, a kind of mental gymnastics, and even as a serious test
of intellectual ability.'

One of the oldest recorded riddles, the riddle of the Sphinx, she
of Thebes in Boeotia—'What goes on four legs in the morning, on
two legs at noonday, and on three legs at night?'—is still to the fore
as a popular 'guess'. When OEdipus solved it as meaning 'Man', the
enraged Sphinx committed *felo de se* by casting herself down from her
rocky hill-dwelling on Phicium. It was perhaps as well; for it would
have been difficult to maintain such a high cryptic standard. Of this
riddle Krappe says: 'It makes such a definite appeal to mankind that
it is known not only in Europe and the Near East, but in Louisiana,
South America and Fiji, where it was carried by European settlers.'

Another of almost equal hoariness—'What we caught we threw
away: what we could not catch we kept'—is said to have puzzled
Homer to such an extent that he died of vexation at not being able to
solve it. But the many warriors of whom he sang must have suffered,
as did those of the Great War, from this minor horror of martial life;
and the Wooden Horse of Troy, having served its primary purpose,
may later have been aptly enough employed, for all we know to
the contrary, as a 'de-lousing' chamber. The riddle itself occurs in a
Scottish string of 'guesses' in which a man coming to a farm 'toon'
asks a small boy various questions about where the other members
of the family are, and what they are doing. The boy describes the

occupation of each—father, mother, brother, sister—in riddles; and in the case of the father assigns to him the hidden occupation which defeated the highly developed intelligence of the Blind Bard.

In the quieter and happier days of our rural past, long before the remote hamlets knew wireless, the motor bus, and all the hoot and hustle of a 'higher standard of living,' the 'guess' shared popularity with song, tale, and a tune on the fiddle as a useful aid to the cheery passing of a long winter 'forenicht' round the farm-kitchen fire. And in going over a list of such riddles, whether carried in memory or collected in print, one is surprised to note that they are comparatively few in number, and led to the inevitable belief that a somewhat jaded courtesy must on occasion have suffered many a 'chestnut' to be hailed as new. But simple things pleased simpler minds; and, just as ballad and tale lost none of their popularity by oft-repetition, so must it have been with the 'guess'. Further, should one subscribe to the belief of the Arabs that there are only twenty-five basic jokes in existence, nineteen of which are unfit to be told to women, one is again surprised to note how seldom these riddles are of the 'broad' or 'naive' type, more especially when the acknowledged 'freedom' of Scots song is taken into account. Such freedom does not seem to have affected the Scots riddle to anything like the same extent.

As befits the theological temperament attributed to our nation, not a few of the riddles have a religious bearing, and may have taken rise in the bygone efforts of some pious caretaker of souls to meet the lower spirituality of a flock who chuckled over the merry knock-about of a mediaeval miracle play. Take, for example,

> There lives a beast into the East
> And nane its age can tell,
> 'Twas at the heicht o' a' its micht
> Before auld Adam fell;
> It was wi' Noah in the ark,
> With Adam in Paradise,
> It helpit Peter on a day
> To gain his soul a prize;
> It wears a ruffle roond its neck
> That's never oot o' fashion,
> His colour is like Joseph's coat
> And worn in every nation.

The answer to this is, of course, 'A cock,' as it is in the case of the less elaborate

> There lives a prophet in the land
> His age no man can tell;

> His coat's of many colours,
> His boots are always new;
> There's no a tailor in the land
> Can shape to him or shew.

The most subtle variant of this riddle is, however, the prose one: 'What prophet was with Adam in Paradise and with Noah in the Ark? He does not believe in the Resurrection, but he does not deny a word of the Christian faith.' Still influenced by the Kirk, we have

> There was a man o' Adam's race
> Wha had a certain dwelling-place,
> 'Twas neither in earth, heaven or hell.
> Come, tell me where that man did dwell?

As answer, Jonah emerges from the belly of the whale; while we meet the prophet again in

> A deep, deep, ditch, and a far-ben cave,
> A livin' man and a livin' grave.

But, besides religious topics, the more common objects of household plenishing offered good material to the wit. The bars of the grate are cryptically suggested to the audience by

> Father, mither, sister, brither,
> A' lies in ae bed
> An' disna touch each ither

while for the bellows we are given

> My back and my belly is wood
> An' my ribs is lined wi' leather,
> I've a hole in my nose
> An' ane in my breist
> An' I'm aftenest used in cauld weather

and for the tongs,

> Lang legs, short thighs,
> Little heid an' nae eyes.

The fiddle we get in two guises, firstly:

> Doon in the wood I aince did grow
> Till the saw did me destroy,
> Syne by the axe I was made alive
> An' noo I sing wi' joy

and secondly:

> Ten teeth withoot a tongue
> It's gude sport for auld and young,
> Tak' it oot o't's yellow fleece
> And kittle't on the belly piece.

A pot of boiling porridge is presented to us as

> Black withoot an' white within,
> An' a' the guts o't wallopin,

but there is, perhaps, somewhat more daintiness in

> Three little ladies a' cled in white,
> Nae use in the mornin,' but a' in use at night,

as a description of candles.

One of the finest, and probably oldest riddles is

> As I lookit owre my faither's castle wa'
> I saw the deid carryin' the livin' awa

to which the answer is 'A ship.' This 'stock' first line—like the 'stock' stanza of the ballads—is not uncommon, as, for example, in

> As I lookit owre my father's castle wa'
> I saw a bunch o' wands,
> An' naebody can coont them
> But God's ain hands.

The answer here is 'The hair of the head.' And again, but with a more attenuated strain of poesy,

> As I lookit owre my father's castle wa'
> I saw a body stan'in',
> I took aff his heid an' drank his bleed
> An' left his body stan'in'.

Answer? 'A bottle'; which also applies to

> As I gaed owre the Brig o' Dee
> I met wi' Geordie Buchan

with the same two last lines as in the preceding one. Was there, of ancient and high renown in Aberdeen, a George Buchan vintner and distiller of usquebagh?

Many of the old 'guesses' were 'catches.' Of this somewhat childish type are the two which follow, both well-known where the answers are respectively 'Ann,' and 'Andrew.'

> An' it's neither Peg, Meg, nor Margit
> Is my true love's name;
> An' it's neither Peg, Meg, nor Margit,
> An' thrice I've told her name.

> As I went to Westminster school
> I met a Westminster scholar.
> He pulled off his hat and drew off his gloves,
> And I've told you the name of the scholar.

This type frequently crops up in the crossword puzzle of to-day. Somewhat more subtle is:

[173]

> The minister, the dominie,
> An' Maister Andrew Lamb,
> Gaed oot to view the gairden
> Whaur three pears hang.
> Ilka ane pu'ed a pear
> An' still twa hang,

the catch being that Mr. Lamb was both minister and schoolmaster.
A similar *motif* inspires

> Three haill cakes, three half cakes
> Three quarters o' anither,
> Atween the piper and his wife
> An' the fiddler an' his mither.
> Divide a' that noo if ye can
> But dinna brak' the cakes, my man.

Here the piper's wife is the fiddler's mother.

Two riddles take us very definitely back to the older days of Scottish rural life. In the first is depicted a shepherd, who, if he had had his dog, would not have seen the wolf steal his sheep.

> As I gaed doon by Humble-dumble
> Humble-dumble dairie, O,
> There I saw Jehoka-poaka
> Stealin' awa' I-peekie, O.
> If I had ta'en my Tit-ma-tat,
> My Tit-ma-tat my Tairie O,
> I sudna ha'e seen Jehoaka-poaka
> Stealin' awa' I-peekie, O.

Its general scheme suggests that this was said by mothers to children, a finger being touched at the mention of each name in the jingle, after the fashion of 'Three little pigs went to market.' But the wolf has long left Scotland, as has the ten-owsen (oxen) pleugh hidden in

> As I gaed to my father's feast
> I saw a great notorious beast,
> Wi' ten tails and forty feet
> An' aye the beast crep' oot and ate.

For a nettle there are several variants, two of these being

> Hey, Jock my cuddy!
> My cuddy's owre the dyke,
> An' if ye touch my cuddy
> My cuddy'll gi'e ye a bite,

and

> Hobbity-bobbity sits on this side o' the burn,
> Hobbity-bobbity sits on that side o' the burn

An' gin ye touch Hobbity-bobbity,
Hobbity-bobbity'll bite ye.

'Robbie-stobbie' sometimes replaces 'Hobbity-bobbity.'

To convey the mental picture of 'An orange' some active mind had evolved

As roond's the mune, as yallow's ochre,
Gin ye dinna tell me that, I'll fell ye wi' the poker,

while physical violence of a graver type is offered to him who fails to see a watch in

As roond's the mune, as clear as crystal,

the all-compelling exigencies of rhyme demanding the addition of

Gin ye dinna tell me that I'll shoot ye wi' a pistol.

Few of us who are Scots left the nursery without knowing, in some of its variants,

Come a riddle, come a riddle, come a rot-tot-tot,
A wee, wee man wi' a reid, reid coat,
A staff in his hand, and a stane in his throat,
Come a riddle, come a riddle, come a rot-tot-tot.

The last line is not infrequently rendered

Come tell ye my riddle, an I'll gi'e ye a groat.

Gregor records a curious example, the answer to which does not at once leap to the eye:

I sat wi my love, I drank wi my love,
And my love she gave me licht,
And I will gi'e you a pint o' wine
To read my riddle richt

for the solution he offers is 'A man murdered his lady love.' 'She gave me licht' is probably the same as 'she lichtlied me,' i.e., 'deceived me'; and in byegone Scottish days, with their French associations, the *crime passionel* would more readily suggest itself as the solution

White bird featherless
Flew oot o' Paradise
An' lichtit on yon castle wa',
An' Lord Landless
Took it up handless,
An' rade awa' horseless

the meaning of which is 'A snowflake,' is a Scottish variant and descendant of the old

Volavit volucer sine plumis,
Sedit arbore sine foliis,
Venit homo absque manibus,
Conscendit illam sine pedibus,

[175]

> Assavit illum sine igne,
> Comedit illum sine ore

a riddle which, according to Krappe, dates back to early in the tenth
century, and 'is known in a considerable number of variants in the
various vernacular tongues of the European continent and extends
over most of Central and Northern Europe, being found even in
Caucasia.'

From snow we can pass to mist:

> Bank-fou an' brae-fou,
> Though ye gaither a' day
> Ye winna gaither a stoup-fou

while of smoke we are told

> Chick, chick, cherry,
> A' the men in Kirry,
> Couldna clim' chick, chick, cherry.
> It sits heich an' cries sair,
> Has the heid but wants the hair

is answered by some as 'A bell,' by others as 'The Town Clock.'

These, then, are some typical examples of the old Scottish rhyming
riddles. But for the end I reserve one which threatens me with the fate
of Homer. It was told me many years ago by the old man who had
forgotten the answer, and I have never seen it in print:

> Fluffy in the fire, stuffy in the sta,
> Pinchbeck ahint the door, an' ruddy on the wa'.

'A sunbeam' has been suggested; but does that throw all the light we
can get on the matter?

26

Some Superstitions of the Fifeshire Fisher-Folk

[From *Folklore* 15 (1904), 95–8]

In Miss Morag Cameron's very interesting notes on 'Highland Fisher-Folk and their Superstitions' in September issue of *Folk-Lore* (vol. xiv., p. 300), mention is made of the fact that most of the superstitions noted were also current on the Fifeshire coast. It struck me that it might be interesting to try to trace how far this is still the case, as one might reasonably expect that the 'Fifers,' being nearer the larger centres of town life, would lose their old beliefs more readily than their northern brethren.

Mining and fishing go largely together on some parts of our country's coast line, the miner taking the fishing season as a beneficial change from his work below ground, while the fisher does not now despise the 'good money' that may be gained in the pit at such time as the harvest of the sea is not available. Hence, as well as the purely fishing and purely mining classes, we have also a mining-fishing class largely imbued with the curious beliefs of both. And yet the miner regards the fisher rather contemptuously as being 'maist awfu' supersteetious' and is a keen critic of him and his ways.

My principal informant, with whom I have gone over Miss Cameron's paper in detail, is an intelligent elderly man who has alternately worked in the pit and the boat for over thirty years. His acquaintance with the subject is thus pretty thorough, and many of the customs and beliefs have been impressed on him through his being 'checkit' for breaches of them. I found that the great majority of 'fraits' mentioned by Miss Cameron are still common to 'the Kingdom.' Some small additions and differences I will mention here.

'Buying wind,' if it ever existed in Fife to the same extent as in the Highlands, has now degenerated into cultivating the goodwill of certain old men by presents of drinks of whisky. The skipper of the

[177]

boat 'stands his hand' (*i.e.* stands treat) freely to those worthies before sailing. 'Of coorse it's a' a heap o' blethers,' said my informant, 'but a' the same I've kent us get some extra gude shots when the richt folk was mindit.'

If one of the crew while at sea carelessly throws off his oilskins so that they lie inside out, an immediate rush is made to turn the exposed side in again. Should this not be done it is apt to induce dirty weather.

At sea it is unlucky, as stated by Miss Cameron, to mention *minister, salmon, hare, rabbit, rat, pig,* and *porpoise.* It is also extremely unlucky to mention the names of certain old women, and some clumsy round-about nomenclature results, such as 'Her that lives up the stair opposite the pump,' &c.

But on the Fifeshire coast the pig is *par excellence* the unlucky being. 'Soo's tail to ye!' is the common taunt of the (non-fishing) small boy on the pier to the outgoing fisher in his boat. (Compare the mocking 'Soo's tail to Geordie!' of the Jacobite political song.) At the present day a pig's tail actually flung into the boat rouses the occupant to genuine wrath. One informant told me that some years ago he flung a pig's tail aboard a boat passing outwards at Buckhaven, and that the crew turned and came back. Another stated that he and some other boys united to cry out in chorus, 'There's a soo in the bow o' your boat!' to a man who was hand-line-fishing some distance from shore. On hearing the repeated cry he hauled up anchor and came into harbour. There is also a Fife belief (although it is chiefly spoken of now in a jesting manner) that after killing a certain number of pigs (some put the number at ten) a man runs the risk of seeing the devil. The hole in the pig's feet is shown through which the devils entered the Gadarene swine. In the popular mind there is always a certain uncanniness about swine, which is emphasised by the belief that a pig sees the wind. It is further said that a pig cannot swim without cutting his throat, and so must inevitably die in the attempt to escape drowning.

It is strange that although it is unlucky to mention the word *hare* while afloat, the leg of a hare should sometimes, as Miss Cameron states on p. 302, be carried in a boat for luck. The fisherwomen of the Forfarshire village of Auchmithie (the 'Mussel Crag' of Scott's *Antiquary*) used to be irritated by school children shouting out, 'Hare's fit in your creel'; also by counting them with extended forefinger and repeating the verse:

Ane! Twa! Three!
Ane! Twa! Three!

Sic a lot o' fisher-wifies
I do see![1]

The unluckiness of counting extends to counting the fish caught or the number of the fleet.

While at the herring-fishing each of the crew is allowed in turn the honour of throwing the first bladder overboard when the nets are cast at night. Before doing this he must twirl the bladder thrice round his head and say how many 'crans' the night's fishing will produce. Should the catch fall below his estimate, he is not again allowed, on that trip, to throw the first bladder; but if successful he throws again the next night.

The Fifeshire fisher does not scruple to eat mackerel, but states that the Highlandman will not do this, owing to his belief that the fish turns into 'mauchs' (maggots) in the alimentary canal. Miss Cameron can perhaps tell us if this still holds good up North. Is the idea secondary to the belief that the mackerel prefers to feed on the bodies of the drowned?

The body of a drowned man is supposed to lie at the bottom for six weeks until the gall-bladder bursts. It then comes to the surface. A man's body floats face downwards: a woman's, face upwards.

In the coast towns and villages of Fife a curious custom prevails with regard to the treatment of any carcase, say of a dog, cat, or sheep, that may be cast up on the beach. School-children coming across anything of the kind make a point of spitting on it and saying, 'That's no my granny,' or 'That's no freend (*i.e.*, relation) of mine.' Others simply spit on the carcase, giving as a reason that it is done to prevent it 'smitting' (*i.e.*, infecting) them. (Almost every one on perceiving a bad smell, spits.) But the probability is that the custom dates from the days when exposed human corpses were not of uncommon occurrence, and the underlying motive evidently is to free the spitter (for luck) from the onus of being responsible for the unburied body and to appease the spirit of the departed.

---

1. *Cf.* Gregor, *Folklore of the North-East of Scotland*, p. 200, where another version of the rhyme is given.

27
New Year's Day in Scotland, 1909

[From *Folklore* 20 (1909), 481–2]

The following notes were compiled from the local paragraphs in the *Aberdeen Free Press* and *The Scotsman* for January 2nd, 1909.

Games[1]

Dornoch. The all but obsolete game of 'bools' was engaged in on the links by about 50 people.

Kirkcaldy. Ravenscraig Castle was, as usual, thrown open to the public for the day, and the ancient game of 'Bawbee she Kyles' was taken part in.

Kirkwall. The chief form of amusement was the ball playing. ...The ball for boys fell to the Down-the-gates; that for youths to the Up-the-gates. The struggle for the men's ball was a most determined one, and...ultimately the Up-the-gates were victorious. (Cf. Gomme, *The Traditional Games of England, etc.,* vol. i, pp. 135-7.)

Wemyss. The 'Kyles,' a game peculiar to Wemyss, was played yesterday, when the medal was won by Thos. Coventry, W. Wyles, a former winner, being runner up. [This game is played with a metal ball and leather thong.][2]

Guizing or Mumming

Kelso. Bands of youngsters were out 'guizanting.' (Guizanting is synonymous with guizing. A long account of 'The Dying Guizard,' or guizer, appeared in *The Scotsman*, Dec. 31st, 1902.)

Lerwick. As on Christmas Eve, a large number of 'guizers,' young and old, were in evidence. The custom of going 'guizing' is decidedly on the increase in Lerwick, and the fun and frolic are entered into largely by young and old.

---

1. Further information as to the games is desired. They are not described in Mrs. Gomme's *Traditional Games* except where indicated. — Ed.
2. Is this similar to the game described in 'More Notes on Old English Games,' *Badminton Magazine*, Jan. 1897, as Kailles or Cayles, played with nine shank bones of cattle and a stick or wooden bowl to throw at them?

North Berwick. 'Guizing' amongst the younger portion of the community was largely in evidence on Hogmanay night.

Other Practices

Auchterarder. Huge bonfires were kindled at the Townhead and the Common Loan.

Banff brought in the New Year with a pipe and drum band and the firing of squibs, rockets, etc.

Berwick, Earlston, Inverleithen, Kelso, and *Kirkcudbright* mention 'firstfooting' as being on the wane, while *Haddington, Hawick,* and *Kilmarnock* mention a good deal of it.

Earlston. The territorials, following the example of their predecessors, had the annual wapinschaw on the range at the Black Hill.

Fordyce. Scarcely had the chimes of the Old Year died away when the village youths were busy at the time-honoured custom of removing the mortar-stone[1] to the door of the young lady whom they wish to see joined in wedlock during the year.

Keith. The Institute Bell was tolled for half an hour, and the engine-drivers at the station kept their engine whistles going for a like period.

---

1. Particulars are desired. — Ed. [See 'Migratory Stones in Banffshire' below.]

28
Scraps of Scottish Folklore: Lanarkshire

[From *Folklore* 21 (1910), 92]

The following appeared under the heading 'An Ancient Custom at Lanark' in *The Scotsman* for March 2nd 1909:

'The ancient honoured custom known as "Whuppity Scoorie" was celebrated by the youth of Lanark last night, and was witnessed by a crowd of several hundred people. The origin of the custom is unknown, but is generally supposed to herald the entrance of spring. From the months of October to February the town bell in the steeple is not tolled at six o'clock in the evening, but during the other months it rings at that hour daily. On the first day of March, when the bell is rung for the first time after its five months' silence, the boys of the town congregate at the Cross with a bonnet to which a piece of string is attached, and so soon as the first peal of the bell rings out the parish church is walked round three times, and thereafter a dash is made to meet the boys of New Lanark. On their meeting there is a stand-up fight, the weapons used being the stringed bonnets. This procedure was followed last night, and about seven o'clock the boys returned and paraded the principal streets singing their victorious refrain.'

29

On Second Sight, and the Cases of 'Theophilus Insulanus'

[From *Caledonian Medical Journal* 9
(1912–14), 70-3, 182–6]

The subject of second sight has been already treated in the *Caledonian Medical Journal*,[1] with such fulness and interest by Dr. Alistair Macgregor and Mr. Andrew Lang, that it may savour somewhat of presumption to take it up again in these pages. But my excuse is that on looking over a copy of *A Treatise on the Second Sight*, by 'Theophilus Insulanus,'[2] at present in the library of St. Mary's College, Blairs, and kindly lent to me by the Very Rev. Monsignor Macgregor, the Rector, I was struck by the interest of several of the cases mentioned, not only from the second sight point of view, but also from the light shed on the times in which, and the people to whom, they had occurred. Dr. Alistair Macgregor refers to 'the cases quoted by "Theophilus Insulanus" in the *Miscellanea Scotica*,' but the volume at present in my hands bears the title of 'A Treatise on the Second Sight, Dreams, and Apparitions; with Several Instances Sufficiently Attested; and an Appendix of others equally Authentic: the whole Illustrated with Letters to and from the Author on the Subject of his Treatise; and a short Dissertation on the Mischievous Effects of Loose Principles. Edinburgh: Printed by Ruddiman, Auld and Company, Printers, Morocco's Close, Lawn-Market, MDCCLXIII.'

Now, although the medical profession at the present day is not

---

1. *Caledonian Medical Journal*, vol. iii, new series, pp. 42, 141, and 178.
2. The identity of 'Theophilus Insulanus' has never been made out. In answer to a question which I addressed to him on the subject, Mr. P.J. Anderson, the Librarian of Aberdeen University, kindly replied as follows: '"Theophilus Insulanus" has long been a puzzle to bibliographers. The British Museum Catalogue does not attempt to identify him, but in the second issue of the *Treatise (Miscellanea Scotica*, vol. iii) he is styled "M'Leod" in the contents. There were several Skye ministers of that name in 1763, and probably T.I. was one of them.'

wholly unconcerned with the mischievous effects of loose principles, I propose only to deal with matters coming under the first part of the heading. And here, as bearing on the subject, I might, firstly, call attention to a recent correspondence in the *Scotsman* on the 'Co-walker,' initiated by Mr. Andrew Lang through a note inserted by him regarding the Norwegian 'Vardogr;' and, secondly, give the only personal knowledge of such matters that I have. When I was practising in a colliery district in Fifeshire I was called to attend a miner who had met with an accident in the pit. While working at 'the face' about eleven o'clock in the forenoon a heavy fall from 'the roof' occurred, and the man, although only sustaining a fracture of the fore-arm, had a very narrow escape from death. After I had attended to him his wife told me, that during the forenoon, while she was engaged baking in the kitchen, her son, a perfectly normal boy of thirteen, was sitting by the fire when he suddenly looked up and said, 'Mother! Father's got his arm broken!' As neither of them had spoken for some time, and had not previously been speaking about the father, the woman was much astonished and alarmed: but the boy repeated and adhered to his statement. Within half an hour the father was carried into the house on a stretcher, and injured as his son had said. I cross-questioned the boy afterwards as to why he had said it, but he could give no reasons. He had been sitting listlessly looking at the fire, and it just, as he said, 'came into his head.' His statement was made practically at the same time as the accident occurred. Whether the acute cerebration of intense fear and the father's thoughts turned with intensity to his home can be scientifically construed as able to send a mind-wave through space to the receptive medium of the son's brain it is for authorities on psychical research to say.

Another case was that of a woman, not of Celtic extraction, who told me that some years before she had been acting as nurse to a neighbour, an old man living by himself. He was very ill, and she had left him for a time to go back to her own home. After an interval she was returning to the sick man's house, and, when nearing the door, she saw him, momentarily, but quite plainly, 'ootside the door, but only as heich as the key-hole.' Although she was somewhat staggered, she entered to find her patient dead. This same woman told me that in her youth she had been servant in a county mansion near Alloa. A fellow-servant there, while making a bed in a room on the ground floor, suddenly looked up, and through the open window 'saw hersel' passing by.' My informant told me that this meant 'either sudden death or lang life,' and in her fellow-servant's case had meant the latter, as she—a middle-aged woman at the time of the occurrence—had lived to a good old age.

In this last case the woman had evidently herself seen her 'co-walker,' who is described by the Rev. Robert Kirk,[1] the author of *The Secret Common-wealth of Elves, Fauns, and Fairies*, as being in 'every way like the man, as a twin-brother and companion, haunting him as his shadow, as is oft seen and known among men (resembling the originall) both before and after the originall is dead; and was often seen of old to enter a hous, by which the people knew that the person of that likenes was to visit them within a few days. This copy, echo or living picture, goes at last to his own herd.'

While cases are common enough in the Highlands and elsewhere of others seeing the 'co-walker' of a friend (there are many such quoted by 'Theophilus Insulanus'), it would be interesting to know more of those who have seen their own 'co-walker' or living picture, and whether in such instances the same interpretation was put on the event.

Of cases where the apparition, shrunk to a smaller size, was seen we have several examples in our author, *e.g.*, Cases VI and VII, and in each case the appearance was the forerunner of the individual's death. Case VI is given thus:

On the twelfth of *November* at even, 1755, Lt. *Keith*, Lieut. *Habden*, with several others of the county gentlemen, went from the Castle of *Dunvegan* to the change-house of that place, where they diverted themselves for some time with a moderate glass of wine; and, as they were to return to the Castle, all on the sudden Mr. *Keith* dropt in his chair with all the symptoms of death. The company suspecting him only in a trance, employed in vain all the ordinary means for his recovery. *John Martine*, the change-keeper, whose office obliged him to give close attendance, imagined to have seen him drop dead in his chair about three hours before he expired, which he told me, as well as several others, and that this was the first time he had the second sight. The said night, *Donald Macleod*, merchant in Feorlig, being of the same company, saw the said Mr. *Keith* shrunk to the bigness of a yuong (*sic*) boy, and in the twinkling

---

1. Quoted by Mr. R. Menzies Fergusson in the *Scotsman* correspondence before mentioned, 11th March, 1912.

of an eye, resume his former size and posture; which he told me once and again: And that he and *John Martine* are still willing to make oath to the premises.

Scoffers will, of course, say that the whole matter may have been unduly affected by 'the moderate glass of wine' aforesaid; but reply might be made that in general the effect of alcohol is not to shrink the size of the individual seen, but rather to double his number. The next case (VII), however, is free from any such suspicion:

JOHN MACLEOD tacksman of *Feorlig*, informed me, That as he and a servant were employed about their labouring, they saw the deceast Mr. *John Macleod*, late minister of *Diurinish*, passing by; and, having followed him a piece on his way, after they returned to their work, he enquired of his servant, if he observed any remarkable circumstance about the minister? who answered he did, and that he seemed to him to dwindle away to the bigness of a boy of six or seven years old, and then recover his former size; which my informer having likewise observed, moved him to put the question to his servant. The minister some short time thereafter sickened, of which he died. And I am told, that this kind of the second sight, is commonly the sure fore-runner of approaching death.

In Case LXXVI our author gives us an instance of second sight found by him in a 'small posthumous pamphlet on the second sight, writ by Mr. *John Fraser*, dean of the western islands, and minister of *Tiree* and *Coll*,' which instance is of interest in connection with the present attempts at salvage of the Tobermory treasure.

I was resolved to pay a visit' (Mr. Fraser writes) 'to an *English* gentleman, *Sir William Sacheverel*, who had a commission from the *English* court of Admiralty, to give his best trial to find out gold or money, or any other thing of note, in one of the ships of the *Spanish Armada* that was blown up in the Bay of *Topper-mory*, in the Sound of *Mull*; and having condescended upon the number of men that were to go with me, one of the number was a handsome boy that waited upon my own person, and about an hour before I made sail, a woman that was also one of my own servants, spoke to one of the seamen, and bade him dissuade me to take that boy along with me, or if I did I should not bring him back alive; the seaman answered, He had not confidence to tell me such unwarrantable trifles; I took my voyage, and sailed the length of *Topper-mory*, and having staid two or three nights with that literate and ingenious gentleman, who himself had collected many observations of the second sight in the isle of *Man*, and compared his notes and mine together; in end I took leave of him. In the meantime my boy grew sick of a vehement bloody flux; the winds turned cross and I could neither sail nor row; the boy died with me the eleventh night from his decumbiture; the next morning the wind made fair, and the seaman to whom the matter was foretold, related the whole story when he saw it verified. I carried the boy's corpse, and, after my arrival and his burial, I called suddenly for the woman, and asked at her, What warrant she had to foretell the boy's death? She said that she had no other warrant, but that she saw, two days before I took my voyage, the boy walking with me in the fields, sewed up in his winding sheets from top to toe; and that she had never seen this in others but that she found that they shortly thereafter died; and therefore concluded, that he would die too, and that shortly. In the isle of *Man*, the inhabitants, under night, before burials, see lights, or a number of candles moving from ships that are at anchor on the coast, or from houses in their cities, to the church-yards, which is a fore-runner of interment the next day. I had this account from a modest person that was on the island when some of these amazing scenes were observed.

Is there any record of the result of Sir William Sacheverel's attempt to recover the Tobermory treasure?

In another case (XLIV) our author, a perfervid Hanoverian, has a reference to Culloden:

MR. ANDERSON (whom I had occasion formerly to mention), assured me, that upon the sixteenth day of April, 1746 (being the day on which his Royal Highness the Duke of Cumberland obtained a glorious victory over the Rebels at Culloden), as he lay in bed with his spouse, towards the dawning of the day, he heard very audibly a voice at his bed-head, enquiring, If he was awake? who answered, He was; but then took no further notice of it: A little time thereafter the voice repeated, with greater vehemence, If he was awake? And he answering, as formerly, He was, there was some stop, when the voice repeated louder, asking the same question; and he making the same answer; but added, What the voice had to say; upon which it replied The Prince is Defeated, Defeated, Defeated! And in less than 48 hours thereafter, an express carryed the welcome tidings of the fact into the country.

XLVIII has no romance in it, and partakes of the nature of a vulgar brawl:

One GORMALA MACLELLAN, who still lives in *Trotternish,* has a particular turn of knowing events attended with the above circumstance, as appears by the following instances, of several sufficiently attested: She happened to be at variance with a woman-servant belonging to *Allan MacDonald* of *Flodegarry,* who, about ten o'clock at night, having Potatoes in her hands, wished one of an extraordinary size in *Gormala's* throat, who was then at six miles distance; but before she could have the least access to hear of the favour intended her, she was by nine o'clock next morning at *Flodegarry's* house, and in a high tone, complained to his Lady of her servant's indiscretion.

Case LXXIII is of interest:

The unfortunate Lord BRUCE, saw distinctly the figure or impression of a mort head, on the looking glass in his chamber, that very morning he set out for the fatal place of rendesvouze, where he lost his life in a duel; and asked of some that stood by him, If they observed that strange appearance? which they answered in the negative. His remains were interred at *Bergen-op-Zoom,* over which a monument was erected, with the emblem of a looking glass impressed with a mort head, to perpetuate the surprizing representation which seemed to indicate his approaching untimely end. I had this narrative from a field-officer, whose honour and candour is beyond suspicion, as he had it himself from General *Steuart* in the Dutch service. The monument stood intire for a long time until it was partly defaced, when that strong place was reduced by the weakness or treachery of *Constrom* the Governor.

I have previously mentioned the interpretation set on seeing a vision of one's self—one's own 'co-walker.' XXVII is a case in point:

MARGARET MACLEOD, an honest woman, advanced in years, informed me, that when she was a young woman in the family of *Grishirnish,* a dairy maid, who daily used to herd the calves in a park close to the house, observed, at different times, a woman resembling herself in shape and attire, walking

[188]

solitarily at no great distance from her; and being surprised at the apparition, to make further trial, she put the back part of her upper garment fore most, and anon! the phantom was dressed in the same manner, which made her uneasy, believing it portended some fatal consequence to herself. In a short time thereafter she was seized with a fever, which brought her to her end, but before her sickness and on her death bed, declared this second sight to severals.

The same type of second sight is noted in Case X as occurring in the lonely island of St. Kilda:

BARBARA MACPHERSON, relict of the deceast Mr. *Alexander Macleod,* late minister of St. *Kilda,* informed me, the natives of that island have a particular kind of the second sight, which is always a fore-runner of their approaching end. Some months before they sicken, they are haunted with an apparition resembling themselves in all respects, as to their persons, features, or cloathing: This image (seemingly animated) walks with them in the fields, in broad day-light; and if they are employed in delving, harrowing, seed-sowing, or any other occupation they are at the same time mimicked by this ghostly visitant. My informer added further, that having visited a sick person of the inhabitants, they had the curiosity to enquire of him, if at any time he had seen any resemblance of himself, as above described? he answered in the affirmative, and told her, that to make further trial, as he was going out of his house on a morning, he put on straw-rope garters, instead of those he formerly used, and having gone to the fields, his other self appeared in such garters. The conclusion was, the sick man died of that ailment; and she no longer questioned the truth of those remarkable presages.

Case XIV throws some light on the habits and customs of the times in which it occurred:

MARGARET MORISON, a widow of good repute, relates from what was told her by her father, that a knot of four women being at supper in his house, and having fish set before them in a kneading trough, one of them, named *Greadach Munro* a notable Seer, rose on the sudden and threw up her meat; being enquired about her ailment, she told them that soon after they began to eat of the fish, she saw a little corps stretched over the trough in his winding sheet, which disappeared in the twinkling of an eye, upon which she turned sickish, so as she had no stomach to partake further of what remained of the fish: In a few days thereafter, *Donald Chisholm*, then tenant in *Glendale*, going with a child to be baptized at *Killmuir*, and night coming on in his return, as he came to Dr. *Morison's* house, took up his quarters there that night, when the child died before day of a sudden ailment. His father having no timber for his coffin, Doctor *Morison* gave him the said trough (not having heard then of the second sight about it), which, with a little help of more boards, served for the purpose; and to verify a prediction of the second sight, which happened but eight or ten days before the completion.

One more case (LXV) may be quoted, because of the method used to procure death in hydrophobia—a variant of the commoner smothering between feather-beds, so often related in the southern parts of Scotland:

About forty years ago, one Mr. ALEXANDER CUNNISON, minister of the gospel on the island of *Mull*, being visited late at night by a neighbouring gentleman, who was followed by a large grey-hound, they took supper; but after they had gone to bed, the grey-hound quarrelled with the house-cat, and soon dispatched it; he then attacked a maid servant, who giving the cry, the minister came to rescue her, but unfortunately was wounded in several parts in the fray; which his wife observing, both she and her sister (a young maid in the house), came to the minister's assistance, and, in the scuffle, received wounds, having, with much ado, turned out the mad dog: He entered a cottage or two hard by, where he destroyed three persons; all that he had bit died in the greatest disorder; only Mr. *Cunnison* caused himself to be bled to death. Mr. *John Cunnison*, his father, being also a minister, and living in *Kintyre*, had a revelation of the above melancholy scene, and told his wife and all the family, that upon that very night, his son, with his wife and severals of the family, had suffered a violent death, exhorting his spouse to patience, and a resignation to the will of God, that she might be prepared to receive these tidings, which ere long would spread, and come to her ears from all quarters. . . .

Was this bleeding to death commonly employed in such an emergency?

As might be expected in a series of cases which number one

hundred and six, with a postscript containing thirteen more, there is great similarity in many of the instances quoted. But in spite of that, the local colour is so vivid, and the narrative so quaint, that 'Theophilus Insulanus' can be read from beginning to end with sustained interest.

30
Queries, Notes, and Extracts

[From *Caledonian Medical Journal* 9 (1912–14), 98, 100–01]

A Folk-belief

The depth of ignorance that still remains in some parts of the French provinces was revealed the other day in France when two brothers, Jean and Henri Favro, and a third man, named François Perron, were charged at St. Brieuc, Department Côtes du Nord, with causing the death of a donkey by kicking and stabbing it.

They put forward the incredible plea that they believed that on Christmas night—when the donkey was ill-treated—priests had the power of transforming themselves into animals. They thought the donkey was the curé of the parish, with whom they were on bad terms. They accordingly overturned it into a ditch and stabbed it to death.

The men were fined £2 and ordered to pay the value of the donkey.

An old custom

In a recent correspondence in the *Scotsman* on the old custom of 'pu'in' the yarrow,' Mr. R. Brown, Bridge of Allan, stated that fifty years ago in Aberdeen the servant lasses used 'to pu' the yarrow,' and say:

> Errie, errie, I do pluck,
> And in my bosom I do put,
> The first young man that I do see
> 'Tis my sweetheart he shall be.

Mr. Thomas Fraser, Dalbeattie, gave the custom as existing in Galloway fifty years ago thus: When a young woman working in the fields came upon a plant of yarrow she would break off a portion, press some of it up her nostrils, and repeat the following:

> Yarrow, yarrow, three times yarrow!
> If ye love me as I love you
> The red, red blood will follow.

Mr. John S. Robertson, Edinburgh, gave the following quotation from a Gaelic song, which he stated was very well known in the West Highlands, and seemed to indicate that the custom was common to both Highlands and Lowlands. The song is the composition of a jilted lover, and is known as 'Mo shuil a'd dheigh'—My eye lingers after thee, Earrthalmhainn. The Gaelic term for the yarrow or milfoil signifies tail or root of the earth:

> I rose early yester morning,
> And cut the yarrow because of my misery,
> Expecting to see the love of my breast,
> Ochone, that I saw her and her back towards me.

The Gaelic ran:

> Gu'n d'eirich mi moch hrath maduinn an de,
> Gu'n ghearr mi'n earr-thalmhainn do bhrigh mo sgeil,
> An duil gu'm faicinn-sa run mo chleibh.
> Ochoin! gu'm facas 's a culthaobh rium fein.

Another correspondent noted the custom as existing in Norfolk, and being still used there by lads and lasses who wish to know what success is to attend their courtship. 'Take one of the serrated leaves of this plant,' says an old authority, 'and with it tickle the inside of the nostril, repeating at the same time the following lines:

> Yarrowy, warrowy, bear a white blow,
> If my love loves me, my nose will bleed now.

If blood follows the charm, success in courtship is held to be certain.

It was also stated that seventy years ago it had its counterpart in Northumberland, but there it was the ash tree that was visited to search for a leaf spray that had no terminal leaflet, the rhyme used being:

> Even, even, ash,
> I've pulled ye from the tree,
> The first young man that I shall meet
> My true love he shall be.

Doubtless some witchery was anticipated, as, if a true 'even' ash was not readily found, and the terminal leaflet furtively removed from a normal spray, the proceeding lost its charm.

31
Migratory Stones in Banffshire

[From *Folklore* 34 (1923), 162–4]

The 'Mortar Stane' of Fordyce, Banffshire, on Hogmanay night is carried by the youths of the village and placed at the door of that young woman whom they wish to see married in the course of the year. In *The Scotsman* of March 29th, 1920, is a letter by 'R.F.,' giving a fuller description of the stone and the ceremony.

'Every year at Yuletide,' he writes, 'the young men gather and deposit the old freestone at the door of one of the maidens of the village, selected by vote, and it sits there till next Yuletide. Its virtue is to bring marriage to the maiden during the year; or, put another way, that she is to have preference over all the other maidens in the village.

'The ceremony is old, beyond the memory of the oldest inhabitants, and is still regularly observed. As a scholar, I have participated in the scenes, which I must confess were very rough and noisy—the stone being conveyed in a farm cart conscripted for the occasion, and pulled by scores of young men. Generally a fiddler was placed on the stone in the cart, and made music for the crowd. Fiddler, fiddle, and the stone were simultaneously dumped down at the door of the selected house. After the ceremony was complete, the cart was taken to the top of a steep brae and sent down into the burn, where the unhappy owner could find it next day. I am informed that now the ceremony is carried through, at the sight of the village constable, with more decorum.

'The original stone was thrown into a deep quarryhole some years ago by some youths, and a substitute had to be found; but the ladies insisted on the quarry being drained, and the original "Mortar Stane" recovered and restored to its historical place.'

Now this Scots stone is a stone of commendation or praise. But in France in 1918 I came across a French stone of accusation and blame.

Some kilometres to the west of the well-known twin towers of Mont St. Eloi, that outstanding and far-seen ancient ruin on a commanding site near Arras, is a village called Gauchin le Gal (*le galet*, or, *patois*, *le gal*, the stone). I went there one day, on duty, to look over the sanitation of the place, but found that, as is usual in a French village, there was not much of that sort of thing to see. Standing, however, in the little *place*, amongst a collection of motor lorries and wagons, were two stones evidently of great age. One, upright like a milestone, had an iron staple let into the top of it; while the other, the shape and size of a large Dutch cheese, had a slice taken off one end. Into the flat surface of the sliced end another staple was fixed, and a small cross was rudely carved beside it. I called on the village schoolmaster to ask about them. 'The stones? Ah, yes! There was a foolish old story about these stones.' 'Could he tell it to me?' 'But, yes, if Monsieur cared for these things. He had it written down some years ago in a little manuscript book.' So with his permission I copied it, sitting at one of the small schoolroom desks. And this was the story.

'On the village square there is to be seen a large round stone chained to an upright stone of sandstone. Various explanations have been given of these stones. The first is that in an ancient fight between two noblemen one made a prisoner of the other, and to perpetuate the remembrance of his victory the upright stone was erected to represent the victor, and the round stone chained to it to represent the vanquished. Another version is that the conquered nobleman was made prisoner and tied to a post in the market-place, where he remained exposed to the public till he died, and hence the small cross that can be seen near the fastening of the round stone. Yet another story exists, which does not redound to the credit of the ladies of the commune who lived in those far-off days, for it says explicitly that this accursed round stone used to go at night and knock at the doors of husbands whose wives were unfaithful to them. As a large number of households were disturbed in this way, the authorities decided to stop the wandering habits of the stone by chaining it up. Since then the inhabitants of the village sleep in peace. Nowadays one would not be afraid to unchain the stone, for unfaithful wives are now rare in this countryside, and the stone would have little opportunity of resuming its old occupation.'

A pretty little tale which it behoved the schoolmaster, as schoolmaster, to call a 'foolish old story.' But enquiry later amongst the peasants revealed more. For the worthy man's little manuscript book had been written before the war, and while 'the accursed round stone' was still chained. When I saw it, it was once again unchained and had been since 1914. Various French troops had been billeted in the village at the commencement of the war, and one lady there had been, to put it mildly, more popular than virtuous. Whereupon some of the scandalised inhabitants took the old round stone, broke its chain, and laid it by night on her doorstep as a delicate and many centuries old hint to mend her ways. She, and some of her *bons amis*, naturally annoyed by this advertisement, seized the nocturnal visitor and buried it in the back garden. But the other inhabitants, indignant as this insult to the ancient guardian of public morals, had gone to the Maire, who had ordered the culprits to disinter it and publicly replace it in the market-place. And in the market-place it stood when I saw it, a tabloid kirk-session once more to pillory 'lights-o'-love.'

32

Hastening the Death of the Aged, Infirm, and Sick

[From *British Medical Journal* (1933), II: 611–12]

The value set on human life has varied in the past and may vary further in the future, but inherent in mankind is the quite understandable belief that this value lessens with age. In the case of the earlier nomadic tribes the infirm seniors interfered with a mobility that was not only expedient but imperative: to be well stricken in years was therefore a call 'for necessary action.' We know that the aboriginal Australian knocks on the head such of his old folk as fall out on the march; certain African tribes throw into the nearest river or otherwise dispose of those who are no longer of use to the community; the Chuckchees of North-Eastern Asia,[1] 'when a man's strength fails, and he is tired of life,' allow his son or some other near relative to dispatch him, granting him, however, the privilege of choosing the manner of his death. Some hundreds of years ago, in this country and in others, the absence—or scanty provision—of such things as hospitals, accommodation, or pecuniary aid for the aged and infirm poor made them a heavy tax upon their poverty-stricken kinsfolk. Did the custom of getting rid of such burdens by accelerating death persist to a fairly recent date? Various things indicate that the lives of the senile, the decrepit, the sick who were a danger to others, and the deformed child were held to be of small account. To my knowledge, in rural Scotland, some forty years ago, the wife of an old bed-ridden paralytic asked if a 'dose' could not be administered to 'let him slip away cannily'; various houses were pointed out as the last places locally where cases of acute mania or rabies had been smothered between feather beds (the then safest and most expeditious way of handling them); while it was frequently suggested that newly born infants with hare-lip, cleft palate, spina bifida, or other malformations should be 'helped out of

---

1. Frazer: *The Dying God*.

the world,' the abnormal being always regarded by the folk with superstitious awe. The old Scottish proverb, 'Tak tent (beware) of them that God has set his mark on,' embodies this idea. It is also still quite common in Scotland to hear the jocular remark from an aged invalid, 'I doot ye'll hae to tak the mason's mell (maul) to me'; or, from a bystander, 'Ay, he'll no dee till ye ca' oot his harns' (knock out his brains). Whether or not lingering traces are to be found here of a previous well-established custom—now, as in the case of many such others, referred to chiefly in jest—it is difficult to say; but we have other evidence that, up to fairly late times, such a custom did exist.

McPherson[1] quotes from the Kirk-Session records of the parish of Alves, Morayshire, a case which came up for discipline on March 15th, 1663. Here, 'the minister represented to the Eldership that he had heard of a verie sinful miscarriage in some people in Easter Alves, viz., the ringing of a Millen Bridle (as they call it) upon ane aged and diseased poor woman, called Margaret Anderson, thereby to hasten her death as they conceived. Their names are Andrew Angus and Agnes Rob.' At a later date 'compeared Andrew Angus and confessed he rang the bridle: he being interrogated what were the words he spake at the ringing of it, answered that he said:

> Cran's flesh or wran's flesh
> Come oot thy way.'

Agnes Rob confessed that 'she went out for and sought for and brought to the house the bridle at the diseased woman her own desire.' As McPherson remarks, there is no association here with witchcraft: the phrase used was a magic formula. 'It appears to be a method of hastening the end, available to any who sought to employ the means.' What 'the Millen Bridle' actually was is unknown; but the expressions used of 'as they call it' and 'as they conceived' suggest that the custom was well known in the district.

Campbell[2] under the heading of 'Killing those too long alive,' states that if a person in the Scottish Highlands is thought to have lived too long, and it becomes desirable to get rid of him, his death can be ensured by bawling to him thrice through the key-hole of the room in which he is bed-rid:

> Will you come, or will you go?
> Or will you eat the flesh of cranes?

Here again, as in the first case, we have the use of 'crane's flesh' in the invocation. I have been unable to ascertain that any evil attribute is

1. McPherson: *Primitive Beliefs of the North-East of Scotland*
2. Campbell: *Superstitions of the Scottish Highlands.*

attached to the crane in the folk beliefs of the Highlands. The 'wran' (wren), however, is a sacred bird; so, as the choice 'cran's flesh or wran's flesh' is given in the Alves case, one would think the former held some power of doing ill.

McPherson also gives, in an interesting extract from Aubrey[1] 'another method of achieving the same object' in seventeenth century England. This is got in a 'countrie storie' of the 'holy mawle w^ch (they fancy) hung behind the church dore wch when the father was seaventie the sonne might fetch to knock his father on the head as effoete and of no more use.'

But Le Rouzic[2], curator of the *Musée Miln* at Carnac, Brittany, provides a more detailed and recent account of such proceedings. He commences with the facetious remark that formerly the Bretons lived to such an age that it was necessary to break their heads with a holy hammer (*un marteau béni*); but goes on to say that every time the death agony is prolonged it is still said by the folk, 'We will need to take the holy hammer to finish him.' This hammer was of stone, and was kept carefully in each district, generally in the old chapels. When it was required, the oldest person in the village used to fetch it, and 'operated'—that is to say, broke the head of the dying—in the presence of all the inhabitants assembled to recite the prayers for the dead. He further quotes a speaker at the Congrès de l'Association Bretonne in 1899 as stating that a ceremony of this kind was carried out at Poulharff as late as 1830.

Here, the daughter of an old paralytic, Mathô-Talen by name, aged 85 and bed-ridden for ten years, desired a neighbour, late at night, to go to a village nearly a league distant and fetch the holy hammer (in the Breton tongue, *er mel béniguet*), for which her father asked to put an end to his suffering. The beadle of the chapel (in this case at Saint Meltro) was the guardian of the mysterious hammer, a heavy and almost spherical stone measuring 42 centimètres in circumference, which was kept in a recess in the church wall, and hidden by an old placard. When brought to the sick man's house, where all the neighbours were already met, the oldest inhabitant (a woman), stooping beneath its weight, grasped the stone to her chest. The paralytic having now with difficulty left his bed for a bench, she thrice made the sign of the Cross with her right hand; and then, with both hands, raised the stone above her head, waving it and saying: 'Mathô-Talen, for the last time commit thy soul to God, for here is

---

1. Aubrey: *Remaines of Gentilisme*.
2. Le Rouzic: *Carnac*.

what will relieve thee from the agonies of death, and lift from thee the burdens of life.' The ends of his fingers having been wet with holy water, he slowly made the sign of the Cross with the right arm. Lowering the stone little by little with both hands, she at last placed it gently on his forehead, steadying it there with her left. Then, again raising her right, she cried in a shrill voice: 'By the Holy Trinity, in the name of the Father, the Son, and the Holy Spirit, thanks to the holy hammer of Saint Meltro, the deliverer of the aged, rest in peace, Mathô-Talen, for thou hast lived well!' Hardly had she finished when the old man drew his last breath: his limbs stiffened and he gave up the ghost while saying, 'God be thanked!'

Le Rouzic mentions that in the *Musée Miln* there are several such *marteaux bénits*; and that at Le Notério, and Saint Germain in the commune of Brech, he had seen similar stones. At the latter place, kept in the sacristy and stated by their keeper 'to have been formerly much in demand,' the 'hammers', were two balls of deep blue schist about 15 cm. in diameter. *Ils avaient cassé beaucoup de crânes.* He also notes *cette légende du rite catholique*, which consists of knocking thrice with a hammer of silver on the head of a deceased Pope.

It is worthy of note that in the cases in Morayshire and Poulharff, and also in the English one mentioned by Aubrey, the instrument of release was in the hands of some guardian. At Alves the 'bridle had to be sought for and brought to the house'; in the other cases it was kept in a church. Again, in Aubrey's case 'the father was seaventie'; while in the Scottish, Breton, and North-Eastern Asian cases the sufferer was not only aged but personally desirous of the 'happy dispatch.' It is interesting, too, to note that the word for hammer or maul ('mell') is the same in both Scots and Breton, and it brings us in touch with the 'millen' of the 'bridle'; for to 'mill,' in the Scottish vernacular, is 'to give one a beating, to drub.' It is possible that the word 'bridle' at Alves in 1633 had another meaning as well as that attached to it now; in Scots it also connotes 'the piece of iron fastened on the end of the beam of a plough, to which the harness is attached,'[1] and is applied too, to a special piece of wood used in carpentry. Taking the usual signification, McPherson thinks that death may have been caused by strangulation; but, whatever the instrument may have been, and however it may formerly have been used, it is not unlikely that 'the ringing of the bridle' was, even by that time, merely a ceremony in

---

1. Jamieson: *Dictionary of the Scottish Language.*

which actual violence had given way to ritual and incantation such as was used in Brittany.

In favour, then, of a once prevalent and long-persisting custom of hastening the death of the aged, infirm, and sick, we have some folk-evidence in Scotland, England, and Brittany that is fairly strong.

33
Chamber-Pots Filled with Salt as Marriage Gifts

[From *Folklore* 45 (1934), 162–3]

Salt, in Scottish folk-belief, is held to have an aphrodisiac action: 'fond o' saut, fond o' the lasses,' is an old saying. Gordon,[1] writing in 1880 of Keith and district, says that on the evening before the marriage the bride's presents and outfit were conveyed to the future home under the superintendence of the bridesmaid, who carried with her 'a certain globular article' filled with salt which was the first part of the bride's furnishings taken into the house. A portion of the salt was sprinkled over the floor as a protection against the Evil Eye. This chamber-pot filled with salt is still a common marriage present with the Scottish folk of the north-east of Scotland: I saw one last year which had been sent (anonymously) to a young man a few days before his wedding. Such articles in miniature—usually with a gilt inscription of 'For me and my girl,' or with an eye on the foot of them—are on sale at the china stalls in the Aberdeen Market, and are frequently to be seen on bedroom mantelshelves, where they serve as emblems of marital union.

As Havelock Ellis[2] says, 'the primitive mind attributes great importance to the excretory functions.' A Scottish example of this is found in the old marriage ceremonies of the tinkers, where a hole was dug in the ground into which both contracting parties passed water. Then, clasping hands across it, they repeated the formula, 'Let them that can sinder [separate] that, sinder us.'

The late Professor Sir Archibald Geikie[3] tells how Mackinnon of Corriehatachan was so indignant over the publication by Maculloch the traveller and geologist—who had been an honoured guest—of derogatory remarks on both him and his clansmen that, on his next visit to Glasgow, he took the engraved portrait of the author to

---

1. *The Book of the Chronicles of Keith*, p. 59.
2. *Psychology of Sex*, p. 140.
3. *Scottish Reminiscences*, p. 394.

a crockery dealer and commissioned 'a set of earthenware' with Maculloch's likeness on each. These articles were distributed over Skye, and, writing in 1904, Geikie said that some of them were still to be seen. Here we have an application of sympathetic magic that found a revival during the late war, when some ultra-patriotic individuals hung up portraits of the Kaiser in their water-closets.

34

Pregnant Women as Pall-Bearers

[From *Folklore* 47 (1936), 230]

James Augustus Blondin, M.D., Member of the College of Physicians, London, in his book *The Power of the Mother's Imagination over the Foetus Examin'd In Answer to Dr. Daniel Turner's Book Intitled A Defence of the XIIth Chapter of the First Part of a Treatise, De Morbis Cutaneis* (London, 1729), says on its page 38, 'And is it not, in England, customary, for Pregnant Women, to be Pallbearers of their Friends dead in Child-bed?' In what part of England was this customary? And when did the custom cease?

On the same page Hesiod is quoted to this effect: 'Don't make Water, facing the Sun, nor in an erect Posture, nor being naked, nor in a publick Place.' Blondin inserts a note in brackets 'The same Superstition is still amongst the Turks.'

35

Stray Notes on the Folk-lore of Aberdeenshire and the North-East of Scotland

[From *Folklore* 25 (1914), 342–63]

A Legend of Buried Treasure

'In one of the fields of Kirktown bordering with Oldyleiper, at the base of a hillock, is a small loch or morass, where it is said a large copper vessel or kettle full of shining gold is hid, and that several attempts were made to find it out, but by some unforeseen event happening they always proved unsuccessful. The last person engaged in a search for this treasure, by perseverance and hard labour, had overcome almost every obstacle, and it was almost within his grasp, when he heard a voice shouting aloud, "The kirk and manse are on fire." The gold-seeker ran to the top of the hillock, in full view of the church and manse, but finding he had gone on an April errand returned with all haste to the "pose," when, behold, he could scarcely recognise the spot where he had spent so many hours of toil and labour. All was covered over again in its usual form, and seeing his hopes thus frustrated he abandoned the project; so here it may still be supposed to be guarded by some supernatural being who has the power to defeat every attempt made to remove its precious charge.' (Dinnie, *History of Birse.*)

A similar story is told of the Corbie Pot, a deep pool in the Crynach burn, parish of Maryculter, Kincardineshire, and also of a pool in the Culter burn, parish of Peterculter, Aberdeenshire.[1]

Fumack Fair

'The ancient name of the parish [Botriphnie] was *Fumack Kirk*, so called from S. Fumack, the patron saint. A little below the

---

1. A similar Buried Treasure story comes from the Rose Hole, Beckhampsted [*sic*] Common, Hertfordshire, where an old man named Rose is said to have discovered that a chest of gold was buried. When the diggers found an

Established manse is S. Fumack's Well. An annual Fair is held in February, on a Green on the opposite side of the Railway line from the Well. According to a "Description of the Parish," *circa* 1726, the "wooden image is washed yearly, with much formality, by an old woman (quho keeps it) at his Fair on the third of May, in his own well there." The Image, having been swept away by a flood of the Isla, was carried down to the mouth of the Deveron, where it was stranded, and afterwards burned, as a monument of superstition, in presence of the Parish Minister. The old custom of a game at Football is still practiced at *Fumack Fair*. Formerly the Gudewives, having "brewed their brewster," used to shake their bags over the still *for luck*. They believed that if the whisky did not operate so as to make the men fight at the Fair and "draw bluid," it would not be a good season following.' (Gordon, *Book of the Chronicles of Keith*, p. 443.)

With the above ritual washing of an image, compare the following:

'In a Niche in the north wall of the church [of Ruthven] is placed the Effigy of Thomas Gordon of Daach, *i.e.* "Tam o' Riven," who fought the Monk of Grange. The effigy is cut in stone, and is known by the name of "Tam o' the stane." The Warrior is in full armour, with his sword by his side. The visor of the helmet is raised, showing the features, which are much obliterated by long exposure to atmospheric influences. No inscription is now to be seen but some of the older Inhabitants say that there was an Inscription on the Sword-belt round the body. The late Gordon of Craig repaired *The Tomb of Tam*; and also an old woman white-washed the Figure annually.' (Gordon, *op. cit.*, p. 409.)

Leechcraft and Witchcraft

The following account of 'the Muckle Wheel Ban' is taken down from the description of an old man, a native of the glen of Cushnie, West Aberdeenshire. The incident narrated actually occurred in the aforesaid glen some sixty years ago, and its truth can be vouched for.

An old farmer, having lost several of his calves through sickness, thought it advisable to mention the fact to Nannie, who had the

---

iron chest, one of them exclaimed, 'Dang it, Jack, here it is!' on which the sides of the pit fell in, and they had barely time to escape premature burial. When they returned next morning they could find no trace of the treasure. W.B. Gerish, 11th Series *Notes and Queries*, vol. i, p. 306 — EDITOR.

reputation in the glen of being a 'canny wifie,' and with whom he happened to be on very good terms. He stated that another of his calves was ill, and Nannie said, 'We'll pit it through the Muckle Wheel Ban', Sanners.' (The 'muckle wheel' was the driving wheel of the old-fashioned spinning-wheel which was driven by hand, by placing the hand on the top of the wheel, and giving it a strong, sharp, backward turn. It was connected by a band—'the muckle wheel ban"—with the spindle, and was at least three times the circumference of the later type of wheel which was driven by a treadle. Only an expert could use it, from the fact that the right hand was constantly occupied with the driving of the wheel.) Having only one calf left the farmer was naturally very solicitous for its well-being, and said so to Nanny. The calf was accordingly brought into the house and the wheel set in motion. Having passed the calf through 'the ban" Nanny gave it a sound smack on the back and said, 'Ye'll live to be a gey ox yet and gang i' the ploo.'

In further conversation with the farmer she remarked, 'They're nae far awa that's interferin' wi' yer caur [calves], Sanners.' 'Nay, Nanny?' 'Na, Sanners, they're nae that! They'll be comin' in sometimes to see ye, bit jist meal doon some breed in a sup milk, an' gae them that to drink. They'll nae be for takkin' 't at first, but press them to tak' it, an' try an' spull some o' the milk on them an' they'll tak' it quick eneuch efter that.' The amount of pressure that had to be exercised, or the celerity with which the proffered refreshment was taken, was evidently the test of guilty or not guilty as regards meditated evil towards the person visited.

The same informant also recounted the following incident which happened in his own family. On one occasion his father had been at a meat market, and had returned home with a lusty porker of some six weeks' old in a poke (bag) slung over his shoulder. On entering his house he flung down the poke in a half-hearted way and said, 'There'll be little thrift wi' that beast!' 'Oh, fat wye that?' asked his wife. 'Weel, I met Mary D. on the road.' Some six months after this, on returning from his day's darg, he was made acquainted with the painful fact that his pig had choked. 'I tellt ye Mary wad dee't' (do it) was his comment.

Following close on this catastrophe a crofter from the 'back end' of the glen was one night wending his way home, 'well primed,' the priming, no doubt, being largely the illicit product of the glen. The night was dark and wild, and as the said Mary's Sheilin' was not far off the crofter's route, he thought it a suitable occasion for giving Mary 'a line of his min" regarding her cantrips and general behaviour. In due time he reached Mary's abode, and as no light was visible he had a difficulty in finding the door. He knocked without reply and knocked again. Then finding the door 'off the latch,' he walked warily in. In the dim light of a dying peat fire he spied a female figure smoking a pipe by the fireside. Without turning her head to see who her visitor was she addressed him in the following words, 'In the name o' God, fat brings ye here in sic a nicht, Jeems?' Jeems explained in strong and uncomplimentary language the reason of his visit, and having exhausted his store of expletives he drew himself up to his full height, and as a parting shot declared, 'Ye chokit Willie Tamson's pig last week; but jist try yersel wi' me, ye bitch!' It is recorded that from this date, having cowed the witch, Jeems prospered in all his worldly affairs, while Mary held him in great respect to the end of her days. (From notes given by Mr J.R., Peterculter.)

The afore-mentioned Mary D. was looked on as a witch, and the usual tale of her turning herself at will into a hare was prevalent in the district.

In the parish of Strachan, Kincardineshire, within the last twenty years, a young servant girl declined to skin a hare which her mistress handed over to her. The girl's refusal was voiced thus: 'Na, na, it micht be somebody's granny!'

Fairies
In the same glen of Cushnie one old man never passed the Fairy Hillock there without holding his cap on, as he always declared the proximity of the hillock made his hair stand on end.

Communing with the Dead
At Coull an old couple lived on a croft—'a sma' croft wi' twa coos.' They lived happily together. On the man's death his wife kept on the croft, but whenever she bought or sold anything she always went to the old man's grave and explained the whole matter to him. He had been a great user of snuff, and on these occasions she always deposited a little heap of snuff on the grave, so that he might regale himself with it till her next visit. (Told me by H.R., aged 75, as having occurred in his youth.)

At Tarland, as a boy, the same narrator was badly scared while coming through the kirkyard at night by 'something white' moving about below a flat gravestone supported on four short pillars. Investigation proved this to be a woman whose husband had been buried there some time previously. She had been a 'bad 'umman,' and her regret made her come there nightly to commune with the dead.

'An old story is still in remembrance about one of the tenants of the ale-house kept at the churchyard of Birse, Aberdeenshire. It is said that having had the misfortune to lose his wife, he, after having her decently buried in the churchyard behind his house, invited his neighbours who had attended on that melancholy occasion to partake of some refreshment before leaving. This they all agreed to, and after consuming a good dinner and several "cups of nappie ale" each, they naturally conjectured that a "jine" would not be out of the question, and as they were now in good spirits, and had been so handsomely treated, before parting they were willing to be their "pint a piece." But the landlord was a man of modesty and feeling, and would not consent to this proposal. However, the cash was collected and laid on the table, and of course he soon gave way to the majority, upon condition of having the liberty to enquire of his wife, and if she gave her consent he would make no objection. This they all agreed to, and away he went to the grave of his newly-buried wife, from which the question, "Will I sell them drink, Nanny?" found answer, "Hae they ony siller, John?" "Awat they hae plenty o' siller." "Weel, weel, gie ye them drink as lang's they hae siller, an' ye'll get plenty o' guid auld bottle't ale i' the amery ahint the hallin door." Some wag in the company had no doubt assisted the dead woman in answering this question.' (Dinnie's *Account of the Parish of Birse*, Aberdeen, 1865.)

The wag may have assisted in the answer, but the fact remains that the man went out to commune with the dead, as in the Coull case.

Funerals
Michie (*Deeside Tales*, p. 20) makes reference to the following: 'It was one of the superstitions of the times that if the perpetrator of a murder could by any chance see through beneath the body of his victim, he would escape the punishment of his crime. So far from proving always true, this belief had sometimes even led to the detection of the murderer, when he might otherwise have escaped. Cases have been known where, during the funeral of a person who had met his death by foul means, the culprit was detected by displaying some anxiety to look under the coffin. This superstition also gave rise to a singular custom, long observed in the Highlands at the funerals of persons supposed to have been murdered. Before "lifting," the coffin was draped with Highland plaids, which hung from its sides to the ground, so that no one might be able to see through beneath it when it was being conveyed to the place of interment.'

'*Reistin*" a funeral. A.M. (died in 1910, aged 83) told me a tale narrated to him by his father as having happened at a funeral in Strathdon in the old days. While the coffin was being carried over a burn it became suddenly so heavy that the procession came to a stand-still in mid stream and no progress could be made. At last one old man asked if any man was present who shaved on the Sabbath day. One of those present acknowledged that he did, and was told to step forward and lay his hand on the coffin. It immediately became lighter, and the procession went forward without further difficulty.

Alexander Thomson, schoolmaster of Strathdon, was drowned in the disastrous floods of 1829. His body on being recovered from the river was taken to a cottage belonging to an old woman, who objected to the corpse being brought in unless it was first 'carried roond the hoose.' This was done; but the flood, later, rose further and reached and destroyed her house. She attributed this to the fact that the body had only been carried once round the house, and not three times. (From A.H., died 1910, aged 75.)

A local verse on the drowned schoolmaster runs:

> Sandy Thomson has been drooned,
>> Schoolmaster o' Strathdon,
> Mony places share the loss
>> Besides the Dee and Don,
> Sandy Thomson has been drooned,
>> Schoolmaster o' Strathdon.

A Resurrectionist Story. In the parish of Newhills, at the beginning of the last century, a funeral had been in progress. The 'lyke-wake' had been unduly prolonged for two days in a barn, until the whisky had run low. One of the company was dispatched for more, and, during his absence, the coffin was, as a practical joke, set up on end outside the door to scare him on his return. He duly reappeared with the fresh supplies, but to the surprise of the rest of the company made no remark about the coffin. At last one man said, 'Did ye nae see onything as ye cam' in? ' 'Na!' he replied, 'Fat wis there to see?' And on going out the assembly duly found there was nothing to see. Some resurrectionists who had happened to pass had seized the opportunity and the coffin with its contents, which never was seen again.

'Canny Folk'

In the fishing villages, in the old days, were certain people, men and women, whose advice it was well to take before setting out to sea or on other important occasions. In the village of Newtonhills, Kincardineshire, such a 'canny man' was, thirty years ago, called into and kept in the house during the progress of a tedious labour, with the idea that his presence would influence its progress favourably.

Birth

If a child cries lustily after it is born, the bystanders say, 'It's gat a gueed brain, ony-wye.' 'Ye may say fat ye like, but I ken this o't,' said an old woman, 'oot o' a' my ten, my aul'est laddie was the only een that grat maist awful' fan he was born, an' he's been cliverer than ony o' them.'

A premature child will live if born at the seventh month, but not at the eighth.

If twins should get husbands and wives, one of them will be childless.

A doublewhorl in the hair of a child means it will live to see two kings crowned, or that it will be 'a great wanderer.'

In olden days two mutches (caps), an inner plain one and an outer one of a more ornamental variety, were put on the child's head. The first inner one, taken off when soiled, was never washed and put on again, but flung in the fire. Similarly, the first soiled napkin was never washed and used again, but was flung out on the green. (*Durris, Kincardineshire.*)

Children baptized after dark will see 'bokies' (ghosts). (*Parish of Keig.*)

Sundry Beliefs and Sayings

Crows building near a house bring luck.

Swallows building also bring luck. It is very unlucky to harry a swallow's nest. A swallow flying beneath the arm causes paralysis of the arm.

If a woman loses her marriage-ring 'she will lose her man.'

It is unlucky to put boots on the table, but the ill-luck may be counteracted by spitting on the soles. Some years ago, after examining and condemning a pair of narrow-toed boots in a plough-man's house, I placed them on the table, and the ploughman's wife immediately removed them saying , 'Would ye hae strife in the hoose afore nicht?' She was consoled when I told her, what she did not know, how the evil might be averted.

It is unlucky to open an umbrella in a house: it presages a death.

It is unlucky to pick up your umbrella yourself if you drop it.

It is unlucky to write a prescription on black-edged notepaper.

[211]

It is unlucky to shake hands twice when saying good-bye.

If shingles meet round the body, the illness will be fatal.

If your left ear burns, your lover is thinking of you; if your right ear, your mother is thinking of you.

If the wind changes when you are 'making a face,' your face will permanently keep the expression: said as a warning to children.

Proverbs and Sayings

'There's great stots in Ireland, but they canna win oure for their horns'; said contemptuously to a boaster.

'We maun just mak' o' the warl' as the warl' wull mak' wi's.'

'The crap fills wi' the corn.'

'Foul saut's gueed eneuch for hairy butter.'

'There's but an ill year betwixt a rich man an' a peer (poor)'; said of farmers.

'Ye never see them gaen fae Auchtermair to Auchterless'' said of ministers.

'I dinna bile my cabbages twice'; said when asked to repeat a remark.

'The fire's the bonniest flower in the garden'; said in cold weather.

'A len' should aye gae lauchin hame'; *i.e.* should be returned with some small addition.

'He's feared o' the death he'll never dee'; said of a nervous man.

> There is a toon ayont the sea,
>> They ca't the toon o' Ayr,
> An' them that winna dae weel here,
>> Winna dae weel there.

(*Aberdeen Evening Express*, Ap. 11, 1907) Cf. Horace, *'Coelum non animum,'* etc.

Local Proverbs

Fyvie.—'The parish o' Fyvie's sap, tends to run into the cap.'

Tomintoul.—It is said that the Deil when flying over Tomintoul says, 'Bonny Tomintoul! ye're a' my ain bairns!' Probably of Protestant origin, as there are many Catholics there.

Buchan.—'There's rowth (plenty) o' a'thing in Buchan, haud awa' freet (fruit).'

Micras.—Of Micras, Deeside. 'There's nae an honest man in

Micras but een (one), an' he stole the cannas' (the canvas on which grain was flailed); used in Micras eighty years ago.

Strathdon.—'Ye can aye tell Nochty-side loons by "thee," "thou," an' "Wilta"'; said in Strathdon eighty years ago. Glen Nochty opens into Strathdon.

Pitfodels.—'Pit fae ye Pitfodels, there's men i' the Mearns!' the Slogan of the Menzies of Pitfodels.

The Mearns.—'The men o' the Mearns canna do mair than they may.' This saying is said to have originated from an unsuccessful attack made by the men o' the Mearns on some caterans in the castle of Birse.

Weather Lore, Seasons, etc.

A caul' May an' a windy
Maks a full May an' a findy.

May birds are aye cheepin'.
May cats are aye meutin' (mewing).

O' marriages in May
Bairns die in a decay.

When the sky's like the waves o' the sea
Wet weather it will be.

'The Gab o' May': cold weather at the beginning of May.

'The Teuchat (lap-wing) Storm': coarse weather at middle or end of April.

'The Cauld Kalendars o' May.'

'The Reedie Rows o' May': large waves that come rolling in, on otherwise calm days in May. (Footdee, Aberdeen.)

'The purse-mou''—lines of clouds converging towards one end: a forerunner of rough weather.

Black cumuli—nimbus clouds sometimes described as 'awfu' swine-looking clouds.'

'Goat's hair'—a cloudy sky resembling this is indicative of wind.

Beef-brose an' bannock day
Please let us home,
For a' the folk in oor toon
Hae gone to Foggie loan.

(Said by Rothienorman school children on 'Faster's-even.' The custom was for the children to write this on the black-board

before the master came in, and he, when he saw it, granted the
holiday.)

> Next comes Candlemas, and then the new meen,
> An' the first Tuesday after that is aye fasteren-e'en.
>
> (Dinnie's *History of Birse*.)

A harden Sabbath's a linen week. (A coarse Sunday is followed by
a week of good weather.)

Three bad Sundays will be followed by a week of fine weather.

> East and Wast
> The sign o' a blast,
> North and Sooth
> The sign o' a drooth.

(Said of the disposition of clouds in the sky.)

> Of fat's before, ye'll hear no more,
> But fat's behin', ye'll bitterly fin.

This is said of parhelia, or mock suns. If seen to the east (*i.e.*
'behind the sun'), they are of ill omen: if to the west (*i.e.* 'before
the sun'), they are of no moment.

> Fin the sea's at Aberdour,
> The ill weather's a' ower,
> But fin the sea's at Auchentumb
> The ill weather's a' t' come.

(*I.e.*, It is considered a sure prognostication of coming bad weather
when the noise of the waves beating on the rocky coast of Buchan is
heard far inland.)

NURSERY TALES AND CHILDREN'S SONGS

The Bannockie[1]

A mannie and a wifie pit oot a bannockie to dry, an' it ran owre
the hills an' owre the hills till it cam to twa waal washers. 'Fat a
bonny bannockie,' they said: 'far cam ye fae?'

'I cam fae a wee wee wifie an' a far less mannie, an' noo I've
come to you.'

They flung their tubs at it; an' it ran owre the hills an' owre the

---

1. Three versions of 'The Wee Bannock,' from Ayrshire, Dumfriesshire, and
   Selkirkshire, are given in Chambers's *Popular Rhymes of Scotland*. The
   Aberdeenshire one is the only one where the bannock survives its visit
   to the tod (fox). — *Cruden.*

hills till it cam to twa barn thrashers. 'Fat a bonny bannockie,' they said: 'far cam ye fae?'

'I cam fae a wee wee wifie an' a far less mannie, twa waal washers, an' noo I've come to you.'

They flung their flails at it; an' it ran owre the hills an' owre the hills till it cam to a mannie an' his clogs. 'Fat a bonny bannockie,' he said: 'far cam ye fae?'

'I cam fae a wee wee wifie an' a far less mannie, twa waal washers, twa barn thrashers, an' noo I've come to you.'

He flung his clogs at it; an' it ran owre the hills an' owre the hills till it cam to a shepherd and his dogs. 'Fat a bonny bannockie,' he said: 'far cam ye fae?'

'I cam fae a wee wee wifie an' a far less mannie, twa waal washers, twa barn thrashers, a mannie an' his clogs, an' noo I've come to you.'

He set his dogs at it; an' it ran owre the hills an' owre the hills till it cam to a tod in the burn. 'Fat a bonny bannockie,' it said: 'far cam ye fae?'

'I cam fae a wee wee wifie an' a far less mannie, twa waal washers, twa barn thrashers, a mannie an' his clogs, a shepherd an' his dogs, an' noo I've come to you.'

The tod shook its tail at it; an' it ran owre the hills an' owre the hills till it cam to a craw on the dyke. 'Fat a bonny bannockie,' it said: 'far cam ye fae?'

'I cam fae a wee wee wifie an' a far less mannie, twa waal washers, twa barn thrashers, a mannie an' his clogs, a shepherd an' his dogs, an' a tod in the burn, an' noo I've come to you.'

The craw flapped its wings at it an' it flew owre the hills an' owre the hills till it flew back to the mannie an' the wifie, an' they catched it.

The Mousie and the Rotten

A mousie and a rotten were to try a race to America. The mousie fell and broke its hinch, and gaed to the souter to get it shewed.

'Souter, souter, shew my hinch unto my pinch, and lat me win my wasie.'

'Na, awyte no,' says the souter, 'I winna shew your hinch unless ye gang to the soo for birse to me.'

'Soo, soo, birse me that I may birse the souter, the souter shew my hinch unto my pinch and lat me win my wasie.'

'Na, awyte no,' says the soo, 'I winna birse ye unless ye gang to the brewster wife for bran to me.'

'Brewster wife, brewster wife, bran me that I may bran the soo, and soo, soo, birse me that I may birse the souter, the souter shew my hinch unto my pinch and lat me win my wasie.'

'Na, awyte no,' says the brewster wife, 'unless ye gang to the coo for milk to me.'

'Coo, coo, milk me that I may milk the brewster wife; brewster wife bran me that I may bran the soo; the soo birse me that I may birse the souter; the souter shew my hinch unto my pinch and let me win my wasie.'

'Na, awyte no,' says the coo, 'unless ye gang to the barn-man for strae to me.'

'Barn-man, barn-man, strae me, that I may strae the coo; and coo, coo, milk me that I may milk the brewster wife; brewster wife bran me that I may bran the soo; soo, soo, birse me that I may birse the souter; souter, souter, shew my hinch unto my pinch and lat me win my wasie.'

The coo got the strae, the brewster wife got milk, the soo got the bran, the mousie got the birse, and the souter shewed its hinch, and the mousie was first in America.

There was a wife an' she dee't, an' her man green't [longed for] for her liver. He took it oot an' roastit it an' ate it; an' she cam in ae day. He said:

> 'Fat maks your feet sae braid?'
> 'I've gaen mair than ever I've read.'
> 'Fat maks your een sae howe?'
> 'It's lyin' sae lang amon' the dowe.'
> 'Fat gars your guts hing oot?'
> 'It was you! It was you!' (*Cruden*.)

> Gowf ba', cherry tree,
> Catch a bird an' gie it me,
> Let the tree be high or low,
> Let the weather be frost or snow.

> Gowf ba', cherry tree,
> How many apples do you give me?
> One for the leddy, an' anither for the laird,
> An' anither for the little boy that sits in the yaird.
> (*Old Aberdeen, eighty years ago.*)

> Whistle Bairdie had a coo,
> White and black aboot the mou,
> Wasna that a dainty coo

[216]

Belonged to Whistle Bairdie?

Ting-a-ling-a-long-tong,
   Fa's that 'at's deid?
Aul' Cattie Gilbert,
   Wi' a sair heid.

A' them 'at kent her
   Fan she wis alive,
Come till her beerial
   Atween fower an' five.

Brose an' butter an' a',
Sowens an' succar an' a',
An' isna she verra weel aff
'At gets brose an' butter an' a'?

Honey an' ham, an' jeely an' jam,
An' a skate like a barn-door.

Dance to your daddy, my little lady,
Dance to your daddy, my bonny lamb,
An' ye'll get a fishie in a little dishie,
An' a whirligiggie an' a supple Tam.

We are a' King William's men,
   Ma thurie an' my thorie,
An' we are a' King William's men
   Within a golden sorie.[1]

Pit the doggie to the mill,
   This gait an' that gait,
Tak' a lick oot o' this wifie's pyock,
An' a lick oot o' the neist wifie's pyock,
An' a drink at the mill dam,
An' gang hame, loup for spang, loup for
   spang, loup for spang!

My father an' mither wis Irish,
   An' I am Irish too,
I boucht a fiddle for ninepence,
   An' it was Irish too,
An' a' the tunes 'at it could play

---

1. Cf. Shetland carol, 'We are a' Queen Mary's Men.' *County Folklore*, vol. iii., p. 253.

Wis 'owre the hills an' far away,'
I bruck it here, I bruck it there,
An' I bruck it through the middle.

As I gaed by my aunty's door
   My aunty wis suppin' sowens,
I socht a sup, I got a sup,
   I socht a suppy mair;
She gaed me in the moo
Wi' the red het spurtle,
An' burnt it an' left but a hair.
   An' here's it!
                    (*Parish of Cruden.*)

Fan I wis een
I gaed my leen,
Fan I wis twa
I shot a craw,
Fan I wis three
I clim'ed a tree,
Fan I wis four
I gaed a glour,
Fan I wis five
I didna thrive,
Fan I wis sax
I got my smacks,
Fan I wis siven
I gaed to Stanehiven,
Fan I wis aucht
I carried a fraucht,
Fan I wis nine
I muckit the swine,
Fan I wis ten
I killed a hen,
Fan I wis eliven
I cam fae Stanehiven.
Fan I was twal
I fell into the draw-waal,
Fan I wis thirteen, fourteen
   I gaed to Aikey Fair,
Fan I was fifteen, saxteen
   Fat to dee there?

Fan I was seventeen, auchteen
  To buy an auld meer,
Fan I was nineteen, twenty
  She was owre dear.

(Parish of Cruden.)

CHILDREN'S SINGING GAMES

Little Sally Walker sitting in the sand,
Crying and weeping for a young man.
Rise, Sally, rise and wipe away your tears,
Fly to the East and fly to the West,
Fly to the one that you love best.
There's a couple got married in joy,
First a girl and then a boy,
Seven years after and seven years to come
This young couple may rise and be done.
Up streets, down streets and a penny glass,
Isn't . . . a nice young lass?
But isn't . . . as nice as she?
Both to be married and they canna agree.
Clean bright candlesticks, clean fireside,
Draw back the curtains and let's see the bride.

A' the men in oor toon lives a happy life,
Except . . . and he wants a wife.
A wife shall he hae, and a widow shall he be,
For look at . . ., she sits on his knee.
She paints her face and she curls her hair,
And she kisses her lad at the foot o' the stair.

The wind and the wind and the wind blows high,
And the rain comes pattering from the sky.
. . . says she'll die,
For a lad on the rolling high.
She is handsome, she is pretty,
She is the flower of the golden city,
She has got lovers, one, two, three,
Pray and tell me who they be?
. . . says he'll have her,
In his bosom he will clasp her,
Lash the whip and away we go,
Off to Newcastle races O!

[219]

Wattery, wattery well flowers, spring up so high,
We are all maidens and we must all die,
Except . . . and she is the youngest one.
She can kick and she can fling,
And she can turn the sofa.
O fie, fie for shame,
Turn your back to the walls again!

We are two lovers come from Spain,
   All in French garlands,
We've come to court your daughter Jane,
   So adieu to you, my darlings.

My daughter Jane, she is so young,
   All in French garlands,
She cannot bear your flattering tongue,
   So adieu to you, my darlings.

If this young man should chance to die,
   And leave his wife a widow,
The bells shall ring, and the church shall sing,
   And we'll all clap hands together.

So a-doaving, a-doaving,
   A-doaving by the hand,
We'll take this pretty fair maid,
   We'll take her by the hand.

Counting out Rhymes

   Eetam, peetam, penny pie,
     Pap-a-lorrie, jinky-jye,
   Stan' ye oot-bye
     For the bonnie penny pie.

   Eenerie, twa-erie, tuckerie, taiven,
   Alamacrackerie ten or elaiven,
   Peen Jean, muskey dan,
   Teedlum, Fodlum, twenty-wan.

Written in Books

   If onybody gets a len'
   Be's gude as sen' it hame again.

   ————is my name,

Scotland is my nation,
————is my dwelling-place,
A pleasant habitation;
And when I'm dead and in my grave
And all my bones are rotten,
Tak' up this book and think on me
When I am quite forgotten.

Old Songs

I set spurs to my neadie
An' awa I did ride,
To fair Lunnon city
Seekin' for a bride.
The girls they cam efter me,
By one, by two, by ten,
I taul them I would mairry,
I taul them I would mairry,
I taul them I would mairry,
But I never taul them when.

I aince had a sweetheart
I loved her as my life,
An' ofttimes I thocht
I would mak her my wife.
But she proved false to me,
For she loved all sorts o' men.
I taul her I would mairry,
I taul her I would mairry,
I taul her I would mairry,
But I never taul her when.

I coorted a widow
Who had great stores of gold.
. . . . .

I coorted her till she gave me
Nine hunner pounds an' ten.
An' I taul her I would mairry,
I taul her I would mairry,
I taul her I would mairry,
But I never taul her when.

I set spurs to my neadie
An' awa I did ride,
To fair Lunnon city,

[221]

Seekin' for a bride.
The girls they cam efter me,
    But catch me if you can,
For I taul them I would mairry,
I taul them I would mairry,
I taul them I would mairry,
    But I never taul them when.

I am a rantin' aul' maid
    An' I've been single lang,
I took into my aul' heid
    That I would like a man.

Chorus: Fal al the diddle al,
        Fal al de day,
        Fal al the diddle al,
        Fal al de day.

I gaed to a singin' class,
    And bonny lads were there,
The first that took my fancy
    Was ane wi' curly hair.

He said to me, 'My bonny lass,
    Fat wye div ye gang hame?'
Richt modestly I answered him,
    'The very wye I came.'

He said to me, 'My bonny lass,
    Fat like's the ane ye lo'e?'
Richt modestly I answered him,
    'He's richt like you.'

He said to me, 'My bonny lass,
    Fat is't they ca' your name?'
Richt modestly I answered him,
    'They ca' me Meg at hame.'

He said to me, 'My bonny lass,
    Am I the lad ye lo'e?'
Richt modestly I answered him,
    'Ye've guessed richt noo.'
                        Parish of Cruden.

As I gaed by yon toonie farm
A barkie cam oot an' doggit at me,

[222]

I took my flauchter shooder fae aff my spad
I gaed it such a lug i' the lasher,
I gart a' its water een again.

(A nonsense recitation with the words transposed.—*Parish of Cruden.*)

'Fustle, fustle, aul' wife,
An' I'll gie ye a hen.'
'I couldna fustle
Altho' ye gied me ten.'

'Fustle, fustle, aul' wife,
An' I'll gie ye a coo.'
'I couldna fustle
Altho' ye gied me two.'

'Fustle, fustle, aul' wife,
An' I'll gie ye a man.'
'F—f—f—f— [Imitation of unsuccessful whistling.]
I'll dee the best I can.'[1]

My ae string walletie,
My twa string walletie,
My three string walletie,
O, weary fa' your dogs, gude wife,
They're rivin' a' my walleties!

(*Strathdon*, ninety years ago.)

---

1. A variant of this is in Chambers's *Pop. Rhymes of Scotland.*

36
The Mining Folk of Fife

[From J.E. Simpkins, *County Folklore VII . . . Fife, Clackmannan, and Kinross* (London, 1914), pp. 385-416]

All the folk-lore notes given here were gathered by me at first hand during a twelve years' residence in Fife, ten years of which were spent in the parish of Auchterderran, an agricultural and mining district. It is not pretended that all the customs, etc., mentioned were universal. Many of them were dying out, and many more were referred to jestingly, often with the semi-apologetic remarks, 'that's an old freit, that's what the auld folk used to say, or do.' But everything I have set down I have tested as having been at one time or another common in the district.

The Fifer, whether he deserves it or not, has the reputation of being more full of 'freits' than the dweller in perhaps any other county in Scotland. He owes much to his isolated situation. The deep inlet of the Firth of Tay to the north, and the equally deep inlet of the Forth to the south, made communication with the outer world difficult and dangerous in these directions for many a long century. Eastwards the North Sea was an effective barrier, while going westward took the Fifer amongst the hills and the Highlanders. The genuine old-fashioned Fife miner has three great divisions of 'incomers' of whom, when occasion arises, he speaks with contempt. These are—(1) Loudoners or natives of the Lothians, (2) Hielanters, who include all from Forfarshire to John o' Groats, and (3) Wast-Country Folk. And these last in his opinion, and not without reason, are perhaps the worst of all. Although present day facilities for travelling, and especially the Forth and Tay bridges, have done much to remove this clannishness amongst the folk, there is no doubt that here and there a considerable amount of it remains. Some time ago a man died in a Fifeshire mining village. He had been continuously resident there for twenty years, but he was not what the Fifer calls a 'hereaboots' man—he was an 'incomer.' And so when he passed away the news went round the village that 'the stranger' was dead.

When I went to Auchterderran in 1894 the great bulk of the mining population was composed of the old Fifeshire mining families, who were an industrious, intelligent, and markedly independent class. They worked in various small privately-owned mines, the proprietors of which in most cases had themselves sprung from the mining class, many of them being relatives of their employés; and a certain family feeling and friendship nearly always existed. With the advent of large Limited Liability Companies there was a corresponding extension of the workings, and a huge influx of a lower class of workman from the Lothians and the West country (involving an Irish element), while the small private concerns went inevitably to the wall.

Most of the old Fifeshire miners had dwelt for generations in the same hamlets, being born, brought up and married, and often dying in the same spot. Many of them were descendants of the old 'adscripti glebae,' the workers who were practically serfs, 'thirled' to pit-work for life, and sold with the pit as it changed hands. It is strange to think that this extraordinary method of controlling labour prevailed in Scotland till 1775, so that an old miner of eighty years of age at the present day might quite well be the grandson of a man who had worked as a serf in the pit. During the earlier part of the nineteenth century the different hamlets naturally kept markedly to themselves. Within living memory all merchandise required for domestic use had to be purchased at the hamlet shop, usually kept by a relation of the colliery owner; any debts incurred to him being deducted from the men's wages. To keep such a shop was therefore a very safe speculation. There were other 'off-takes,' *e.g.* for medical attendance, pick-sharpening, etc.; and as wages ruled low the total sum received every fortnight on 'pay-Saturday' was often small enough. The good type of miner always handed over his wages intact to his wife, who bought his tobacco for him along with her household purchases, and returned him a sum for pocket-money, usually spent on a 'dram.' An occasional excess in this line was not harshly judged, and good comradeship prevailed. An interesting comment was once made by an old Fifer after the influx into Auchterderran of 'Loudoners' and 'wast-country folk' occurred—'Ay, this is no' the place it used to be: ye canna lie fou' at the roadside noo wi'oot gettin' your pooches ripit!'

In the parish of Auchterderran the collieries in the days gone by were small, and only the more easily-got-at surface seams of coal were worked. The first seams to be worked out were those which cropped out to the surface, and the seam was simply followed in as far as it could be got at (an 'ingaun e'e'), and when it got too deep for this method a shaft was driven. It was the custom for both man and wife to work in the pit. The man dug the coal and the woman (before winding machinery was introduced) carried it to the surface in her creel, either up the 'in-gaun e'e' or up the side of the shaft by a circular ladder.

That this work of coal-bearing was coarse and degrading work for women, and that it attracted to it or caused to be forced into it the unfortunate and friendless, is shown by the following extract from 'The Last Speech and dying Words of *Margaret Millar*, coal-bearer at *Coldencleugh* who was execute 10. *February* 1726 at the Gibbet of *Dalkeith*, for Murdering her own Child.'

> The place of my birth was at *Dysert* in *Fife*. My Father *John Millar* was a Salter under my Lord *Sinclar* there, and I being in my Nonage left to the care of an Uncle, who put me to the Fostering, and after being wean'd from the Breast, was turn'd from Hand to Hand amongst other relations, when my Friends being wearied and neglecting me, I was obliged to engage with my Lord *Sinclar's* Colliers to be a Bearer in his Lordship's Coalheughs; So being unaccustomed with that Yoke of Bondage, I endeavoured to make my Escape from such a World of Slavery, expecting to have made some better thereof: But in place of that I fell into a greater Snare.

Ventilation in the earlier part of last century was a negligible quantity, and the air was often too foul for the naked-light lamps to burn in. One old man, the husband of Mrs. H. mentioned later, told me that he remembered some sixty years ago working below ground by the phosphorescent light of decaying fish-heads, in a low part of the mine where the air was too foul to allow his tallow lamp to burn. He said they gave enough light to show him where to 'howk' his coal.

The following interesting account of mining life in bye-gone days was written in 1896 by an old miner, A.C., Lochgelly, then aged about seventy years:

> I will now give you my little essay on the rise and progress of the mining industry in Lochgelly for a hundred and fifty years back. You will find it both interesting and amusing, and at same time all truth. Their work and mode of living was the constant fire-side talk. We are the oldest race of miners that belongs to Lochgelly, and have been all born in that little old row of houses called Launcherhead, and the mines where they

wrought were round about it. It was the custom at that time for the man and his wife to work both. The man digged the coals, and his wife carried them to the pit bank on her back. They were called Bearers, and if anything went wrong with the man she had to be both miner and Bearer both. Such was the case with my Grandmother. She was left a widow with five of a family, three girls and two boys. My Father was six months old, and my uncle B. was two years, there being no other way for her to support her family but to make herself a general miner. So she put her two boys in her coal creel, carried them down the pit and laid them at the stoop side until she digged her coals and carried them to the pit bank on her back. When she rested she gave my father a drink and my uncle a spoonful of cold stoved potatoes. Potatoes formed the greatest part of their living at that time. That was in about 1725.[1] There was only nine miners in Lochgelly at that time, and at the end of the year my grandmother had the highest out-put of coal on Lochgelly work. Their daily output was little over ten tons. Last time the mining industry of Lochgelly was brought up she was the leading character. After her family grew up she drove both coal mines and stone ones. She drove a great part of the day-level leading from Water Orr. The air was sometimes that bad that a light of no description would burn: the only light she had was the reflection from Fish Heads,[2] and her family carried the rade[3] to the bank. The name of this remarkable female miner was Hannah Hodge. Sir Gilbert Elliot was the laird of Lochgelly at that time. He had them all up at Lochgelly House two or three [times] every year and had a proper spree with them. There was two Englishmen, father and son, the name of Chisholm, took Lochgelly work and keept it as long as they lived and their sons after them. They invented the first machine here for raising coal and that was a windlass and they raised the output from ten to fifteen tons. The only machine for raising coal before that was the miners' wives. As time rolled on the Father and Son got married on my two aunts. Such a marriage has not taken place in Lochgelly for one hundred and fifteen years [before that]. William Stewart carried on the work after their father's death. They introduced a Gin and brought the output up to

---

1. *Sic*, but the date is obviously wrong. Probably it should be 1795.
2. Cf. old H.'s description, Auchterderran.
3. "Redd," refuse, material not coal.

25 tons. Mr. Henderson and company got the work next and they raised the output up to 30 tons. And it has increased every year since that time. When the Nellie workings got up through on the old workings that I heard them talk so much about I travelled [walked] a whole day to see where my Father and Mother wrought, and I saw my Uncle B.'s mind ['mind' = mine, Fifeshire] where he made such a narrow escape of his life. He was driving a mind from the parrot seam to the splent to let off a great quantity of water that was lying there. It blew the side out of his mind. It knocked him up to the high side which saved his life. If he had gone out the day level with the water he [had] never been seen [again]. He was very jocular and about as good of walking on his hands as feet. He got himself rightly arranged with his lamp hanging on his backside and walked up and down past Launcherhead doors and every one that looked out thought they were no use of them going to work that day after seeing a man walking about the place wanting the head. All the miners in Lochgelly lived in Cooperhall and Launcherhead and was full of superstition.

After dealing with Lochgelly in recent times the old man says:

For every holing a miner takes off he can sit down and say to himself 'I sit here where human foot has never trod nor human voice has rung,' and that is more than Stanley could say after his travels through Africa.

Miners' Freits
The old-fashioned miner had a strong objection to meeting a black cat or a woman, especially an 'old wife,' and more so one with a white mutch on, while on his way to work. Many colliers even yet will turn back and lose a day's work rather than proceed in face of the possible ill-luck involved. It is supposed to mean accident, either to the man or to the place he is in. The cases are cited of a man who, in spite of the meeting, went to work and got his leg broken, and of another who went to work and found his 'place' fallen in.

When an accident happened in the pit, all who heard of it used to 'lowse,' *i.e.* cease from work. In these days of large collieries the news does not always reach the working places; but in the event of any serious accident, involving say, two or three deaths, the whole of the men employed usually come to the pit bank and cease work for the day.

The following are common freits noted at Auchterderran:

It is unlucky to begin work or start on a journey on a Friday.
It is unlucky to turn back after you have started out from the house.
It is unlucky to shake hands twice on saying good-bye.
It is unlucky to dream of eggs; eggs mean 'clashes' (evil-speaking: disputes).
To dream of rats is unlucky; rats mean enemies.
To dream of washing means a 'flitting' (removal).
To dream of the loss of teeth means a death.
To dream of the loss of fingers means the same.
To rub the nose when you rise in the morning means that you will hear of a death before night.
It is unlucky to meet a woman with untidy shoes or stockings.
If a man's (or woman's) bootlace comes undone, his (or her) sweetheart (or wife or husband) is thinking of him (or her). (Evil wishing ties knots; good wishing looses them.)
It is unlucky to put your shoes on the table, it will cause 'strife.' Ill luck can be averted by spitting on the soles.
If two people wash their hands together in a basin, the sign of the cross should be made in the water.
It is unlucky to go under a ladder.
It is unlucky to spill salt. If done some salt should be thrown over the left shoulder.
Breaking a mirror means ill-luck for seven years.
It is unlucky to give a present of a knife or scissors. It 'cuts love.'
Sudden silence means that an angel is passing through the room.
It is unlucky to look at the new moon through glass.
On first seeing the new moon you should turn a piece of silver in your pocket.
It is unlucky to give undue praise to horses, cattle, etc., or children. If this is done it constitutes 'fore-speaking' and evil will follow. Hence probably the Scots invalid on being asked how he is says he 'is no ony waur'—he avoids fore-speaking himself.
A cat will 'suck' a child's breath and so cause death.
A horse 'sees things' invisible to the driver. 'What are ye seein' noo?' is a common remark when a horse shies without apparent cause.
It is lucky to have a horseshoe in the house.
A woman whose child had died, said to me: 'This comes o'

laughin' at freits.' On enquiry I found that she had always condemned those who kept a horse-shoe at the fire-side (a common custom). She immediately procured one.

A pig sees the wind.

The 'hole' in the forefoot of a pig is where the devils entered the Gadarene swine.

A man who has killed a lot of pigs in his day has a good chance of seeing the Devil.

It is unlucky to 'harry' a swallow's nest.

If a swallow flies below your arm that arm will become paralysed.

Swallows or crows building near a house are unlucky.

It is unlucky to have peacocks' feathers in the house.

GAMES

Hainchin' the bool
A game played in the earlier half of the nineteenth century amongst the Fifeshire miners was called 'hainchin' the bool.' The 'bool,' which weighed about 4 lbs., and was somewhat larger than a cricket ball, was chipped round from a piece of whin-stone with a specially made small iron hammer. The game was played on the high-road where a suitably level piece could be got. The ball was held in the hand, and the arm brought up sharply against the haunch, when the ball was let go. Experts are said to have been able to throw it over 200 yards. The game was ultimately stopped by the authorities. This form of throwing is very frequently practised by boys to throw stones over a river or out to sea from the beach. How long 'hainchin' the bool' had been practised in Fife it is hard to say, but the stone ball was the same type as the 'prehistoric' stone-balls fairly common in Scotland, some of which at least may have been used for a similar purpose.

Shinty formerly took the place of the present-day universally popular football.

The dulls or **Dully** (Rounders) was also formerly popular.

Cock-fighting was formerly very common amongst the Fifeshire miners. Even yet, in spite of legal repression, many game-cocks are bred and matches held on the quiet. A disused quarry in the parish (*Auchterderran*) was a favourite amphitheatre for large matches (*e.g.* an inter-parish or inter-county combat), and Sunday a favourite day. Quite a large crowd of men would collect, often driving long distances, to view the combat. In Fife the cocks were always fought with the natural spur.

Quoits is an old game still played with great interest and skill.

MARRIAGE

'Marry for love and wark for siller' runs the Fife proverb, setting forth the principles on which matrimony should be undertaken.

On hearing of an intended marriage, the customary enquiry is, as to the man, 'Wha's he takkin'?' but in the case of a woman, 'Wha's she gettin'?' Other common sayings are: 'She's ower mony werrocks[1] (bunions) to get a man': and, 'Mim-mou'ed maidens never get a man; muckle-mou'ed maids get twa.' 'When ye tak' a man, ye tak' a maister,' is a woman's proverb. But when once the wedding-ring was on, it was unlucky to take it off again. 'Loss the ring, loss the man.'

> Change the name and no' the letter,
> Change for the waur and no' the better.

It was quite common in the parish for a married woman to be referred to by her maiden name in preference to the surname she was entitled to use by marriage.

The following account of old-time marriage customs among the mining folk was taken down in 1903 from the description of Mrs. H., of Auchterderran, aged seventy-five. She had been born, brought up, and had lived all her life, in one hamlet in the parish, and had never been further than ten miles away from it.

When the 'coortin'' had been successfully accomplished, the custom was to celebrate 'the Contrack night.' This was the night that 'the cries' had been given in (*i.e.* the notification to the minister to proclaim the banns of marriage) and a convivial meeting was held in the house of the bride. The food was plain (perhaps 'dried fish and tatties'), and there was much innocent merriment; one outstanding part of the programme being the 'feet-washing' of the bridegroom. This performance varied in severity from plain water and soap to a mixture of black lead, treacle, etc., and the victim always struggled

---

1. *Wyrock*, a sort of hard excrescence. — Jamieson.

against the attentions of the operators. In spite of his efforts at self-defence the process was always very thoroughly carried out. As regards the 'cries,' the proper thing was to be 'cried' three Sundays running, for which the fee was 5s. But if you hurried matters up, and were cried twice, you had to pay 7s.6d., while if your haste was more extreme and you were only cried once, you were mulcted in the sum of 10s.6d.

The marriage usually took place in church. On the marriage-day the bridegroom and bride with best-man and bridesmaids set out in procession for the Kirk, the bride and groom sometimes being 'bowered,' *i.e.* having an arch of green boughs held over their heads. All the couples went 'traivlin' linkit' (walking arm in arm) sometimes to the number of thirty-two couples, while guns and pistols were fired on the march, and all sorts of noise and joking kept up. In the parish of Auchterderran it was the rule (owing to damage having been done on one occasion to the sacred edifice), that all this had to cease when the procession came in sight of the kirk at the top of Bowhill Brae, about two hundred yards from the building. Money was dispensed by the bridegroom, which was called the 'ba' siller.' All this is done away with now, with the exception of the ba' siller, which is always looked for.

On returning home, the bride had a cake of shortbread broken over her head while crossing the threshold. This is still sometimes done. In the evening a dance would be held and 'the green-garters' (which had been knitted in anticipation by the best maid) were pinned surreptitiously on to the clothing of the elder unmarried brother or sister of the bride. When discovered they were removed and tied round the left arm and worn for the rest of the evening. The green garters are still in evidence. The unmarried women present would be told to rub against the bride 'for luck,' as that would ensure their own early marriage. The proceedings terminated with the 'beddin' o' the bride.' When the bride got into bed her left leg stocking was taken off and she had to throw it over her shoulder, when it was fought for by those in the room, the one who secured it being held as safe to be married next.[1] The bride had to sit up in bed until the

---

1.   The bride was now laid in her bed,
         Her left leg ho' was flung,
      And Geordie Gib was fidging glad,
         Because it hit Jean Gunn.
      ALLAN RAMSAY, first supplemental canto to 'Christ's Kirk on the Green.'

[232]

bridegroom came and 'laid her doon.'[1] Sometimes the roughest of horseplay went on. In one case mentioned by an old resident in the parish, practically 'a' the company' got on to the bed, which broke and fell on the ground.

'The Kirkin'' took place the following Sunday, when three couples sat in one seat; viz. the bride and bridegroom, the best maid and best man, and 'anither lad and his lass.'

On the first appearance of the newly-married man at his work he had to 'pay aff' or 'stand his hand' (stand treat). Failing this he was rubbed all over with dust and grime. This was called 'creelin.'

This 'creelin'' is a very attenuated survival of the custom mentioned by Allan Ramsay in his second supplemental canto to 'Christ's Kirk on the Green,' where the day after the marriage the bridegroom has 'for merriment, a creel or basket bound, full of stones, upon his back; and, if he has acted a manly part, his young wife with all imaginable speed cuts the cords, and relieves him of his burden.'[2]

BIRTH AND INFANCY

Of the three stages of life round which old customs and beliefs cluster—namely, marriage, birth, and death—the second has perhaps the greatest amount of folklore connected with it. Some part of what is here set down has already appeared in the *Caledonian Medical Journal*, vol. v.,[3] but all of it is the fruit of many years' personal experience as a medical practitioner among the folk of Fife, more especially among those who daily go down into the coalpits of the country to earn their bread.

. . . . .

The belief in maternal impressions is of course fixed and certain; and wonderful are the tales told of children born with a 'snap' on the

---

1. ...The bride she made a fen',
   To sit in wylicoat sae braw, upon her nether en'. *Idem.*
2. *The Works of Allan Ramsay*, vol. i. p. 328. A. Fullarton & Co., London, Edinburgh, and Dublin. 1851.
3. 'The Scottish Bone-setter,' 'The Obstetric Folk-Lore of Fife,' and 'Popular Pathology'; also 'Some Fifeshire Folk-Medicine' in the *Edinburgh Medical Journal*, 1904.

cheek (through that favourite piece of confectionery having been playfully thrown at the mother), or with a mouse on the leg.

. . . . .

Any start or fright to a pregnant woman is considered dangerous, as the child may 'put up its hand and grip the mother's heart.' I have heard sudden deaths in pregnancy attributed to this. Each pregnancy is supposed to cost the woman a tooth.

A barren woman is often told chaffingly to 'tak' a rub' against a pregnant woman and 'get some o' her luck.'

If a woman is presented with a bunch of lilies before her child's birth, the child will be a girl. This is believed to be of French origin, as it was narrated by a daughter of a Frenchman who was taken prisoner at Waterloo. She lived in Ceres, Fife.

. . . . .

The placenta was usually burned, sometimes buried.

After the birth the mother had to be very careful till the 'ninth day' was past. Till then, she was not allowed to 'redd' her hair, or to lift her hands 'abune the breath' *i.e.* higher than her mouth.[1] . . .

'Nurse weel the first year, ye'll no nurse twa,' was the advice given by experienced elders to young mothers.

'A woman was in seeing a neighbour who had had a "little body." The patient got up while the caller was in. The caller was going out again, but she was brought back until the mother got into bed again. Before leaving, the caller got "the fitale dram."' (*Cowdenbeath*).

. . . . .

If the child's first cry can be twisted into 'dey' (father), the next comer will be a male.

. . . . .

If the child is pronounced to be like father or mother, some one present will say, 'Weel, it couldna be like a nearer freen'!'[2] It is held that the child will be liker the parent who has either been fonder of the other at the time it was begotten, or fonder of the other during the pregnancy, 'because he or she looks often at, and thinks often o'' the other. Or again, that the infant will be more like the parent who has the stronger constitution.

---

1. Cf. Neuburger, *History of Medicine*, vol. i. p. 74.
2. Friend, *Scot.*, a relative.

If the little stranger is a well-developed child, we are told: 'That ane hasna been fed on deaf nuts.' (Deaf nuts are worthless withered nuts.)

. . . . .

First Ceremonies

The ceremony of drinking the child's health at birth ('wettin' the bairn's heid') is laid stress on, and those not 'drinkin' oot the dram' are expostulated with thus: 'Ye wouldna tak' awa' the bairn's beauty? (or luck).' The refreshments, usually shortbread and whisky, are called 'the bairn's cakes.'

A visitor going to see a newborn child must not go empty-handed but must carry some small gift for presentation to the youngster, or he or she will carry away the child's beauty.

The child should always, when possible, be carried upstairs before it is carried down; and where this is impossible, a box or chair will give the necessary rise in life.

'The bairn's piece' was a piece of cake, or bread and cheese, or biscuit, wrapped in a handkerchief and carried by the woman who was taking the child to the kirk for the christening. This woman was always if possible one of good repute in the district, and the office was considered an honour. 'Mony an ane I carried to the kirk,' said old Mrs. H., with pride. The first person met with on the way, whether 'kent face' or stranger, was presented with 'the bairn's piece,' and was expected to partake of the proffered refreshment. Sometimes he or she would indulge in prophecy and say, 'A lassie the next time,' or, 'a laddie'; but failing this it was considered that if the person met was a male, the mother's next child would be a female, and *vice versa*. The custom is now practically extinct, even in country places.

'Children that are taken to be christened are taken in at the little gate instead of at the big gate now, since suicides are not taken over the church wall to be buried, as it was supposed that the first child that was taken in at the gate would commit suicide.' (Verbatim as given. *Cowdenbeath*.)

If on a Sunday a boy and a girl are being christened, the girl must be christened before the boy, otherwise she will have a beard.

. . . . .

If a mother thinks she is not to have more children, and so gives her cradle away, another child will be born to her.

If you see a baby about six weeks old watching smoke going up a chimney, it will never have a birthday.

. . . . .

If the child 'neezes' (sneezes), the correct thing is to say, 'Bless the bairn!' If it 'gants' (yawns), the chin is carefully pushed up to close the mouth.

When the child's nails require shortening, they should not be cut with scissors, but bitten. If a child's nails are cut before it is a year old (some say six months), it will be 'tarry-fingered,' (a thief).

. . . . .

Families

If twins grow up, and both marry, only one of them will have children.

An addition to a miner's family, if a boy, is described as 'a tub o' great'; if a girl, as 'a tub o' sma'.'

A family of two is described as 'a doo's cleckin'' (*i.e.* a pigeon's hatch).

A family of three is looked on as ideal: 'twa to fecht an' ane to sinder' (separate). Sometimes another child is allowed, and it becomes 'twa to fecht, ane to sinder, an' one to rin an' tell.'

The last of the family is described as 'the shakkins o' the poke,' (bag). 'Losh, wumman! this'll surely be the shakkins o' the poke noo!'

LEECHCRAFT

'Folk-medicine,' says Sir Clifford Allbutt (*British Medical Journal*, Nov. 20, 1909), 'whether independent or still engaged with religion and custom, belongs to all peoples and all times, including our own. It is not the appanage of a nation; it is rooted in man, in his needs and his primeval observation, instinct, reason and temperament. . . . To Folk-medicine doubt is unknown; it brings the peace of security.'

The Leech

'A drucken doctor's clever,' is the popular opinion expressed in a curiously unwise proverb. But even he does not always command the undoubting faith that is reposed by the ignorant in the unwashed oracles of the roadside, the tinker and the tramp, who have successfully dodged the dominie, but who nevertheless are reputed to be

'skeelie wi' simples.' For 'ye'd wonder what gaun-aboot folks kens.'
If the 'cure'—these remedies are always known as 'cures'—can be got
from anyone invested with a slight touch of the uncanny, so much
the better. One old lady told me, 'My mither got the cure from a
man wantin' the legs, that was drawn aboot by two black dogs.' A
man with two legs, drawn about by a horse, can be met with and
consulted any day; but one wanting the legs and drawn about by two
black dogs is something out of the usual run, and naturally his advice
should be something 'by-ordinar,' and implicitly to be trusted.

. . . . .

Popular Physiological Ideas

It is believed that there is 'a change in the system' every seven
years.

Hair. If a grey hair is pulled out three will come in its place.
(*Auchterderran* and *Fife generally*.)

A horsehair put into water is supposed to turn into a worm
or an eel. Many people otherwise intelligent fully believe this.
(*Auchterderran* and *Fife generally*.)

Hair and nails should not be cut on Sunday. 'Cursed is he that cuts
hair or horn on the Sabbath,' was quoted against a resident who had
dishorned a 'cattle-beast' on Sunday. (*Auchterderran*.)

An excessive amount of hair on a new-born child's head is an
explanation of the mother having suffered from heartburn.

'A hairy man's a happy man—or, a "geary" (wealthy) man—a
hairy wife's a witch.'

A tuft of hair on the head that will not keep down when brushed
is called 'a coo's lick.'

Red Hair. A red haired first-foot is very unlucky.

'He's waur than daft, he's reid-heided.'

There is a schoolboy rhyme:

> Reid heid, curly pow,
> Pish on the grass and gar it grow.

Large Head. 'Big heid, little wut.'

The Heart. 'To gar the heart rise,' to cause nausea.

'To get roond the heart,' to cause faintness. ('It fairly got roond
my heart.')

Sudden death is explained as due to the heart having been 'ca'ed
(pushed) aff its stalk.'

Any injury, however slight, near the heart, is looked upon as
dangerous. 'Far frae the heart' is used to mean, not dangerous, not
of much importance, trifling. 'O that's far frae the heart!' not worth
bothering about.

[237]

'Whole at the heart,' courageous, in good spirits. 'But a' the time he lay he was whole at the heart.'

'Something cam' ower the heart,' *i.e.* a feeling of faintness occurred.

'I saw her heart fill,' I saw she was overcome with emotion.

Hiccough is supposed to be caused by 'a nerve in the heart,' and at every hiccough 'a drop o' blude leaves the heart.'

Jugular vein. Great importance is attached to any injury 'near the joogler.' Fear will be expressed lest any swelling in the neck should be 'pressin' on the joogler.'

. . . . .

Nerves. A 'nervish' person is a nervous person: a 'nervey' one, a quick active person.

Hysteria is described as 'the nerves gaun through the body.'

A highly neurotic imaginative person is described as 'a heap o' nerves'—'a mass o' nerves.'

A *pot-bellied* individual is described as 'cob-weimed.' The 'cob' is the grub found at the root of the docken, and is a favourite bait with fishers.

Sneezing ('neezing') is held to clear the brain.

Spittle, spitting. Fasting spittle is a cure for warts and for sore eyes.

The spittle of a dog ('dog's lick') is a cure for cuts and burns.

Spitting for luck. At the conclusion of a bargain the money is spat on 'for luck.' Money received in charity from one for whom the recipient has a regard is similarly treated.

A man meeting a friend whom he has not seen for a long time will spit on his hand before extending it for shaking hands.

Along the coast, any dead carcass is spat on with the formula, 'That's no my granny.'

A schoolboy challenge is to extend the right hand and ask another boy to 'spit owre that.' If he does so, the fight begins. A schoolboy saying (contemptuous): 'I'll spit in your e'e an' choke ye.'

Teeth. Toothache is caused by 'a worm in the teeth.'

To extract eye-teeth endangers the sight.

'He's cut a' his teeth,' he is wide awake.

'He didna cut his teeth yesterday,' he is an experienced person.

'A toothful,' a small quantity of anything.

Thumb. An injury to the thumb is supposed to be specially apt to cause lock-jaw.

Tongue. 'Tongue-tackit,' tongue-tied.

'The little tongue,' the uvula.

If a magpie's tongue has a piece 'nickit oot' between two silver sixpences, the bird will be able to speak.

A seton passed in below the tongue of a dog will make it quiet while hunting. A poacher's dodge.

'To have a dirty tongue,' to be a foul speaker.

'To gie the rough side o' the tongue,' to swear at, to speak harshly.

'Her tongue rins ower fast,' or 'She's ower fast wi' her tongue,' said of women.

Unconsciousness is described as 'deid to the warl'.' 'I was deid to the warl' for sax hoors.'

Wind (flatulence) has extraordinary powers attributed to it: 'gettin' roon' the heart,' 'gaun to the heid.' An acute pain in the chest or belly is often said to be caused by 'the wind gettin' in atween the fell (skin) and the flesh.'

. . . . .

Pathological Ideas

Popular Conception of Disease. An implied belief in the existence of disease as an entity—an entity that can be fed, or starved, or transferred—is often peculiarly prominent. There is always for example, a fear of taking anything that may 'feed the tribble.' A fight is going on between the trouble and the 'system,' and unsuitable medicine may go to help the former at the expense of the latter. 'For ony favour,' said one woman, 'dinna gie me onything that will gar me eat, for a' I tak just gangs to the hoast and strengthens it.' Again, in the case of a poultice, there is an underlying idea of the transference of the 'tribble' from the afflicted body to the poultice, and it is with this idea that the poultice is usually burnt. The poultice is held to 'draw the tribble': the disease is 'in' until it has been extracted: it has to be got out. Some poultices, such as carrot or soap-and-sugar poultices, are described as 'awfu' drawin' things.' 'Is it no' drawin' it owre sair?' is a common query regarding a poultice or a dressing. When a blister does not rise readily it is looked on as a bad sign: the trouble cannot be drawn out: 'it is ill to draw,'—'dour to draw'— 'the tribble's deep in.'

Disease may also be 'drawn out' from a human body to that of a lower animal, as appears from the treatment of syphilis noted below and other cases.

Contagion. 'Ay, an' wha smittit (infected) the first ane?' is often said contemptuously as an argument against instructions to isolate an infectious case. Measles, scarlatina, etc., are looked on as 'bairns' tribbles' and to 'pit them a' thegither an' hae dune wi't' is often practised. On the other hand, it is believed that all bedding and clothes belonging to a deceased phthisical patient should be burnt. It is also held that those who are not 'feared at' a trouble will not take it. Another belief is that a younger person cannot 'smit' an older. 'She's safe to wash his claes: she's auld be's (compared to) him.' An older person sleeping with a younger is considered apt 'to tak the strength frae' the younger one (*Auchterderran*).

Boils are looked upon as a sign of rude health. *Swollen glands* (referred to as 'waxen kernels' or 'cruels') are looked on as a sign of the system being 'down.'

Cancer is referred to as 'eatin' cancer.' A common expression is 'They say an eatin' cancer will eat a loaf.' Of one case of cancer of the breast a woman said, 'It used to eat half a loaf o' bread and a gill o' whisky in twa days' (*Auchterderran*).

Celibacy in a male is held to be bad for mental conditions. 'His maidenheid's gaun to his brain': said scoffingly of an eccentric single man.

Delirium. A delirious person is spoken of as 'carried.' One who is excited is spoken of as 'raised' or 'in a raptur',' and a confused person as 'ravelled' (*i.e.* tangled—a ravelled skein of wool is a tangled skein).

Drunkenness. A drunk man, if very drunk, is described as 'mortagious,' 'miracklous,' 'steamin' wi' drink,' or 'blin' fou'.' A chronic drunkard ('drooth') is spoken of as 'a sand-bed o' drink.' A man wanting a drink will ask you to 'stan' your hand,' or ask 'Hae ye ony gude in your mind?' or 'Can ye save a life?' (*Auchterderran*).

. . . . .

Mumps. Local terms for this are 'Bumps,' 'Buffets,' and 'Branks'— 'Branks' meaning the halter for a cow (*Auchterderran*).

. . . . .

Suicide. It is often said of a suicide 'he maun hae been gey sair *left to himsel'* afore he did that.'

. . . . .

Health Maxims

Better haud weel than mak' weel.

Better wear shoon than sheets.

Feed a cold and starve a fever.

If ye want to be sune weel, be lang sick: *i.e.* keep your bed till you are better.

'He's meat-heal ony way,' is said of an invalid whose illness is not believed in.

Nervous people are said to be 'feared o' the death they'll never dee.'

[240]

'He'll no kill,' and 'He has a gey teuch sinon (sinew) in his neck,' are said of hardy persons.

'Let the sau sink to the sair,' was said jestingly as a reason for drinking whisky instead of rubbing it in as an outward application.

Hygiene and General Treatment

The time of day or year is held to exercise an influence on birth, death, or disease. If a woman in labour passes 'the turn o' the nicht,' it is said, 'She'll maybe gang the roond o' the knock (clock) noo.' So too with a moribund person.

Skin eruptions are often explained as 'just the time o' year.' Boils, pimples, rashes, etc., are held often to come out in the spring.

Spring Medicine. In springtime there is a necessity 'to clear the system;' which is best done by a purge and a vomit. A well at Balgreggie, Auchterderran (mentioned in Sibbald's *Fife*), was once resorted to for this. This well has now fallen in, and is simply a marshy spot.

Sulphur and cream of tartar is a favourite spring drink.

Water. On coming to another place, the 'cheenge o' water' is held to cause boils, pimples, and other skin eruptions.

Living too near water causes decay in the teeth.

It is dangerous to give cold water as a drink in fevers and feverish conditions, or in the puerperium.

It is held that 'measles should not be wet,' and this is often a valid excuse for keeping the patient lamentably dirty.

Too much washing is weakening. The old-fashioned Fife miner objects, on this account, to wet his knees and back.

A pail of water should not be left standing exposed to the sun, as the sun 'withers' it.

Air. The smell of a stable or byre is wholesome for children and invalids. Change of air is advantageous in whooping-cough. (The length of time the change lasts is of no moment.) On one occasion a miner took his child down the pit into the draught of an air-course for change of air. It died of pneumonia two days later. In some cases men have been known to take more bread with them for their 'pit-piece' than they needed, and the surplus bread, which had received the change of air, was given to the patient.

Earth. Breathing the smell of freshly-dug earth was held to be good for whooping-cough, and also for those who had been poisoned with bad air. A hole was dug in the ground and the patient 'breathed the air off it.' A 'divot' of turf was sometimes in the old days cut and placed on the pillow.

Blue flannel is held to be 'a rale healin' thing' when applied to bruises, sore backs, etc. The working shirt of the Fifeshire miner is always of blue flannel.

Ointment. Butter wrapped in linen and buried in the ground until it becomes curdy is held to be a fine natural 'sau' (salve) for any broken surface.

Diseases and Remedies

For *Bleeding at the Nose.* A door-key put down the back, or a cold cloth or sponge applied suddenly to the perinaeum.

Burns. Holding the burnt part near the fire 'draws oot the heat' from the burn.

'*The drinking diabetes.*' In 1904 a child suffering from 'diabetes' was directed by a 'tinkler wife' to eat a 'saut herrin'.' After it had done this, the child's arms were tied behind its back and it was held over running water. A 'beast' (which had been the cause of the trouble), rendered very thirsty by the meal of salt herring and hearing the sound of water, came up the child's throat, and the child recovered. (Cf. Worms, *infra.*)

'*Fire*' (any foreign body, metallic), *in the eye*, is removed (short of working at it with a penknife) by the operator (1) licking the eye with his tongue: (2) drawing the sleeve of his flannel shirt across the eyeball: or (3) by passing a looped horsehair below the lid.

Headache. A handkerchief (preferably a red handkerchief) tied tightly round the head is good for headache.

Hydrophobia was treated in the old days by smothering the patient between two feather beds. A house in Auchterderran was pointed out where this is said to have been done.

Inflamed eyes are cured by wearing earrings: by application of fasting spittle; by the application of mother's milk; and by cow's milk and water used as a lotion.

Piles, treated by (1) sitting over a pail containing smouldering burnt leather; (2) the application of used axle-grease.

Rheumatism ('Pains') is treated by (1) switching the affected parts with freshly-gathered nettles; (2) carrying a potato in the pocket; (3) supping turpentine and sugar, or (4) sulphur and treacle; (5) wearing flowers of sulphur in the stockings, or rubbed into blue flannel; (6) by inunction of bullock's marrow twice boiled; (7) rubbing in 'oil o' saut' or 'fore-shot.'

Ringworm is treated with (1) ink; (2) gunpowder and salt butter; (3) sulphur and butter; (4) rubbing with a gold ring.

Toothache is caused by a worm in the tooth, and is cured in women by smoking (*Auchterderran*). It may also be cured by snuffing salt up the nose (a fisher cure, St. Andrews), or by keeping a mouthful of paraffin oil in the mouth (*Auchterderran*). A contemptuous cure advised to a voluble suffer is, 'Fill your mouth wi' watter and sit on the fire till it boils.'

Warts. Cures: (1) rubbing with a slug and impaling the slug on a thorn. As the slug decays the warts go; (2) rubbing with a piece of stolen meat, as the meat decays the warts go; (3) tying as many knots on a piece of string as there are warts, and burying the string, as the string decays the warts go; (4) take a piece of straw and cut it into as many pieces as there are warts, either bury them or strew them to the winds; (5) dip the warts into the water-tub where the smith cools the red-hot horse-shoes in the smithy; (6) dip the warts in pig's blood when the pig is killed. Blood from a wart is held to cause more.

Whooping-cough. Besides the cures for this mentioned above, there are the following. (1) Passing the child under the belly of a donkey. (2) Carrying the child until you meet a rider on a white (or a piebald) horse, and asking his advice: what he advised had to be done. (3) Taking the child to the lime-kiln. (4) Taking the child to a gas-works. During an outbreak of whooping-cough in 1891, the children of the man in charge of, and living at, a gas works did not take the complaint. As a matter of fact, the air in and near a gas-works contains pyridin, which acts as an antiseptic and a germicide. (5) Treating the child with roasted mouse-dust. (6) Getting bread and milk from a woman whose married surname was the same as her maiden one. (7) Giving the patient a sudden start.

Worms. Medicine for worms had to be given at the 'heicht o' the moon.' The worms are held to 'come oot' then.

Another method was to make the sufferer chew bread, then spit it out and drink some whisky. The theory is that the worms smell the bread, open their mouths, and are then subsequently choked by the whisky! (Cf. Diabetes, above.)

Materia Medica. 1. Animal Cures
Cat. A black cat's tail rubbed on a stye in the eye cures the trouble.

Cattle. I have seen cow-dung used as a poultice for eczema of the scalp, for 'foul-shave,' and for suppuration (abscess in axilla). The general belief among 'skeely wives' is that a cow-dung poultice is the 'strongest-drawin' poultice' one can get.

Cow's milk mixed with water is used as an eye-lotion.

[243]

The marrow of bullock's bones, twice boiled, is used as an inunction in rheumatism.

One often hears of an ox having been killed and split up 'in the auld days,' and a person who was 'rotten' (syphilitic) put inside it, to get 'the tribble drawn oot.' Told of 'the wicked laird of B.' A horse is also said to have been used.

Dog. On the advice of a 'tinkler wife,' a litter of black puppies was killed, split up, and applied warm to a septic wound on the arm.[1] (*Auchterderran.*)

Donkey. Children are passed under the belly of a donkey to cure whooping-cough. Riding on a donkey is supposed to be a prophylactic measure.

Eel-skin is used as an application in sprains. It is often kept for years and let out by the owner as required. It is kept carefully rolled up when not in use.

Hare. A hare-skin is worn on the chest for asthma. The left fore-foot of a hare is carried in the pocket as a cure for rheumatism.

Horse. The membranes of a foal at birth ('foal-sheet') are kept, dried, and used as a substitute for gutta-percha tissue in dressing wounds.

The advice of the rider on a white or piebald horse is good for whooping-cough.

Limpet shells are used as a protective covering for 'chackit' (cracked) nipples.

Man. Saliva is rubbed on infants' noses to cure colds. 'Fasting spittle' is used for warts and for sore eyes. Woman's milk is also used for the latter purpose.

The smell of sweat is held to cure cramp: the fingers are drawn through between the toes to contract the smell.

Urine is used as an application for 'rose' (erysipelas).

Rubbing a birthmark with the dead hand of a blood-relation will remove it.

Mouse. The 'bree' in which a mouse has been boiled is used as a cure for bed-wetting in children. Or the mouse may be roasted, after

---

1. 'Among the odd remedies recurred to to aid my lameness,' says Sir Walter Scott, 'some one had recommended that so often as a sheep was killed for the use of the family, I should be stripped, and swathed up in the skin, warm as it was flayed from the carcase of the animal. In this Tartar-like habiliment I well remember lying upon the floor of the little parlour in the farmhouse, while my grandfather, a venerable old man with white hair, used every excitement to make me try to crawl.' (Lockhart, *Life of Sir Walter Scott*, chap. I.)

cutting off its head, and then powdered down and given as a powder, both for bed-wetting and for whooping-cough.

Pediculi capitio are supposed to be a 'sign of life,' *i.e.* they only appear on the head of a healthy child. By a curious piece of confused reasoning I have known them to be deliberately placed on the head of a weakly child with the idea that the invalid would thereby gain strength.

Pig. A piece of ham-fat tied round the neck is good for a cold, bronchitis, or sore throat.

'Swine's seam' (pig-fat) is an universal application for rubbing to soften inflamed glands; to rub the glands of the throat 'up' when they are 'down' (*i.e.* when the tonsils are enlarged and easily felt externally); for sprains; for rheumatism, lumbago, sciatica, etc.

Pig's blood is a cure for warts. When the pig's throat is cut, the warty hand is applied to the gush of blood.

Pig's gall is a cure for chilblains.

Skate. 'Skate-bree' (the liquor in which skate has been boiled) is held to be an aphrodisiac. 'Awa' an' sup skate-bree!' said tauntingly to a childless woman.

Slugs. The oil of white slugs is used as a cure for consumption. They are placed in a jelly-bag with salt, and the oil dripping out is collected.

The oil of black slugs is used as an external application for rheumatism. The slugs are 'masked' in a teapot with hot water and salt.

Spider. 'Moose-wabs' (spiders' webs) are used to check bleeding, and are used as pills for asthma.

2. Vegetable Cures

An infusion of *Bramble-leaves* is used in diarrhoea.

Infusions of *nettles* and *broom-tops* for 'water' (dropsy).

Infusions of *dandelion-root* for 'sick stomach.'

'*Tormentil-root*' is used for diarrhoea.

Yarrow, horehound, and *coltsfoot* for coughs and colds. An infusion of *ivy-leaves* is used as an eye-lotion. Ivy-leaves are sewn together to form a cap to put on a child's head for eczema. *Kail-blade* (cabbage-leaf) is used for the same purpose. Ivy leaves are applied to corns.

Marigold leaves are applied to corns.

'*Apple-ringie*' (southernwood) and *marsh-mallow* poultices are used as soothing applications in pain, in 'beelins' (suppurative conditions).

[245]

'*Sleek*' (long, thin, hairy seaweed) is used as a poultice in sprains, rheumatism, etc. (*Buckhaven*).

A '*spearmint*' poultice is used as a galactagogue.

Potato, *carrot*, and *turnip* poultices are often used.

Poultices of chopped *leeks*, or chewed *tobacco-leaf*, and of *soap and sugar*, are common for whitlows.

A *potato* carried in the pocket is good for rheumatism.

Freshly gathered *nettles* are used for switching rheumatic joints.

3. Mineral Cures

Coal. A piece of coal is sucked as a cure for heartburn.

Sulphur. Sulphur is a cure for cramp. A piece of sulphur under the pillow would protect all the occupants of the bed. It is sometimes worn in the 'oxter' (armpit), and sometimes sewn in the garter, when it is called a 'sulphur-band.'

Flowers of sulphur are dusted into the stockings for rheumatism, or rubbed into blue flannel and applied for lumbago.

Sulphur and cream of tartar is taken as a 'spring drink.'

DEATH AND BURIAL

A cock crowing, an owl hooting, or a dog howling at night, are all signs of death.

If a corpse keeps soft and does not stiffen, there will be another death in the family within a year.

If two deaths occur in the place, a third will follow. This is a very common belief. The brother of a man who was seriously ill accompanied me to the door on one occasion and said, 'I've sma' hopes o' him mysel', doctor; there's been twa deaths in the parish this week, and we're waitin' the third.' The patient nevertheless recovered.

The clock is stopped at death; the mirrors are covered, sometimes also the face of the clock; and a white cloth is pinned up over the lower half of the window (*Auchterderran*).

Cats are not permitted in a room where there is a dead body, owing to the belief that if a cat jumped over the corpse, anyone who saw the cat afterwards would become blind (*Auchterderran*).

A saucer with salt is sometimes placed on the chest of the corpse (this is not a general custom). Pennies are laid on the eyelids to keep them shut, and the falling of the jaw is prevented by propping up with a Bible.

The presence of the minister at the 'chestin'' (coffining) is still quite common in Fife. This is the outcome of Acts of Parliament in 1694 and 1705, which enjoined the presence of an elder or deacon to see that the corpse was clothed, in the former case in linen, in the latter in woollen garments. See H. Grey Graham, *Social Life in Scotland in the 18th Century*.

PROVERBS

A cauld hand and a warm heart.

A' his Christianity is in the back-side o' his breeks (said contemptuously of one whose professions do not match with his mode of life).

A hoose-de'il and a causey-saint.

An ill shearer never gets a gude heuk.

As the soo fills, the draff sours.

A scabbit heid's aye in the way.

Auld age disna come its lane (*i.e.* other troubles come with it).

A woman's wark's never dune, an' she's naethin' to show for't.

Betwixt the twa, as Davie danced.

Ca'in' awa', canny an' pawkie,
Wi' your ee on your wark an' your pooch fu' o' baccy.
(An adage on the best way to work. *Auchterderran.*)

Daylicht has mony een.

Dinna hae the sau (salve) waitin' on the sair (*i.e.* do not anticipate trouble).

They're queer folk no' to be Falkland folk. (Possibly referring back to the days when foreigners were common at the palace.)

Falkland manners.

Fife. He's Fifish.

He's a foreigner frae Fife.

He's a Fifer an' worth the watchin'.

It taks a lang spune to sup wi' a Fifer.

He's got the Fife complaint—big feet and sair een. (An 'incomer's' saying regarding the Fifer, and naturally resented by him.)

He's got a gude haud o' Fife (of a man with big feet).

As fly as the Fife kye, an' they can knit stockins wi' their horns.

Why the Fife kye hinna got horns; they lost them listenin' at the Loudoners' (Lothian people's) doors. (They were so astonished at the Lothian dialect that they rubbed off their horns in listening to it. N.B.—The Fifers have an old dislike for the Loudoners.)

Fools and bairns shouldna see half-dune wark.

Freens (= relations) gree best separate.

Go to Freuchie and fry mice! (*i.e.* get away with you!)

He's as fleshly as he's godly (said of anyone laying claim to piety).

He has a gude neck (*i.e.* plenty of impudence. 'Sic a neck as ye ha'e!').

He pits his meat in a gude skin (said of a healthy child with a good appetite).

He's speirin' the road to Cupar an' kens it.

He's speirin' the road to Kinghorn and kens't to Pettycur (*i.e.* some distance farther on).

He's ta'en a walk roond the cunnin' stane.

I'd soom the dub for't first (*i.e.* I would sooner cross the sea than do it).

It's lang or the De'il dee at the dyke-side.

It taks a' kinds to mak' a warl'.

Just the auld hech-howe (*i.e.* the old routine).

Marry the wind an' it'll fa'.

Maun-dae (must do, *i.e.* necessity) is aye maisterfu'.

Seein's believin', but findin' (feeling) 's the naked truth.

Sing afore breakfast, greet afore nicht.

Sodger clad but major-minded (*i.e.* poor but proud).

Spit in your e'e and choke ye.

That's a fau't that's aye mendin' (*i.e.* youth).

That beats cock-fechtin'.

The De'il's aye gude to his ain.

The nearer the kirk, the faurer frae grace.

They're no gude that beasts an' bairns disna like.

Twa flittin's (removals) is as bad as a fire.

When ye get auld ye get nirled.

[Whaur are ye gaun?] 'I'm gaun to Auchtertool to flit a soo.' (*Auchterderran*. Said to impertinent enquirers. Auchtertool is a village in the neighbourhood about which there is a saying, and a song, 'There's naught but starvation in auld Auchtertool.')

Ye canna be nice (particular) and needfu' baith.

Ye dinna ken ye're livin' yet (said to a young girl making a moan over any pain or suffering).

Ye'll be a man afore your mither (jocose encouragement to little boys).

Ye maun just hing as ye grow. (It is often said of neglected children, 'they just get leave to hing as they grow.')

Your e'e's bigger than your belly (said to a greedy child).

(See also *ante*, Marriage, Birth, and Leechcraft.)

SCHOOLBOY SAYINGS

'D'ye see onything green in my e'e?'

'I'm no' sae green as I'm cabbage-looking.'

'I'll spit in your e'e an' choke ye!'

'Spit owre that!' Said with hand extended; challenge to fight.

'Coordie, Coordie, Custard!' To a coward.

'Clypie, Clypie, Clashpans!' To a tell-tale.

A boy going to school in a kilt would be greeted with:

Kilty, kilty cauld doup,
Never had a warm doup!

A child unduly proud of any article of dress would be humbled by the other children chanting:

A farden watch, a bawbee chain,
I wish my granny saw ye!

Any one wearing a new suit of clothes is given a severe nip by his comrades. This is called 'the tailor's nip.'

WEATHER LORE

A cat washing itself over its ears means wet weather.

Crows flying about confusedly, rising and falling in the air, means windy weather to follow.

'A near hand bruch (halo round the moon) is a far awa' storm: a far awa bruch is a near hand storm.'

'There's somethin' to come oot yet,' said when cold weather persists continuously, or 'There's somethin' ahint a' this.'

'It's blawin' through snaw.' Said of a cold wind.

'It's waitin' for mair,' said of a persistent wreath of snow on a hill-top or hill-side.

A duck looking at the sky is said to be 'lookin' for thunder.'

'Rainin' auld wives,' 'Rainin' cats and auld wives,' and 'Rainin' auld wives and pipe stapples (pipe-stems)' are all said of a heavy wind and rain storm (*i.e.* the kind of weather witches would be abroad in).

When mist comes frae the sea,
Gude weather it's to be,
When mist comes frae the hill,
Gude weather it's to spill.

Mist on the hills, weather spills,
Mist on the howes, weather grows.

[249]

(Of the position of clouds in the sky.)

North and South,

The sign o' a drouth;

East and Wast,

The sign o' a blast.

'Clear in the South droons the plooman.'

'It's cauld ahint the sun' (*i.e.* warm when the sun is out, but cold when it sets).

If the oak afore the ash,

Then we're gaun to hae a splash;

If the ash afore the oak,

Then we're gaun to hae a soak.

Rain in May maks the hay,

Rain in June maks the broom,

Rain in July maks it lie.

37
Upper Donside Fairs and Feuds: A Minister's Memoirs

[From *Scots Magazine* 20 (1933–34), 429–42]

From notes made by the late Rev. Alexander Forbes Moir,
arranged by David Rorie
  A native of Upper Donside, born in 1822, the writer of these
notes was for many years a minister of the Free Kirk of Scotland,
first at St. Fergus, and later at Woodside. On his retirement he
settled at Cults, Aberdeenshire, where he died in 1907. Some
years before his death he wrote, at Dr. Rorie's request, various
recollections of his youthful days, and from these this article has
been compiled.

Upper Donside comprises two parishes, Strathdon and Glenbucket,
with part of Tarland and the whole *quoad sacra* parish of Corgarff.[1] It
can be taken as beginning at the Brig o' Kindie and extending some
twenty-five miles west along the river to the Springs of Don which
issue from the side of a bare, wild hill within less than a couple of
miles of Inchrory on the Avon, that well-known tributary of the
Spey. The scenery is very varied, here rugged and barren, and then
again wooded and cultivated, always pleasing, but never rising to
the stern majesty which gives so great a charm to the strath of
the Dee. By a curious pre-Reformation arrangement the parish of
Tarland cuts that of Strathdon in two, and the long drawn out tongue
of the famous Deeside parish meets and marches with Kirkmichael
or Inveravon in Banffshire. Whatever may have been the origin of
this arrangement it must have tended more to the profit of the then
ruling ecclesiastical authorities than to the edification of their flocks,
many of whom resided at more than ten miles distance from their
parish church. At the end of the eighteenth century, and for many
years later, there were, owing to this arrangement, more than fifty

---

1. Mr. Moir's notes were written about 1900.

householders residing on the Don and its tributaries who had no ecclesiastical rights in the church that they attended, but sat in it by sufferance, communicated as a matter of convenience, and were probably never once in their lives in their own parish kirk. None of the Donside 'Tarlanders' cared to let it be known that he was born in his native parish; for it had then, and for long before and after, that evil reputation for fighting which gained for its inhabitants the far known cognomen of 'The Teuch Tykes o' Tarland.' In fact, the name of the parish was so notorious that I have, in my student days, heard the street urchins of Aberdeen calling a maimed crow, which had fallen into their hands, a 'Tarland blackbird.' It can be understood, then, that a Donside Tarlander might be proud of his native strath and yet chary about acknowledging his native parish.

The parishes of Glenbucket and Strathdon are physically what the names import, the one a glen, the other a strath with a number of smaller glens branching out on either side. Glenbucket is, at its widest, about two miles, and seven or eight in length, bounded by bare and barren hills, with one solitary plantation of a few acres extent covering a rocky cone of no great height. It was at one time the property of the Earl of Fife; that earl who ruined himself in the respectable company of the Prince Regent; but who nevertheless was best remembered in Strathdon as a benevolent if somewhat eccentric old gentleman whose early follies were covered out of sight by the kindly charities of his later years.

In all physical features no two places could well be more different than these contiguous parishes. The Donside lairds at the beginning of the nineteenth century were some of them resident for most of the year and all of them for a longer or shorter part of it, and had an interest and a pride in their native strath—which resulted in its hills being clothed with wood and the grounds around their mansions being more or less well kept. I question if the Earl of Fife ever saw his Glenbucket property; at any rate, although a just and even liberal landlord, he did nothing to beautify it.

One curious and very marked diversity then existed in the physical economy of the two parishes. On Donside the homesteads were scattered singly in picturesque loneliness, each with its few trees surrounding its kailyard, always at least a rowan or two if there were no others. One homestead you would find in a sheltered nook, another on a sunny knowe, a third on the brow of a steep grassy bank, and a fourth close by the river's brim; thus bespeaking a people who for many generations had dwelt secure. In Glenbucket, on the other hand, the farmers' dwellings were with few exceptions (and these mostly in the lower end of the glen) gathered into hamlets, six, eight, or even ten families in the group, each tilling its little farm, as if gathered together for mutual aid and succour in unquiet or dangerous times.

These little farms were as curiously arranged as the dwellings. The land was considered to be of two qualities; the richer, which had been cultivated for centuries, lying well down in the valley along the banks of the stream. Such land was known as 'intown' or 'infield' (or 'infeidle'). The newer and shallower, which had come under the plough at a much later date, ran up the hillsides, and were, naturally, much less fertile. These were known as 'outfield' (or 'outfeidle'). It is obvious that the man whose holding consisted of infield would be in clover, while the occupant of an outfield holding would be reduced to 'windlestrae' for a living. This was obviated in Glenbucket by a method which was, I suspect, a relic of a more patriarchal system than now obtains, a reminiscence of a time when the soil was held as the common heritage of the clan. In Belnaboth, for example, there were seven crofters whose rigs would run side by side, a rig of outfield alternating with one of infield. This system was known as 'run rig' or 'rig about,' and secured that each holding in the hamlet had its due share of good land and less good, while the hill pasture was held to be the common heritage of all. I remember well how much grumbling and discontent prevailed when the plan was altered, and each occupier had his lands brought together and laid out as an ordinary farm or croft. That, as I suppose, was to be expected until things had settled down and the plough got accustomed to the new furrow. I cannot tell how these village groupings and the run rig system came to survive for so long in Glenbucket—and, though only to a small extent, in Glen Noughty as well—unless it were that the people there were more exposed to inroads from their unquiet neighbours, the cateran of Badenoch, Cabrach, and Glenlivet.

The mention of Glen Noughty reminds me of a saying we had at school: 'Ye can aye ken Noughtyside loons by "thee," "thou," and "wilta'" (wilt thou). Whether or not this was a trace of a Quaker family having at one time settled there I cannot tell, but the children were recognised as speaking differently from the rest of the scholars.

Just where Noughty falls into Don there stands one of the most remarkable monuments in the county of Aberdeen in the shape of a fortress of the prehistoric age, or at any rate of an age where there is no record. It is called the Dune of Invernoughty, and no local tradition, so far as I remember, exists to show its origin, although some antiquarians refer it to the Roman period. Why it was erected there, or what there was for it to guard, has always been a mystery to me. A thousand years ago these glens must have been very thinly peopled, and have consisted of moor, marsh, and forest, with little property to be protected and few to hold in subjection. Yet here stands a huge fortification—a mound fifty feet high, flat on the summit, walled round with stone and lime enclosing not less than half an acre, and moated with a ditch thirty feet wide at bottom and not less than twelve feet deep even now. Other scarpments are to be seen in the neighbourhood of a less elaborate kind which may have been subsidiary to this one. But why was it planted there? Had there been a large population in the glens above, or had it stood on any route by which the far highlands of Badenoch and Lochaber were accessible, then it might have checked inroads upon the Aberdeenshire lowlands. But it is not so: the only route to the far highlands is by Corgarff, Inchrory, Tomintoul and Grantown, routes roundabout and tedious. Another fortress of the same class and period I have seen upon the farm of Fechley, in Towie, and a third is the Peel at Lumphanan, neither of the two, however, so complete nor so remarkable as that of Invernoughty.

I would turn now from the topography of the district to the social and domestic affairs of an age which has wholly passed away, and try to record, as I have frequently been asked to do, some of the recollections of my earlier years. The condition of things then existing in Aberdeenshire, and, doubtless, in many other parts of Scotland, has gone for ever; yet with all its drawbacks, and they were not few, it afforded us as much happiness, so far as my memory serves me, as I see current round me to-day. Certainly the essential factors of happiness were as plentiful as they are now. The domestic affections, with obedience to and reverence of parents, were then as flourishing as now, the latter more so. We had food, raiment and shelter; and, though neither one nor the other was within sight of the level of luxury, we were content with such things as we had and were happy. Money, to be sure, was scarcer, and things that are to-day necessaries of life were then luxuries which seldom appeared in the menage of households fairly well-to-do; but true happiness is not bound up with luxurious living, and one can be happier in spending pennies than in spending pounds. The cannon of Waterloo were, in my childhood, still echoing over the land in the shape of taxes that enhanced the price of almost everything. The people had little to sell; the market was far away; and they got small return for their grain, cattle, butter or eggs, were there any superfluity of these to dispose of. So, while there was rarely want, there was seldom luxury, and very little money circulated.

I was born on the 27th December 1822, on a small farm called Faichley, on the north side of the Don, next door to Candacraig, the seat of the laird. The farm was of the size and type current in the Strath—flat haugh land embraced on two sides by the river. My father was the last tenant who tilled it, and he left it about a year after my birth. Long afterwards he told me that he was seven years upon it 'without getting seed or breid'[1] from it; for its low level made it peculiarly liable to the frosts which were the great trouble in those days in Strathdon, Corgarff, and all other parts of the north of Scotland of a like elevation above sea level. Improved methods, better drainage, and better seed have remedied this trouble to a great extent; but even now, and especially in late seasons, much corn is injured by autumn frosts. Since my father left it, Faichley has been let as grass parks, the only thing it is suitable for.

As there was then no doctor within many miles of Strathdon, the services of the parish minister of Coldstone (who was also an M.D., and held in great repute) were requisitioned at the time of my coming into the world. It was probably due to this lack of available medical skill for the district that, out of seven children born, I was one of the two who survived birth and infancy.

My mother's maiden surname was Kellas. In the earlier part of the eighteenth century, three brothers appeared in Strathdon, strangers from the north, James, Alexander, and John. They had either been out with Mar in 'the '15,' or involved in some local feud: at all events they had found it convenient to drop their clan and family name of Macdonald, as at the same time (or perhaps later at 'the '45') did some of their kinsmen who also settled in the Strath and took the name of Callum. But whatever induced the brothers to settle in Aberdeenshire and drop their patronymic they must have been honourable men, for their descendants took a good position on Donside, and have kept it to this day. The brothers, when asked where they came from, answered 'from Kellas,' a barony in the parish of Dallas in Morayshire. Whether they came from there or not, they were thenceforth known on Donside by that name, and my mother's father, John Kellas of Midtown, across the river from Colquhony, was a son of one of the brothers. He was twelve years old when Culloden was fought, and had got, at first hand, vivid

---

1. 'Bread,' in those days, meant oatmeal cakes.

accounts of the battle from those who had taken part in it. Not a stone now stands upon another, nor grows a solitary rowan tree, where his homestead once stood: for more than forty years the plough has gone over where his hearth-stone lay: only a greener spot on the brae marks where six lads and six lasses were born and brought up creditably on the few acres that constituted the little farm, or croft as we would call it now, although such a name was unknown in my youth. All these twelve children grew up to be men and women, the former, with one exception, making in due time for Glasgow, Edinburgh, and Aberdeen, to push their fortune, but each in turn to die before his father, save the one who stayed in the Strath. It is in favour of country as against town life that he lived to the age of 81, while his sisters attained the ages of 96, 90, 82, 80, 74, and 70.

Though only a crofter, John Kellas was in many ways a remarkable man, and commanded the respect of the whole glen, not only on account of his years, which were many, but for his force of character and sterling integrity. He was a man of powerful frame, a little above the middle height, and, in his heyday, possessed of great strength. At the time when I knew him from my fifth to my twelfth year, he was over 95 years of age, and even then was a hale, stalwart man walking about his croft, leaning upon a two-handed staff as tall as himself, and in full possession of all his faculties save those consisting of muscular suppleness and strength. He always wore knee breeches with blue stockings and a Kilmarnock striped cap, save on high occasions when he assumed a broad woollen bonnet, a compromise between the narrow-brimmed 'cockit' bonnet and that immensely broad 'divot' worn at funerals by the Aberdeen Shore Porters. I do not believe that the good man ever wore a hat: if he did I never heard of it nor saw a vestige of such headgear about the house. He was looked up to with reverence by his children; and it is characteristic of the time and people that none of the family would have ventured to speak in his presence unless he had spoken first.

In his younger days all the crofters and farmers in the Strath and the glens opening into it had the right of pasturage on 'The Hill' (the wild uninhabited portions of Glen Noughty, the Bunyach at the head of Deskry, and Glencoury and Glenearnan) for more or fewer sheep according to the size of their several holdings. The Bunyach, a valley opening from the base of Morven, was where John Kellas had his grazing, and on one occasion a 'yowe' of his went amissing, the popular voice accusing a noted family resident there of being the culprits, and even going the length of putting that accusation into a ballad, orally circulated, which had for its name 'The Fate of Midnies'

Yowe.' The suspected family, notorious for their love of and skill with the cudgel, believing that the ewe's owner had originated the rumour, sent two of their most powerful members to his croft to give him a thrashing. On reaching there they threatened to beat him within an inch of his life; but the big strong man, 'calm as a mountain lake,' simply faced them, neither lifting a hand nor saying a word. Knowing his great physical strength, and utterly cowed by this unexpected reception, the men left as they came, without a blow having been struck.

Tarland and Aboyne were at that time the chief outlets for the cattle, sheep and horses of Strathdon. How often the markets were held at Tarland I have forgotten; but there was one which I 'stood' myself oftener than once as a herd in part charge of cattle for sale. That market was known as 'Lonach Fair o' Tarland,' or 'St. Luke's Fair.' The village of Aboyne was then called 'Charleston of Aboyne,' so named after one of the Earls of Aboyne, the marquisate of Huntly not falling to that house until 1836 when the last Duke of Gordon died. There were also fairs frequented by our Donside people at Braemar, Tomintoul, Dufftown, Huntly and Alford; while some folk, more enterprising than the general run, might very occasionally go as far afield as Elgin o' Moray, but that was reckoned as a very great adventure indeed. Tarland bulks the largest in my boyish memory, outwith the bounds of our own parish where we had Tambreck Market once or twice a year, and, the biggest of all, 'John's Fair' held at Heugh-head in the month of August, in honour of which we always had a school holiday. For a local fair it was a large one, attended by many people from the low country as well as from the glens, with numerous cattle and sheep and not a few horses for sale. Still another market was held on a flat moor on the border of Leochel Cushnie and Alford, which rejoiced in the somewhat distinguished name of 'Scuttery,' or, if you wanted to be genteel, 'Muir o' Foulis.' Tarland Fair was notorious for the fights which took place at the end of it, when men had finished their business and been often enough in the tents to have developed each his little weakness, whether it might be quarrelsomeness or brag or whatever his peculiar tendency might be. Sometimes the fight arose out of an immediate personal quarrel: very often it was the outcome of an old grudge and might involve a couple of families with all the fighting strength they could muster. Not infrequently the feud was a standing one, the origin of which dated back to former generations, and was fought out over and over again as often as a sufficient number of kith, kin and allies gave prospect to the 'clan' of adequate support and hope of victory. The usual site was either the market stance or the village street; but many pitched battles occurred on the road home. I never was the witness of any serious encounters; for by the time I was taking notice of such things the arm of the law had reached up to the farthest glens and the fights had degenerated into mere drunken squabbles. But in my father's time it was different; for any man under 55 might be involved in a bludgeon fight—fists were never used—either on his own account or in aid of some of his kin; and it was reckoned no dishonour to be defeated, only a mishap to be put right at some other more fortunate time. It was a dishonour, however, to shirk the combat if it was your own quarrel or a question of helping kinsmen or friends. And yet, bitter as were these battles, and heavy as were the strokes given and taken, it was seldom that they left any serious effects—perhaps an arm disabled for a time, or a 'cloured heid' that mended in a couple of weeks. As I have said, most of this was tradition to me; but my father has told me he has seen forty men on each side cudgelling each other in the streets of Tarland; Couttses on the one side and Andersons on the other; the weaker in number with their backs to the walls of the houses. The Couttses were a big clan in the valley of Cromar, which comprised the parishes of Tarland, Logie Coldstone and Glentanar, and the Andersons, allied with whom was a noted fighting sept of Essons, were widely spread over the same locality. Even in my day some of the Essons were given to cudgel play when they had had a 'gey roch dram,' and duly displayed, for some time after, 'tied up' heads and other souvenirs of serious strife.

My father has told me of many fights in which he was engaged, either as a principal or an accessory. Here is a story illustrative of the darker side of the period's social life.

Two families nearly related—the mother of one family being sister to the mother of the other, the children, therefore, being first cousins—were tenants of one big holding, each possessing a half. A quarrel had arisen, the cause of which I cannot tell unless it was that the eldest son of the one family was accused of having seduced the eldest daughter of the other; but family feuds can be intensely bitter, and so was this. For clearness I shall call the one family 'Gillespie,' and the other 'Machardy.' The Gillespies were older than the Machardys, who were little more than boys or girls, the eldest being a lad of only eighteen or nineteen, and the youngest not over eight. Their cousins watched their opportunity and caught the father as he came in from his labours in the gloaming, disabling him with a broken head. The boys and girls as they came in were each dispatched in like manner. The eldest son, who alone showed fight, caught hold of a spade with which to defend himself, but he was knocked down and struck on the head with a bludgeon as he lay on the causeway before the byre door. The only unbroken head in the house that night was the head of the mother. Then these cowardly villains went before the nearest Justice of the Peace, and, swearing that they were in danger of their lives at the hands of the cousins whom they had so badly misused, took out what was called 'lawburrows' against them, binding them over to keep the peace.

Yes, they were a fighting race, these men of the glens, and they were not more afraid of a cracked crown than the borderers of Dandie Dinmont's day: their feuds and personal grudges were many and deep-rooted. Even the minister had sometimes to make his hands the friends of his head. On one occasion the Rev. George Forbes, minister of Leochel Cushnie—a son of Bellabeg, and father of the first Sir Charles, who succeeded his uncle, John, at the head of the great Bombay banking house of Forbes, Grant & Co.—went, at a Tarland market, into the little inn there to have some refreshment. He was a big powerful man, and had his own feuds like most of his flock. Shown into a room, he found that he had stumbled into a nest of unfriends, and well knew that he would not be allowed to retire scatheless. All the same he sat down, called for and got his refreshment, and proceeded with great deliberation to prolong his meal, knowing—such was the etiquette of these feuds—that he would not be disturbed while eating, and trusting that some allies might turn up. So indeed it fared, for two cousins, one of whom was my grandfather Kellas, and both of them stalwart, active men, happened into the room on the same errand as himself. No sooner had they appeared than the minister sprang to his feet shouting, 'Now, lads! We're a match of them a',' and, suiting the action to the word, he seized the nearest man by the shoulders, raised him up, and smashed him down right through his chair on to the floor. This act of derring-do sufficiently demonstrated the possibilities of further action, and neither the doughty minister nor his allies received any molestation from their now thoroughly cowed enemies.

There were at one time two families, or rather clans, on the little stream of Deskry, which arose at the northern base of Morven. The head of the one clan, the Grassicks, was Peter Grassick, farmer in Foggiemill. There was just one farm betwixt that and Deskry farm, the headquarters of Lachlan Bremner, head of the Bremners, two of whom were the visitors who had once come to Midtown to attack my grandfather. Between the Grassicks and the Bremners there had been a longstanding feud, which brought about repeated fights whenever they met at roup or market. There is a tradition that they at last arranged to fight it out to a finish at a solitary place where there is a level space, surrounded by peaks and high ground on every side, just above Rough Neuk. Here there is a dark tarn whence there seems to be no outlet. The place is known as the Pots o' Poldye, and there a desperate battle was fought with which side as victors I cannot tell. I can tell, however, the result of a single combat between the two heads of the respective clans. Both had flocks in the Bunyach, and, as it happened, both had gone one day to see after their welfare. They met with no living soul within sight or hearing, and there in God's wilderness, with none but sheep and wild birds to see what they did, they fought it out. When the combat was over Lachlan Bremner was unconscious, and Peter Grassick raised his enemy's head on a little green, mossy tuft of benty grass to let the blood run from his mouth lest he should choke. There he left him 'to come till himsel'.' That was the kind of men they bred in those days.

I do not know when the next incident I will tell occurred: it must have been more than a hundred years ago.[1] My grandfather Kellas was not a quarrelsome man and was never known to be a party in a fight. John's Fair, the biggest tryst in the Strath, was held, I think, in August, and even in my schooldays it rarely passed without a fight, although by then it was regarded as a drunken, disreputable affair. But at the end of the eighteenth century it was a very different thing; the perpetuating of an old feud or the settling, in what was then held to be a legitimate way, of a new quarrel. That night there had been a big fight, and the parties worsted in combat had taken the very unusual course of summoning the victors before the sheriff at Tarland. My grandfather was called as a witness, much against his will, and was being cross-examined by a very exacting lawyer for the defence whose wish it was to prove that the blows struck by the accused had not been of a heavy nature, and to try to get the witness to agree with this point of view, insisting that he should show exactly how the blows were delivered. My grandfather protested that he could not; and as the lawyer persisted that, being on his oath, he was compelled to do so, the good man's patience became exhausted. So, leaning forward from the witness box, with the exclamation: 'An ye will hae't an' winna want it— *that's* hoo they strack!' he dealt the lawyer a blow on the side of

---

1. i.e., previous to 1800.

his head which sent him along with his table and his papers flat on the courthouse floor. As he wrathfully gathered himself and his belongings up, the Sheriff drily remarked, 'Weel, my mannie, ye've got it noo!'

But enough of fights and what they brought about. Let me now tell you some other phases of the primitive social life of the Strath. The principal industry of the matrons and girls in every household was the spinning wheel. The wool clipped from their sheep about midsummer was washed, bleached and dyed by the housewife and her daughters. Every homestead had its 'lit-pot,' and the dyes in vogue were those obtained from logwood, indigo, or 'stane-raw,' a lichen which grew profusely on exposed rocks and old stone fences. The. dye produced from this was similar in its purple sheen to that obtained from another lichen then imported from Sicily. At the beginning of the nineteenth century this foreign dye became so scarce, owing to the hazards of ocean transport during the Napoleonic wars, that it was sold sometimes for £100 a ton, resulting in an increased demand and a good market for the native product of our Highland rocks; so much so, that women and boys in the Strath could, by gathering it, make as much as half a crown a day where it was plentiful. In autumn you will often see it in purple patches on the stones, the purple being caused by acid in the birds' droppings, that being the season when many of them live mostly, if not entirely, on various kinds of wild berries. This dye, either by itself or in combination with others, was much used for the yarns employed in making winceys for women's wear, although I have often when a child seen men wearing wincey coats and even suits. The wool, as such, was seldom dyed, unless to make indigo blue stockings, but, after bleaching, was carded into half-arm's-length 'rowes' by means of hand cards. From these rolls it was spun into yarn, or, if meant for stockings, into worsted. If intended for blankets the yarn was not dyed, but if for clothing it was dyed such colour as was wanted or the local skill could reach, and then either sent to the weaver or stored until needed. All this work was done at home by the daughters or maids of the family. In like manner was produced the linen wanted for bed, table, or body wear; for every holding had its patch of flax and its 'lint-hole' where the flax lay in water till rotted sufficiently for the fibre to be separated. This was done by beating it on a large flat stone with a smooth bit of wood, the 'beetle' or 'bittle.' It was then sent to the lint mill, at Dinnet, or Glenkindy, to be cleaned and straightened. Brought from the mill it was ready for spinning. When the flax was to be spun it was twisted round an upright spindle (the 'rock') which was inserted in its socket on one of the frame arms of the 'little wheel'; and then with both hands the spinner drew it out on to the 'flichts' which, revolving rapidly, both twisted and rolled up the yarn on a spool which could be removed when full. In the case of carded wool the roll was spun upon the same spinning-wheel, but directed into the 'flichts' from the lap of the spinner. I have also often seen in action what we knew as the 'muckle wheel,' wrought by a spindle suspended from the thread that was in course of formation which was gathered or rolled on the spindle by its being twirled by the hand of the spinner. This wheel, of simple construction, was four or five feet in diameter, while the fly wheel of the 'little wheel' would have only been two feet six inches.

The winter evening, known as the 'forenicht,' was invariably spent in spinning. The fireplace of the living-room was always a large one, often without any chimney; but where there was one the 'cheeks' would be wide apart. On each side of the fire was the 'ingle-neuk,' the assigned places of the goodman and the goodwife if they cared to assert their claims; but unless advanced in years they would have scorned even that slight indulgence. The goodwife would be plying her wheel at the head of her maids or daughters while the goodman would be pursuing some profitable employment such as mending the family shoes or constructing baskets (called 'sculls') with 'etnach' (juniper) withes. Usually he had some skill in these and various other ways, and few houses were without the 'buist,' an open box containing a very varied collection of tools. The males of the family, with visitors come to spend their forenicht, would be seated in a circle round the fireplace, sons and men-servants without distinction, for the man-servant was almost always son of a neighbour whose family was larger than his holding needed. Outside this circle sat the women-folk with their wheels; members of the family and neighbour lasses who had carried theirs with them to visit their friends, as these, possibly, had visited them the night before. Songs, stories, chat, clashing wits and laughter, to the accompaniment of the steady birr of the wheels, were the order of the evening; while the dambrod entertained the goodman (if otherwise unoccupied) and his cronies until it was time to disperse, always at what would now be deemed an early hour. A weel-faured lass would be sure to have some one proud to see her home and to carry her wheel.

A sad thing once occurred in the Strath of the eighteenth century. A girl, and a very beautiful one, was trysted to spend the forenicht with her wheel at Dykeneuk, five or six hundred yards from her home. While she was going along the lone braeside in the darkness with her wheel on her arm, a young man sprang out upon her from behind a bush, his head adorned with the horns and hide of a stirk, with the foolish intention of giving her a 'fleg.' From this sudden shock, although she lived till the age of 96, she never mentally recovered, in spite of every means being employed for her benefit that the simple skill of the place could suggest; and the author of the mischief was so looked down upon by young and old that he left the glen for parts unknown. Amongst other things tried she was taken on a horse behind her father to Whitehills, near Banff, for change and sea bathing—through Glenbucket, through the Cabrach, down Deveronside by Foggieloan and Boyndlie, no slight undertaking in those days for such as he. But, faring home from Whitehills through the Upper Cabrach along the side of the hills, the father's horse shied and cast him off the saddle with his foot fast in the stirrup, and then galloped along a track, full of stones and unmade save by the winter torrents, until its fright abated. When the rider came to himself he found that his scalp was torn from the back of his head and the skull laid bare. Going into the nearest cottage he had his wounds washed and bound up by the good woman of the house; and then, again clambering into the saddle, he rode home the remaining twenty miles. Ministrations such as those of the Cabrach wife made up all the surgical skill his head received, yet he lived to count his hundred years. For such was the hardy type of men living in these glens a century and a half ago.

As soon as anyone died in the Strath arrangements were made by friends and neighbours to meet and sit with the family in presence of the deceased every night until the funeral. This was called 'the lyke-wake,' and refreshments were offered as visitors came in. The proceedings were quiet: sometimes a chapter of the Bible would be read, and reminiscences would be recounted of notable events in the life of the departed, all being done in subdued tones and in a manner becoming the occasion. Great preparations were made for the funeral: masses of oatcake, kebbucks of country cheese, oceans of whisky, with pipes and tobacco. Those expected to be present had all been 'bidden' by an authorised person, or by a member of the family. The barn was 'redd up,' extemporised tables laid and covered with tablecloths, delft-ware plates were set at intervals with pipes and tobacco. Jugs of the same ware were provided to hold whisky toddy. The head of the house, or a son, stood at the door with bottle and glass to welcome each guest as he arrived, and each as he entered was expected to drink his glass of whisky neat—his eating and drinking afterwards was at his own pleasure. A couple of hours would be spent in consuming the plentiful refreshments provided before they 'lifted.' There was no hearse; the coffin was very plain and borne upon spokes to the grave. As soon as the procession came in sight of the church the sexton rang the bell and continued to ring until the mourners had reached the graveside. There was no religious service: the minister might or might not be there, just as any other neighbour might be bidden or passed over. Old hatreds might be shown on these occasions by withholding a 'bidding.' In one case I knew of a neighbour who was thus passed over shook his head and remarked: 'Just wait or I hae an occasion mysel' an' see if I dinna pey him back!'

There was an old tale, often told, of a funeral procession which, when crossing a burn, was suddenly 'reistit' in midstream. The burden became excessively heavy, and the bearers could neither move forward nor back. In this dilemma the minister, who was present, demanded of the company: 'Is there any man here who shaves on the Sabbath day?' One man confessed shamefacedly to the grievous fault, and was told to come forward and lay his hand on the coffin. On this being done the bearers moved froward without any difficulty. Shaving was always done on the Saturday night to prevent any breach of the Sabbath day.

Marriages were also great occasions in the Strath. There was a party called 'the send,' consisting of two or three friends of the bridegroom, who were detailed to go in advance of his procession to the door of the bride's house to demand her on his behalf. Her father, or a brother, standing in the doorway was expected to make some demur, or at least hold some parley as to what the demand meant, before yielding the bride up. Then, at some period of the day, there was the 'riding of the broose,' a race on horseback when mounts were available, otherwise on foot. To 'win the broose' was a great distinction, often talked about afterwards in the winter evenings.

38
Stray Notes on Scottish Folk–Lore

[From *Folklore* 49 (1938), 85–91]

A REGIMENTAL WRAITH

In the *Sunday Times* (4/10/36) 'Bydand' writes:

Jane Maxwell, Duchess of Gordon, who is said to have helped to raise the Gordon Highlanders by giving a guinea and a kiss to the recruits, was buried at Kinrara, a lovely spot in the Inverness-shire parish of Alvie, where she spent the last sad years of her lively life. When the estate was sold a few years ago by the Duke of Richmond and Gordon, who bears the title Earl of Kinrara, dating from 1876, the land containing the Duchess's grave was bought by the officers of the Gordon Highlanders.

My Cabrach correspondent tells me that an apparition appears at the Duchess's grave 'before dire disaster overtakes the Gordon Highlanders. It was seen before Magersfontein, and several times before and since, taking the form of a weeping lady with long fair hair.'

WISHING WELLS[1]

(*Aberdeen Press and Journal*, 3/5/37 and 24/5/37.)

(1) Culloden Wishing Well Trek

Despite the protests made by prominent figures in the Free and Free Presbyterian Churches against the annual pilgrimage to the Wishing Well at Culloden Moor, the numbers taking part in yesterday's trek were greater than ever.

The brilliant weather was no doubt largely responsible for the record crowd which took part in the centuries-old custom of dropping coins in the well, drinking the water, wishing a wish, and tying a rag to one of the nearby trees.

The pilgrimage started at an early hour. Shortly after sunrise

---

1. See *British Calendar Customs, Scotland*, vol.i, p.141.

the first of the visitors set out on foot to the well. As midday approached the numbers grew, and by early afternoon the crowd reached unprecedented proportions.

The trek continued until sunset, when the trees round the well hung heavy with 'clouties,' and a big heap of silver and copper coins lay at the bottom of the well, to be collected later and handed over to local charities.

The crowd was drawn principally from Inverness and Nairn and the intervening districts, although some of the pilgrims came from as far north as Dingwall and as far east as Elgin.

Hundreds came by car, motor cycle, push bicycles, and even on foot, and bus companies which provided special services from Inverness and Nairn reported that they never had a bigger demand for transport to the well.

A conservative estimate is that 12,000 people took part in the pilgrimage.

The money found at the bottom of the well amounted in value to £27 7/-.

(2) Orton Pilgrimage
To Historic Well of St. Mary

Brilliant weather favoured the annual Roman Catholic pilgrimage to the historic well of St. Mary, Orton, yesterday.

The large gathering, which met in a wood a short distance away, was led by Mgr. Cronin, rector of Blairs College, who was accompanied by Mgr. M'Donald, Buckie; Canon Wiseman, Keith; and Father Joseph Thomson, Kingussie. Then followed the altar boys, Girl Guides, and Children of Mary from Keith, Buckie and Tomintoul, and Sisters of Mercy from Elgin, Tomintoul and Keith.

The address at the well was given by Father Thomson, who said that the gathering represented people from a wide area.

'Here on the banks of a noble river we take our stand by the humble well,' he said.

'Just as the river from its source in the distant hills has grown in power and majesty with the addition of its tributaries so has this assemblage.

'The natural attractions of this spot are far indeed from accounting for our presence here. There is about this spot an attraction that is sacred, a beauty that is of another world. Here it is said were first preached the tidings of the Holy Gospel to our progenitors, and from time immemorial a tradition has been centred round this spot—a tradition that has outlived the prejudice, persecution and apathy of well nigh 400 years.'

(Like most, if not all, wells dedicated to St. Mary, this well was probably a fertility well. Gordon, in the *Book of the Chronicles of Keith*, and writing in 1880, says on p. 60: 'Orton has ceased for many years, and is now only a feeble, filthy, stagnant driblet for the use of cattle. Formerly the Well was in the shape of an *Ichthus* or *Oval*, which was resorted to at certain seasons for the cure of whooping-cough and eye and joint diseases. Some "miraculous stones" still abide.' In the past few years the Roman Catholic Church has put it in repair and instituted pilgrimages thereto. D.R.)

A CURSE STONE

(*Scotsman*, 27/4/37.)

Considerable excitement was aroused in the district of Artafaillie, on the Allangrange estate, in the Black Isle of Ross-shire, when it was reported that an ancient basin stone was to be removed from its site to Inverness Museum, to ascertain its dimensions and weight.

Inquiry was made into its history, and it was discovered that the stone was the subject of a legend, according to which, if it were removed, misfortune would happen. The tradition, as recorded in the *Proceedings of the Society of Antiquarians of Scotland*, published in 1882, is that 'Some fifty years ago, an old man who occupied the farm of Teandore carried the stone to his house, either from a belief of some latent virtue or for some more prosaic purpose. For three successive nights after its removal the family were disturbed by loud, mysterious noises, which on the third night reached a climax. The grounds affected were extensive. Cattle bellowed, dogs howled all over the valley, and a dread voice, in tones of thunder, exclaimed in distinct syllables: "Put back the stone." Instant obedience was given by the terror-stricken inmates, and the stone has rested untouched since then, and its mystic guardian has been silent.'

It was further stated that within forty-eight hours of the removal of the stone in 1832, news was received at Teandore of a fatal accident to a relative of the occupiers of the farm, and the sheep farmer at Teandore collapsed.

As feeling is strong in the district that misfortune will follow if the stone is again removed, Mrs. Fraser Mackenzie, the proprietrix of the estate, has given orders that the vegetation round the site should be cleared and a suitable fence erected, to preserve it from interference by thoughtless sightseers. The proposal to remove it to Inverness has been dropped.

PIE-BOYS' CALL AT NEWBURGH, FIFE

(*People's Journal*, 6/8/32, from article by Provost George Anderson, Newburgh.)

The cheery call of the pie-boys occasionally comes back to one over sixty years of time. Those pie-boys were a weekly feature of life in Newburgh sixty years ago. As they went about the streets selling their wares on Saturday nights they sang the refrain:

> Buy my hot penny pies,
> Stovin' and reekin',
> Hettin' and pipin',
> O, the juice o' the maut,
> O, the sweet o' the saut,
> O, the tap o' the tree,
> Come a' tae me, come a' tae me
> For hot penny pies.'

USES OF POWDERED CUTTLE-FISH BONES IN SHETLAND

(*Scotsman*, 8/3/37.) In a letter, R. Stuart Bruce writes:

In olden times Shetland families often used finely powdered cuttle-fish bone for drying their letters. This was thought much better than sand for absorbing the ink. Another very curious use for the powdered bone was that sheepmasters in Shetland long ago blew the fine powder into the eyes of sheep which were thought to be going blind. This was said to be a certain cure!

I have heard it said that in fairly recent times the Shetland people sent cuttle-fish bones south, to be ground into bone manure.

WITCHES AND WARLOCKS AT KEMNAY, ABERDEENSHIRE

(*Aberdeen Press and Journal*, 21/3/36.)

Tradition has it that in the days when witches and warlocks still held sway in Scotland, his Satanic majesty paid one of his not infrequent visits to north-east Scotland. In the course of a hame-ower crack with one of the 'witch wives' of the neighbourhood, Auld Clootie threatened to claim the carline as his own unless she was able to make for him before nightfall a real rope of sand.

The Donside witch merely grinned, and said that to her such a task was but the merest child's play. The witch anyhow won her wager; and though her Devil's rope broke, its remnants are still to be seen in the Kembs of Kemnay, a chain of low, rounded sandhills, or rather hillocks, which run along the northern boundary of the estate and terminate on the borders of the parish of Cluny on the south-east. According to popular tradition, the parish derives its name from the Kembs or sand chain woven by that old-time Donside witch.

THE CORN-CRAKE
(*Aberdeen Press and Journal*, 26/6/35.)

The Corn-crake is being welcomed again in the evenings in the Cabrach district, after an absence of many years. Its presence is said to give promise of a bumper harvest, as well as a good salmon season.

ILL OMENS

At a hotel fire in Edinburgh some few years ago, three persons were fatally burned, and a honeymoon couple were amongst the injured. It was noted in the local press at the time that this couple, on leaving the house after the marriage ceremony and finding they had forgotten something, had returned to it in spite of the guests warning them that this was a most unlucky thing to do. Another ill omen lay in their friends having scattered lentils over them owing to the supply of rice having run short.

Some months ago an Aberdeen trawler was lost at sea with all hands. One of the widows informed a reporter that 'she knew something was to happen,' as she had dreamt that she was being followed about by a black and white dog.

39

Some Folklore and Legends of
Lower Deeside

[From *The Book of Aberdeen*, ed. David Rorie (1939), pp. 206-17]

It was my good hap to live and work for over quarter of a century amidst the ever pleasant surroundings of Lower Deeside. And if you chance to be one of those who still believe in wearing out shoe leather by other means than pressing it on an accelerator or, less frequently, a brake, it may fall in with your mood to come with me for a walk through the three parishes of Banchory-Devenick, Maryculter, and Peterculter, trying as we go to recapture that earlier and better atmosphere when a man could confidently sally forth 'to take the air' and not the exhaust products of petrol, and averting any possible fatigue on our voyaging by easy and familiar converse after the placid fashion we learnt long ago from The Compleat Angler.

Meet me, then, at the Auld Brig o' Dee; and, firstly, as we set out to cross it, let us make up our minds to leave recognised history severely alone, so that we may the more readily hear what were the current 'cracks' and tales of a countryside where the folk of old lived a quiet and peaceable life—with a due modicum of godliness and honesty—and had minds as yet unmuddled by wireless or the contradictory captions of a morning and evening newspaper.

Yes, of course, we know that Bishop Elphinstone projected the bridge, and that another bishop, Gavin Dunbar, brought the scheme to fruition: thus it is written. But the man who interests us at the start of our stepping out is the actual builder, Thomas Franche, later to serve King James V as his master mason. For it must be to the said Thomas that an old local saying applies, a saying that was prevalent up to the middle of last century, namely, that 'the brig was biggit for auchteen pence, and the man that biggit it had a saxpence left till himsel'.' Who, or what, originated this cryptic piece of legendary lore I cannot tell: it may be that the builder's fee was fixed at one third of the total cost; but whether that was the customary and proper percentage of his day, or any other day, I must leave architects to tell us.

But there is a definite moral for us all in another old saying about the bridge, which runs,

> There was a wifie sat on the Brig o' Dee
> An' aye she cried, 'Gie me! Gie me!'
> An' there was another wifie
> An' she aye took what she had
> An' sae she never wantit—
>   Which o' thae wifies wud ye be?

Another rhymester tells us that,

> Willie Buck had a coo,
> Her name was Billy Binty,
> She loupit owre the Brig o' Dee
> Like ony cove-o-ninty,

the last word probably being a corruption of 'Covenanter' and referring, though vaguely, to the capture of Aberdeen in 1639 by Montrose.

And we may note in passing, also, the rhyming chronicler who

> . . . . lookit owre Dee
> And saw a skate flee,

a vision suggesting the culmination of a series of prolonged and hilarious visits to the vintner; while

> Goukit Geordie, Brig o' Dee,
> Sups the brose an' leaves the bree,

was a verbal stimulant of old to the young child who was slow 'to clean the caup.'

Now that these innocent, if trivial, recollections have taken us over the bridge—or, perhaps more correctly, across it—we turn to the right, trying not to see the huddle of petrol stations and bungaloid growths desecrating the scene, and commence to go up Lower Deeside, coming, after a mile or so, to the kirkyard of Banchory-Devenick, the site, like many of its kin, of at least one ghost story. For, 'lang, lang syne,' it was haunted by the restless spirit—wandering by night and wailing 'Nameless! Nameless!'—of an unchristened bairn; and this to the mortal fear of those who had to pass the spot after dark on their lawful occasions. As custom required that such apparitions had to be 'well and truly laid' by one qualified so to do, the child's grave was baptised by a cleric; the name given to the occupant being 'Godfrey,' so as to bring in that of the Creator and thus secure rest to the wandering 'ghaistie.'

Here we have the idea of the restlessness of the unchristened child—an idea giving rise to many similar stories all over this country and others. Of old, in Scotland, they were called 'Tarans' and were frequently seen wandering in woods and solitudes, lamenting their sad fate, and to go over their graves was very 'unlucky.' The stain of namelessness had to be removed; and the spirits were, now and then, easily pleased. At Whittingehame in East Lothian, for example, a child had, before baptism, been murdered by its mother beneath a large tree, and for years the villagers were scared by the ghost 'running in a distracted manner between the tree and the churchyard and crying.' The villagers believed that it could not rest on account of wanting a name, 'no anonymous person,' says Chambers, 'being able to get a proper footing in the other world. Nobody durst speak to the unhappy little spirit from a superstitious dread of dying immediately after; and to all appearances the village was destined to be haunted till the end of time for want of an exorcist.' But fortunately, at long last, a merry-maker, fearless in his cups, fell in with the spirit during the small hours, and hailed it cheerfully with, 'How's a' wi' ye this morning, short-hoggers?' Whereupon the ghost straightway and for all time vanished, first exclaiming gleefully

O weel's me noo, I've gotten a name;
They ca' me Short-hoggers o' Whittingehame!

Not so pathetic as our local story: and more prosaic into the bargain. For the name that so delighted the Lothian ghost arose from the fact that it was wearing short stockings without feet; this lack being probably due, as one commentator gravely observes, to the long series of years during which the ghost had walked.

Now, before leaving the vicinity of the kirkyard, let us take a look at the picturesque pool in the Dee a little west of the church, because it is probably the last place on Lower Deeside where a genuine water kelpie made its appearance. Some 'hundred years ago and more' a salmon fisher was rowing his coble across the pool and paying out his net as he went. It was in the gloaming, with a thick 'haar' on the water; and as he turned his boat he glanced over his shoulder and saw the water kelpie on a rock, with a large chain ready to throw at him. Pulling harder than he had ever done in all his days, the terrified oarsman got to his 'home' side and breathlessly told his companions what had happened. The mist prevented them seeing anything; but plain to their ears was the sound of the chain 'gaun clickin' doon the garth'; a garth, as I trust you know, being a stretch of shingle. And the kelpie was (alas!) never again seen in Banchory-Devenick.

But, as we walk westward along the south Deeside road and it is yet a mile or so to our next halt of legendary interest, let me remind you that the kelpie was a fairly common frequenter of both Dee and Don. You may remember how Farquharson-na-Bat, 'Farquharson of the Wand,' so called from his trade of basket-weaving, lost his footing in the river while crossing it one dark night of long ago just above the Linn of Dee beyond Braemar. Swept down the rough channel, he was drowned, and for some days search was made for his body in vain. 'At last his wife, taking her husband's plaid, knelt down on the river's brink and prayed to the water-spirit to give her back her dead. She then threw the plaid into the stream. Next morning her husband's corpse, with the plaid wrapped round it, was found lying on the edge of the pool.' They believed, those folk of that day, that a certain ritual would make the water-spirit give up his prey.

More fortunate in his dealings with the kelpie was the ferryman at Potarch, in days before the bridge was there, who was much annoyed by the knavish tricks of his fellow claimant to the water. One night, in answer to a loud hail from the other side, the ferryman crossed with his boat and shipped a passenger—'a very grim fellow indeed, with a remarkably dark countenance, and eyes shining like a pair of live coals.' Weighty he was, too, sinking the boat almost to the gunwale, and causing the rower to labour at his oars and comminations. Then, as the passenger landed, the affrighted boatman caught sight of an extensive cloven hoof, and uttered an immediate prayer for safety. On hearing this, the water kelpie (for of this breed he was) changed into a horse, and, neighing and laughing derisively, splashed up the middle of the river and disappeared. And never thereafter did the honest ferryman go out at night without the family Bible open in the bow of his boat, to keep off kelpies and 'a' sic like.'

Was it this plethora of kelpies that gave the Dee its unenviable character for drowning? For the old rhyme runs

> Blood-thirsty Dee
> She needs three,
> But bonny Don
> She needs none,

a rhyme, by the way, that evidently sprang from a Donside brain, and is not without a touch of smug complacency.

But who can say? At any rate we know that all over the Highlands and Lowlands there was the same belief in the existence of a water-spirit, sometimes in the shape of a man, sometimes in that of a woman, a horse, a bull, or a cow. Hugh Miller tells of the water-spirit haunting the Ross-shire river Conan and appearing as 'a tall woman dressed in green, but distinguished chiefly by her withered meagre countenance, ever distorted by a malignant scowl. At dangerous fords she used to start out of the river before the terrified traveller, to point at him as in derision with her skinny finger, or to beckon him invitingly on.' And then he goes on to tell us how, in swimming at sunset over some dark pool 'where the eye failed to mark or the foot to sound the distant bottom of the river,' the twig of some sunken bush struck against him as he passed, and he felt as if touched with the cold bloodless fingers of the goblin.

I am afraid the kelpie was in most cases the product of fear and imagination, aided by the objective phenomenon of a half submerged tree-trunk or a foam-crested wave swirling in the wan moon's light: you will recall to mind William Watson's line on the breaker with its 'white fingers wildly grasping at the sky.' And in the days when travelling was toilsome, whisky cheap and strong and home-made, fords many, and bridges few, we can readily understand how the fingers became joined to hands, arms, and a human shape; or, mayhap, the crest of the wave became that of a horse. So that, if we take Tam o' Shanter as typical of a time when ferlies were more easily seen, we may be almost certain that the average water-spirit had more spirits than water in his composition.

Now, note as we pass it, that fine old beech on the right, covered, where it is get-at-able, with copious and deeply cut initials of lad and lass. By the older folk it had been known and used as 'The Trysting Tree,' and to associate yourself by the knife with its vigour and strength was considered to be health-giving and 'lucky.' Note, too, the arrow of Cupid which pierces a heart here and there; a lingering and popular carving traceable, some suggest, to the Roman occupation, although as a fertility symbol it has an even older origin than that.

And now we have come to where the Crynoch Burn goes under the South Deeside road; and if we follow the water up to the Corbie Linn, with its picturesque 'pot,' we come in touch again with one of the kelpie tribe. For right at the foot of this pot is a goodly treasure of gold. Many years ago, it is said, two enterprising worthies diverted the course of the stream above the linn, and set about emptying the pot of its water. When they had nearly accomplished this—so nearly, mark you, that they heard the jingling of the treasure—a voice shouted to them to hurry out as a neighbouring farm was on fire. On clambering to the surface they found the alarm to be false; but on looking down into the pot they saw that it was again filled with water and that their labour had been in vain. Yielding victory to the kelpie, they left unrewarded.

Stories similar to this are found all over Scotland. Locally they are told of the Leuchar burn at Culter as well as of the Crynoch; and not so very far away in the parish of Birse near Oldyleiper, a large copper vessel or kettle 'full of shining gold' is lying hid at the foot of a small loch. Many attempts, so the story goes, have been made to recover it, and all unsuccessfully. One man nearly got it, but, when just within his grasp, a false alarm of 'The kirk and manse are on fire!' called him away to find that he, too, had been fooled. Curious, is it not, how the water-spirit so often fell back on fire as an aid to his knavery?

Now, not so far west from the Crynoch burn is the old mansion house of Maryculter, once the site of a Preceptory of the Knights Templar, former owners of a large extent of land in the district. And associated with the stirring days when they sent their regular contingents to the Crusades is a legend dealing with the sad fate of one of their number, by name Godfrey Wedderburn. Of noble birth and descent, as was required of them all, he in due time set out for the Holy Land, where in a fierce battle with the Saracens he fell sorely wounded on the stricken field. But, viewing the scene of her father's prowess by moonlight, the fair daughter of the Paynim leader was so attracted by Godfrey's manly beauty that she bound up his wounds, concealed him in a cave near a neighbouring oasis, and visited him and tended him by night until he had gained a fair measure of health and strength. And in the process, of course, she had, as all such stories demand, fallen deeply in love with her charge, giving him as a love-token a talismanic ring, and hanging it round his neck by a golden chain.

But, alas! for her romance, one fine day a detachment of Crusaders stopped at the oasis, and to them Godfrey declared himself and was carried away, ultimately reaching his old headquarters at Maryculter, to resume his former strict and almost monastic life.

And there he stayed while many moons waxed and waned, until one fateful morning when, as he passed in procession with his comrades to chapel, a dark but comely maiden rushed forward with a glad cry—and flung her arms round his neck.

Well, of course, this was simply not done in the best Templar circles, and one can easily imagine the raised and knowing eyebrows of his fellow warriors and the promptitude with which the Commanding Officer put him under arrest. Brought before the Grand Master, he told his innocent story, was not believed, and, furious that his word was doubted, struck him. Condemned to death, but on account of his previous good service permitted to die by his own hand, he plunged a dagger into his heart in the presence of all the members of the Preceptory, duly paraded by torchlight and at midnight in a field behind the chapel. As he fell, the lovely Saracen again rushed on the scene, and with a shriek, drew out the blood-stained dagger along with the ring he wore suspended round his neck as her farewell gift.

Raising it on high with its large single gem sparkling in the ruddy glare, she dared the Grand Master to adorn himself with it; 'for,' she cried, 'it can only be worn in safety by one who is pure of heart.' In this awkward situation, challenged as he was in face of his command, what could the unfortunate man do but put it on? And as he did so there came an awesome peal of thunder and a flash of lightning that carried his corpse deep into the ground; while the maiden, in turn, plunged the dagger into her breast and fell lifeless across the body of her beloved. The parade broke away in confusion, and refused to return to the scene till dawn. Doubtless you, with the rank materialism of to-day, shrug a sceptic's shoulder; but, had we time, I could show you in the field the depression which is still known as 'the Thunder Hole,' and thus put you to shame.

And so, away up the side of the burn, were buried in the same grave a gallant knight and a dark but comely lady of high degree; for Godfrey's last request after sentence of death had been passed on him was that he might lie where he could hear the wimple of the linn, and so be reminded of that far away oasis and the trickling water he had heard there by day but could never drink until nightfall brought his faithful nurse. The ring is said to have been cast away in the fields by the horror-stricken Templars; and as each anniversary of the tragedy came round, the folk of the district used to hold that the gem could be seen twinkling like a star among the grass, though none would ever dare draw nigh it. And if death was near at hand in any home it was said that the figure of the Saracen maid could be seen gliding past the window, a sure fore-runner of the end. Some say she would even enter the room and beckon to the sufferer in token of his release; others, that she could be seen and heard singing at the Corbie Linn; while there are those who declared that at dead of night Godfrey, in full armour, would gallop his steed through the neighbouring lands of Kingcausie and over the hill. Certain it is that even within recent years there have been instances of his ghostly visitation of the scene of his sorrows.

And now let us cross the Dee and proceed from the North road up that which leads us past a building once the Free Kirk of Contlaw. Like all of its kind, it must have been erected after 1843, and it is strange, therefore, that the tale I tell should be associated with it. For it is said that a belated reveller found his way into it one Saturday night, and, prowling about for a suitable sleeping place, had gone up the pulpit stair. Above the pulpit was a hatch opening into a loft; and, pushing it open, the trespasser climbed in, shut the trap-door behind him, and fell into a deep and drunken sleep. Next forenoon he was wakened from slumber by the hearty singing of the congregation; and, forgetting where he was and how he had entered, started walking about to find an exit; the sound of his heavy tread being audible to all except the minister, who was definitely hard of hearing.

Now here comes a catch in the story; for what perturbed the congregation was an idle tale that the building was haunted by the Deil; and it is obvious that the last place any sane man would look for 'Auld Clootie' would be in a Free kirk, especially one of the older variety. Nevertheless, no sooner was the service finished and the minister out of the pulpit than the congregation started to 'skail' with unwonted haste; a haste developing into panic as the legs of the man aloft, who had now found the trap-door, commenced to waggle in the air as he sought for foothold. And when at last the dazed drouth got down to the floor, the only man remaining seated in a pew was an unfortunate little tailor, a cripple whose crutches had been carried away in the rush. As the intruder, black of face with dust and with dishevelled locks adorned with cobwebs, found his way towards the terrified tailor, he was greeted with the agonised appeal—'Eh, bonny Deil, dinna tak' me! I'm nae a reg'lar member!' Neither was he; and it certainly seemed a pity that a mere casual visitor should become scapegoat for the 'lave.'

But however unfounded the tale may be as applying to the kirk at Contlaw, let us go on to the crest of the hill and pause to look at one of the finest views on Lower Deeside; a glorious sweep of hill and dale from Benachie through Lochnagar and Cloch-na-ben on to Cairn-mon-earn. And then, by descending into the dip and taking the farm track to the right, we come to the small farm of Westfield, with an old tree in front of the house. Till recent years the name of the place was 'Broonie's Graif'; the grave not of a brownie such as he of Blednoch, but of a poor and persecuted human being. For here on the tree, far back in the days gone by, Broonie hanged himself, and here he was buried, else would we not have the 'graif' beneath a large boulder in the farmyard. But while we know neither his age nor the rest of his history, we do know the verse which, oft recited to his annoyance, hastened his tragic end; and that verse ran:

> Brent Broonie o' the Brae
> Maks sheen baith nicht an' day
> An' clips a bit frae Sunday.

Broonie, then, was probably a souter who, clinging to the 'Old

Faith,' had not 'come over' at the Reformation, and had thus failed to attain the hyper-Sabbatarian standard of his neighbours and their new clerical masters. Close at hand, until recent years, were both the 'Priest's Tree' and the 'Priest's Well,' indicating that here had dwelt a cleric who may have stiffened Broonie's nonconformity. Let us say our *requiescat in pace*, for he probably was as worthy as those who 'misca'ed' and killed him.

Now away up to the right of us is the estate of Binghill, and 'somewhere' in the vicinity lies buried a bullock's hide filled with gold. Treasure again; and again never yet discovered. Nor is it too safe to attempt it, even with supernatural aid, and to prove it we can take an instance from Fife. In Largo Law, which looks down on Largo Bay of song fame, is a gold mine—no less. And a ghost who knew the exact site offered to disclose it to a shepherd, whose chance acquaintance he had made, on the conditions that

> If Auchindownie cock doesna craw,
> And Balmain horn doesna blaw,
> I'll tell ye where the gowd-mine is in Largo Law.

Chanticleer happened to keep silence, but unfortunately, and just as the great secret was about to be told, the cow-herd of Balmain (who, of course, knew nothing about the arrangement) blew a blast both loud and shrill, whereupon the ghost vanished, exclaiming furiously

> Woe to the man that blew the horn,
> For out of this place he shall ne'er be borne!

Nor was he; for the luckless wight, Tammas Norrie by name, was there and then struck dead, and so firmly pinned to the earth that his body could not be removed. And in complete proof of this story is there not a cairn, now grown into a green hillock, called Norrie's Law, to confound all disbelievers? Nor is that the only instance on record of how dangerous it is to meddle with buried treasure. But let us get back to Aberdeenshire.

We have left our rough track and got on to a wider road which takes us up the hill to Black Tap, whence, if you look westward, you will once again be rewarded by a truly lovely view of the hills. Here, too, you will see good specimens of 'consumption dykes,' the rough, wide, and solid walls made of stones of all shapes and sizes, collected with infinite stress and toil by the hardy race who of old turned boulder, whin, and heather into arable land. Why 'Black' Tap? Well, in times gone by there abode here a certain John Black, who in his day must have been unable to enjoy in peace his glorious view of the hills: for he, honest man, owned sheep, and from these hills one night came caterans, as John slumbered, who gravely lessened the sum total of his woolly wealth. Nor was this all; for when the farmer, by the dim light of dawn, examined the door of his dwelling, he found written thereon in chalk:

> John Black o' Black Tap,
> Your yowes are unco' fat.
> Oot o' three score and seven
> I hae ta'en eleven.
> Did ye but ken my name
> Ye would hang me for the same.

Hanging? Hanging was too good for a man whose verse was even worse than his morals! The only excuse one can make for him is that he would probably have been more at home in the language of Ossian, and that this house-door effort was mere 'writing down' to the mental level of the lowlander.

In this vicinity, too, were till lately the remains of some prehistoric 'bee-hive' dwellings, and two good examples of 'cup-and-ring' stones. One of these last having, many years ago, been shown by a local antiquary to a visiting, appreciative, and learned brother from the south, was found later to have no markings; the newcomer having evidently returned with a skilled stonecutter and removed the part of the boulder bearing the inscription; a proceeding which would have strained the conscience of even Jonathan Oldbuck at his keenest.

And now, as we descend the hill to the right, we come to a wood in which is an old stone circle, one of the many for which Aberdeenshire is famous. To a former generation this wood was known as the Scare Park or Scare Wood, and held to be uncanny, as 'feart' things were to be seen there. It is curious that when, some forty years ago, a new road was made through it, a prehistoric stone coffin was dug up; the local story of uncanniness being doubtless due to the vague tradition of a burial place being there. For tradition, more especially of this nature, is often truer than it gets credit for. In Glenlyon, for example, there was discovered, some half-century ago, a similar stone coffin containing a headless skeleton; and long before it was unearthed children had been warned by their elders against going near the place where it was found, 'as a ghost might spring upon them.'

So, with a proper appreciation of the cautious wisdom of our forebears, we can leave the Scare Park, pass through Cults to its famous little suspension bridge—'The Shakkin' Briggie'—and, crossing the river, get once more on to the South Deeside road at the kirk of Banchory-Devenick. And as we come back again—footsore perhaps but not, I hope, unedified—to the Brig o' Dee and the rough-and-tumble of a to-day which, like Gallio, cares for none of these things, at least such of them as you and I set out to consider, I cordially grasp your hand on parting and thank you for the ready courtesy of a hearing ear.

40
The Lighter Side of Leechcraft

[From *Scots Magazine* 8 (1927), 211–4]

When grizzled country medicos foregather—or those mayhap whose hair has, as Russell of the *Scotsman* once said of his own, 'preferred death to dishonour'—there is one point whereon they agree, *videlicet*, that the present medical generation 'dinna ken they're livin'.' Gone are the days of saddle and gig, when sun, rain, wind, frost, hail and snow gave our Gideon Grays the all-weather visages of Baltic skippers; a choice blending of the colours of a 'finnan haddy' and a brick. 'What do they know of hardship who only motors know?' (And saloon-bodied motors at that!) Time has in the past thirty years brought about as big a change there as from the old wind-jammer to the modern craft with its oil-engine.

And Time has also changed the nature of the country doctor's erstwhile unsophisticated clientele. For the old peasant is passing. Sanitarians have robbed him of his box-bed and his red 'Kilmarnock': corrugated iron has taken the place of his thatch: above his tin roof swings an aerial so that his mind, once a receptacle of old ballads, pithy proverbs, and honest Scots song, can be riddled and ruined, into hours of unholy lateness, with negroid jazz, and his decent dour dialect sapped by the monotonous tones of some R-less metropolitan 'announcer.' The days are past when about 8 p.m.

> Auld Simon sat luntin' his cutty,
> And lowsin' his buttons for bed,

after a solid 'twa-handed crack' about sheep and neeps with a crony who by now, at his own ingle, was doubtless similarly engaged in shedding his breeks with a view to slumber.

Nothing but good have I to say of Simon: mark that. Uneducated? Yes—measured by modern standards: but a shrewd, observant 'character,' infinitely preferable to many of his successors, intoxicated with their poor standard half-pint of the present 'fushionless' Pierian spring. *Vale* Simon! And to thee this tribute! . . .

In the early part of last century a farmer in Buchan was despatched at midnight post haste for the howdie. It was a wild night of wind and rain, he had a good ten miles to ride, so that on reaching his destination he considered himself justified in taking a good dram. The handy-wife, also duly fortified against the elements, mounted pillion behind him, and the worthy pair started hell-for-leather on the return journey. His horse reeking with sweat, the farmer reached his own door, and an excited woman rushed out with a lantern and the exclamation, 'Thank the Lord ye've come!' Then holding up the light, she added in dismay, 'But whaur's the nurse?' Sure enough, nurse there was none; and the mystery was cleared up by the horseman dismally muttering, 'I'se warrant that was her that played clyte at Insch!'

An old practitioner in Forfarshire was, many years ago, sitting at the bedside of a wealthy and garrulous old lady patient, who was volubly detailing her many infirmities. The bed was hung with print curtains on which were depicted two figures. On these the doctor was gazing, while apparently respectfully listening to the old lady's interminable story. Suddenly he astonished her by smiting his knees with both hands and exclaiming triumphantly, 'I hae't noo! I hae't noo! Patie an' Roger! Patie an' Roger!' He had solved the puzzle of the curtains and lost one of his best patients: for the indignant dame refused to play second fiddle to Allan Ramsay and never asked him to darken her door again.

A quaint request was once made by the wife of an old bedridden man who caused her much annoyance by his restlessness at night. Following the doctor to the door one day, she asked confidentially, 'Doctor, could ye no' gie him a poother?' 'A powder? What kind of a powder?' 'Well, my sister's man in the Wast Country was juist like Wullie here, and the doctor there gied *him* a poother, and efter that he neither moved ee nor broo!' The powder, needless to say, was not forthcoming.

During one of the earlier influenza epidemics of the nineties, in a small country town where cases were numerous, the doctor, for the convenience of those taken ill after the chemist had shut his shop, used to carry some antifebrile powder with him. Called late one night to see a frail old man, he laid a small paper packet on the mantel-shelf and said to the wife, 'Give him that with a good glass of whisky.'

'Listen to the doctor's orders noo, mistress!' anxiously said the patient, who was usually rather stinted as regards that commodity. 'Listen to the doctor's orders! A guid gless o' whisky, he says.' Next morning, on calling, the doctor found the patient much better, but the powder still where it had been laid. 'Why on earth didn't you take your powder?' he asked rather testily. 'Weel, ye see, sir,' said the patient, 'There was a mistak aboot that poother. Ye wesna weel doon the stairs las' nicht when I mindit ye hadna said whether I was to tak it afore or efter the speerits, sae for fear o' ony hurt I jist took the whisky by itsel'.' Canny soul!

Knocked up one mirk night by his bell going thirteen to the dozen in the small hours, a doctor stuck his head out of the window and asked, 'What do you want?' Back came the counter query, 'Can ye tell me the composition of speerit varnish?' 'What on earth do you want to know that for?' 'Man, I've juist swalla'd a gless o't!' 'What for?' 'What for? I thocht it was whusky!' 'And didn't you know the difference in taste?' 'I niver kent ony differ till I felt my moo-tash gettin' a' stiff!' And then the excited sufferer added, 'But dinna stand bletherin' there, man! Tell me what I'm to dae!' And before closing the window the doctor told him to swallow the brush.

Another and similar 'drooth' had after a fortnight's spree gone to the chemist's for a pick-me-up to break him 'off the dram'; next day he met a crony whom he had not seen for some time, who asked after his health. 'Oh! I'm juist in my frail usual an' aye stappin' aboot,' he replied, 'but I'm takkin' a mixtur' I got frae Droggie, an' I'm fair lossin' my taste for drink.' 'Lossin' your taste for drink?' exclaimed his horrified friend, 'Man, if I was you I would be d——d carefu' what ye're daein!' Now firmly convinced that he had been trifling with the gifts of the gods, the man of mixtures hastened with his friend to the nearest pub to endeavour (and successfully) to recover the lost talent.

Many are the wonderful tales brought back to the country after a visit to the hospital of a large town. One patient sent to Edinburgh was on his return asked by the doctor, 'Well, did you see the professor?' 'See the perfessor?' exultantly said the man, who had been made the subject of a clinical lecture; 'see the perfessor? I saw aboot twa hunner o' them! Some o' them was blecks, and the heid ane was that pleased wi' my complaint that he drew a pictur o' my puddens on a black-boord!' He had got full value for his train fare.

To take the eyes out, lay them on the cheeks, 'clean them,' and put them in again is a possible operation if popular testimony be proof. One such case, when doubt was thrown on his statement by his doctor, said desperately, 'Ane o' them was oot, onywey!' 'How do you know?' 'Man, I was keekin' for five meenutes richt doon my left lug!'

Take this description of going under chloroform: not so poetic, maybe, as Henley's, but realistic enough in its way. 'Syne twa student-billies cam' rinnin' into the ward wi' a hurly, an' I was liftit aff the bed on till't. Syne they yarkit it richt roon: *that* was to make me unconscious—I kent fine what they were efter—but it didna. Syne they pit a nepkin wi' a queer smell on't a' ower my face, but I was aye conscious o' what they were daein' till a muckle deep voice said, "Gie him mair." An' *this* time they drappit somethin' fair in my ee. Losh; it nippit till my lugs was bummin' like the clapper o' a mill—and I mind nae mair!'

And how curious the *fons et origo mali* in some cases! 'To lat ye understan' my complaint,' said one old dame to her doctor, 'ye'll hae to gang back to the year auchteen hunner an' seeventy-twa, the nicht auld Mrs. S. was in at her tea. Her an' me was awfu' chief, an' a rale herty tea the body took, an' syne stappit awa' hame. Aboot hauf an hoor efter a neebor o' mines pit her heid in at the door, an' says she, "D'ye ken Mrs. S.?" "Ken Mrs. S.?" says I. "The cratur's juist had her tea here!" "Weel, she's deid," says she. An' wi' that there was somethin' like a fiddle-string played plunk in my inside, an' I've niver been the same woman since!' I understand that the exact nature of the musical occurrence was never ascertained.

In the 'Kingdom' a doctor who was conducting an Ambulance Class asked one of his pupils what he would do if he came upon a man lying unconscious by the roadside. 'Gie him a gless o' whusky,' was the prompt reply. 'But if he could not swallow a glass of whisky, what then?' 'Weel, I wouldna fash wi' him further: if he's a Fife man an' canna swalla a gless o' whusky, he's deid.'

Will as much legendary lore gather round the present medical generation as did round its predecessors in the days gone by? There was one old hero of medicine whose sayings and doings were retailed fifty years after his decease by those who in their youth had known him and now gloried in the fact. On one occasion this doctor was attending an old cattleman who had been gored in the abdomen by a bull. It was long before the days when Lister had made abdominal surgical work a possibility, but the patient had nevertheless been pulled round and was convalescent. Needless to say his diet had been of the strictest. One day on calling at the cottage the doctor found the wife engaged in making broth for her dinner. As he left, the patient called after him, 'Doctor, can I no' take my denner wi' the wife?' 'Oh ay,' said the old medical, 'tak your denner wi' the wife an' ye'll tak your supper wi' the Deil!' Under the circumstances the patient adhered to his 'skilly'; the necessity for so doing had been vividly brought to his notice.

41
At the Sign of the Blue Pill

[From *Caledonian Medical Journal* 11 (1918–22), 325, 328–9, 364; 12 (1923–5), 43-5, 45-6, 224–6; 13 (1926–8), 441; 14 (1929–31), 202, 276–7; 15 (1932–6), 363–4; 16 (1937–40), 235–9]

Many are the stereotyped stories told about outstanding members of our profession, the same old stories, possibly Babylonian, fathered now here and now there. To the credit of how many old country doctors all over Scotland has 'If it's watter there's a trootie intil't' been laid? And here, in this cutting from a French newspaper, we find Du Bois Raymond as the hero of a tale with which all old Edinburgh men connect the name of the immortal 'Bilirubin'; although he, if my memory serves me right, used a visiting card to point his moral.

'La *Gazette de Voss* publie à l'occasion des dernières sessions d'examens, une série d'anecdotes dont furent tour à tour les héros des professeurs et des étudiants. Celle-ci concerne le professeur Du Bois Raymond, un illustre Neuchâtelois qui a fait sa carrière scientifique à Berlin.

'Le professeur interrogeait un candidat en médecine qui ne répondait à aucune des questions posées. Du Bois Raymond prend une feuille de papier et la partage en deux moitiés. A la question suivante, également adressée à un muet, deuxième partage; à la troisième, même jeu, et ainsi de suite jusqu' à ce qu'il ne reste qu'un tout petit carré de papier dans la main de l'examinateur. Alors le professeur tend ce reste au candidat et dit. "Ecrivez-moi là-dessus ce que vous savez de médecine."' ['The *Gazette de Voss* publishes, when the last examination sessions take place, a series of anecdotes whose heroes are in turn the professors and the students. This one concerns Professor Du Bois Raymond, a renowned Neuchâtelois who has pursued his scientific career in Berlin.

The professor was examining a candidate in medicine who was not responding to any of the questions asked. Du Bois Raymond takes a sheet of paper and folds it in two. With the next question, addressed likewise to a mute, another fold; with the third, the same performance, and so on until there remains only a very small square of paper in the examiner's hand. Whereupon the professor proffers it to the candidate and says "Write down what you know about medicine on this."']

I remembered a voyage I had once made on the famous East Neuk of Fife branch of the N.B.R. from Thornton to Leuchars. I was going to Elie, and in the carriage, as that train wended its habitually slow way, was, amongst several others, a somnolent horse-couper in a severe state of intoxication. Also present was a brisk little bright-eyed inquisitive man. As the train passed station after station the little man got anxious, and, addressing us *en masse* said, with an eye on the horse-couper, 'He'll be missing his stop!' Then, shaking the dealer, he asked, 'Whaur are ye gaun tae?' Waking with a snort his victim said, angrily, 'Coupar-Angus,' and relapsed into slumber. 'Mercy me,' said the little man, 'he'll never get there the nicht—no' possible ava'!' When the philanthropist had got out at the next station the 'couper' slowly sat up, glared round at us, and said portentously, 'I'm gaun to Pittenweem; but it disna dae to tell every★★★★★★fool your business!'

What's in a name? A good deal, after all is said and done. You can usually tell a man's nationality from it, and after you have got that, can often deduce his county or even his parish. Mistakes, of course, can be made. Was it not the case that on one occasion a German waiter—before the war, pray Heaven!—announced the decent and respectable name of McCorquindale as 'Max Körchenthal,' thereby indulging in a little bit of folk-etymology by making something he could understand out of something else that he could not?

It is an old game. Take the names 'Forbes' and 'Gordon,' *par exemple*, the former, alas! now almost universally, even in Scotland, vulgarised into a monosyllabic 'Fawbs,' instead of its ancient and proper pronunciation, 'For-bes.' Why do we all so weakly yield to this? It is one of the many signs of a wilting national backbone. For how do the folk explain its origin? Thus. In the days gone bye a large boar—a famous fellow; he ravaged many parts of Scotland—attacked and killed, amongst other maidens, a lady yclept Elizabeth. Her bereaved lover met him in single combat and slew the tusker with a large two-handed sword, shouting with each mighty stroke his war-cry, 'For Bess! For Bess!' And if we bear this in mind, the question of one syllable or two is settled for ever.

But there is a variant, which also explains 'Gordon.' According to this tale there were *two* lovers of *two* maidens, both slain by the boar. The pair of gallants pursued, overtook, and knocked him over. Whereupon one cried, 'Ye haud the fore-birse an' I'll gore doon.' Hence, easily and properly, the two gentlemen were thereafter known—as have been their descendants—by the names of Forbes and Gordon. What their original names were, or whether they were altogether nameless before their deed of derring-do, history sayeth not.

Stracathro, too, was visited by the savage animal, and here, also, he is claimed to have been killed, the slayers shouting the battle-cry of 'Strike an' ca' through!' From which it is no far cry to 'Stracathro'; the transition is easy and acceptable, unless to the hardened unbeliever.

One of the finest, I think, is the reason given for Cruden—famous for golf and fresh air—being so called. Here the Danes landed in days long past and made a sanguinary raid, penetrating far inland. The inhabitants, rallying their broken forces, gradually drove the invaders back. Nearing their ships, the Danish retreat became a rout, and their leader, standing on the prow of his flagship, yelled in his excitement 'Crood in, boys! Crood in!' Why he thus deserted the language of his fathers in favour of the vernacular of his foes we are not informed. But 'Cruden,' as a place name, is satisfactorily explained. Is it not so?

Nor should one miss Lumphanan. Years back, a Scots King, one of the 'Jamies'— which of them, I regret to say, I do not recollect—spent the night in a house there. While sitting by the fire a loose stone came rumbling down the chimney, and the surprised king ejaculated, 'Losh, me! The lum's fa'in' in.' His sudden remark survives as a place name. Why not?

And then to go South a bit, we have Alloa and Tillicoultry. Alloa, apparently, was at one time not only nameless, but also extremely desirous of securing a proper designation. So a 'council of notables' met and sat into the 'sma' hoors,' discussing, quarrelling, and suggesting, until at last, in disgust or despair, or both, one of the worthiest of the worthies got to his feet and remarked 'Ah'll awa'.' Light at once burst on all present, and there was an unanimous shout of 'Alloa, so be it!' Alloa so was it, and Alloa it still is.

So with Tillicoultry. For long had the inhabitants searched for a name, and in vain. One of them, seeking inspiration, sat beside a pond on the outskirts, sad at heart. A Highland drover passed by with his herd, and the local solitary asked, 'Will ye no gie your beasts a drink?' 'Na,' said the Highlander, 'There's deil a coo dry.' Inspiration again! Off hastened the Tillicoultry man, and his town got a name that still survives.

Well, well; thus it is that many honest people think, and find the problems in question satisfactorily solved. Which, after all is something. For in these present, evil, strenuous, materialistic days a little honest belief in something—even if the belief is obviously wrong—is worth chronicling. If you believe a thing you often save yourself a lot of bother, and you at least possess the grace of acknowledging that someone else may know more than you do. And it sweetens ordinary conversation a good deal.

. . . some people do believe in re-incarnation. In the Kingdom of Fife was an old mansion house near a loch—it still stands there, so far as I know—which house, ruinous somewhat, had only the lower storey inhabited as a cottar house. It fell to my lot, one summer's day, to pass several tedious hours there, what time the population of the parish gained one more. The garden was in ill repair, and full of mole-hills. To pass the time I took a convenient spade and dug—unsuccessfully—for moles. In a little out came the handy-wife and said, brusquely: 'I widna dae that, if I wis you.'

'Why?' I asked.

'Ah weel, there's gude reasons.'

Later, with some difficulty, I got the reasons. Over a hundred years ago an old lady had lived there, much attached to her old ancestral home, and especially to her garden, which was then carefully kept, and in which she spent much of her time. On her death-bed she talked much of it, and her last words were that after her decease 'she would come back as a mowdie-wort and bide there!' And I had been carelessly trying to dig up old Miss Euphemia!

A fine old house it had been, haunted not only by the mowdie-wort spinster, but also by a white horse—probably a water-kelpie story, as the loch was there. However that may be, the white horse 'appeared' on occasion; of that there was no possible doubt. The farmer of the place, coming home one night from market, met it face to face in the court-yard, and promptly retired some distance down the road to spend the night in a convenient, though cold, ditch. In the morning he reconnoitred carefully, to discover that a white cow, which had broken loose, had been the real cause of his alarm. But even his adventure did not destroy the story of the white horse. Long may his hoofs clatter!

At the Sign of the Blue Pill

I have often wished that a collection could be made of the tales told by old folk about the famous (to them) country doctors of the past. One old man, talking of a long dead medical stalwart of his youth, said to me the other day, 'Ay! he was a winnerfu' lad that! Did ye ever hear aboot him and the man wi' the bad leg? Na? Weel, this man had been lyin' a lang time, an' ae day the doctor gaed till him, an' says he, "John" (he ca'd him John because his name was John, ye see), "John," says he, "I'm gaun tae dae my verra best for ye?" "Weel," says John, "I'm a puir man, an' mebbe no fit to meet your chairges, doctor, but ye can hae your wull o' my leg," says he. Sae the doctor yokit till him an' cut his leg a' roon an' roon' jist like the strips on a barber's pole lang syne. An' that dune, he blew poothered gless intil a' the cuts, to keep them festerin', ye see, an' draw the tribble oot. An' that man mendit ilka day efter't, and had a soond leg for 'ears and 'ears till he dee'd!'

Now, what kind of a leg had the man got when the doctor 'yokit till him'? And what did the doctor do to it? I suppose that concerns the legend very little. Possibly he only made some fairly large incisions, and 'blew in' some boracic acid powder. But the fact remains that he did something sufficiently 'by-or'nar'' to start a story that out-lasted him, a story, too, that casts a slur upon the originality and daring of the present rural medico—who merely passes such a case into the hospitals. And, once there, have the staff the courage to use 'poothered gless' blown into barber's pole 'strips'? Nay!

I remember another old chap who, thirty odd years ago, told me a tale about the famous Danny Ferguson, the Stirling bone-setter. It was something 'ootside banes,' as my informant said, and showed Danny breaking new ground. 'I ken some o' you doctors dinna haud wi' bane-setters, but ootside banes a'thegither I kent a case whaur Danny fair beat some of the best doctors in Edinburry—ay! an' in Lunnon forbye! There was a leddy cam' till's door ae day— a real leddy, min' ye, carriage an' pair an' twa fitmen an' a' the rest o't—and speirt for Danny. Danny had her in, an' she telt him a' her story. Awfu' pain in her side she'd had for 'ears and 'ears, an' naebody could dae naethin' for her. Weel, Danny didna say onything, juist lookit at her, an' syne oot wi' his pen-knife an' made a nick in her side wi't—richt through her claes, min' ye!—and took oot—what think ye, doctor?—*a bag o' lice!* Ay, man, juist that! *That* was what had been batherin' her a' thae 'ears, and *nane* of the doctors had fan' it oot. Aha! Danny was the lad, I'm tellin' ye!'

Here, again, what *did* happen? And how did *this* story gain credence? 'A real leddy; carriage an' pair,' &c.

[289]

And it was there, too, [a town in Fife] that the famous race meeting occurred. One worthy in the town had a bucket-leg and a crutch, and another had an old white mare. In which of the numerous 'pubs' the match was hatched, and after what debate, history deponeth not. But it was ultimately agreed that a race was to take place from the cemetery gate to the town cross, the conditions being that the bucket-leg man rode the 'mear' while the mare's owner, with one leg trussed up, used the other fellow's crutch. The distance was about half a mile, and all the town was out to see the joyous affair, and to bet on it. It was a close race, and both the principals were 'well-oiled.' Surrounded by a cheering crowd they came panting up the cobble-stones, 'Bucket' with his 'pin-leg' sticking out at right angles from the back of his mount and 'Hiltie' scrabbling madly on the 'causey' with his opponent's crutch. And, behold! it was a dead heat; for a yard or so from the winning post 'Hiltie' got his stick in between his mare's front legs, and the 'hale jing-bang' lay in a confused, struggling heap, circled by a crowd convulsed with Homeric laughter! 'It fairly beat cock-fechtin'.'

'Singing's the thing,' as Sir Harry Lauder very properly remarks; an appropriate addendum to 'It's a poor heart that never rejoices.' And singing often comes in handy enough. You remember the old yarn of the stammering sailor who, seeing a shipmate fall into the sea, rushed to the skipper, and in his excitement could only make various splutterings and facial contortions. 'Sing it, you lubber!' said the captain. Whereupon the seaman emitted the informative chanty,

> Overboard is Barnabas
> And half a mile a-starn of us!

In Sir Walter Scott's recently published letter-books we find reference to the silver c.p. [chamberpot] of a lady of title which occasioned trouble at a house where she was visiting. For the chamber-maid there declared that as the c.p. was of silver it obviously ranked as plate, and thereby, for polishing and other proper care, came under the jurisdiction of the butler, and was no affair of hers; a nice point that required judicious handling. And to cap this, Sir Walter introduces the tale of the large silver c.p. which, in another establishment, was always solemnly brought in by the butler after dinner and placed, when the ladies had left the room, on the table for the convenience of such as required it. Unfortunately one day the ladies had, without the butler's knowledge, stayed later than usual; and his solemn entry with the silver 'michael' caused confusion—to none more than to himself. It is a tale worth reading as throwing light on the manners and customs of a not very remote period.

All of us know the old eighteenth century sideboard with the small recess at one end containing a c.p. In the days when there were no inside 'lavatories' for handy and repeated visiting, such a convenience ranked high in the minds of our three-bottle forebears as an evidence of thoughtful hospitality.

In the literature of the eighteenth century, and the centuries preceding it, the chamber-pot had a secure place. No comic interlude seems properly complete without it. Sterne, Swift, Smollett, and Fielding all toy with it: Le Sage in *Gil Blas*, Cervantes in *Don Quixote*, Boccaccio, Margaret of Navarre, and Montaigne, to mention only some of its adherents, recognize its quaint and peculiar humour. The last-named mentions a friend of his, a hypochondriac of the first water, whose chief delight was to give clinical lectures on his case to such as would gather round the contents of half a dozen c.p.'s. I do not know that the type is quite extinct even yet.

Scarron, the curious, embittered and deformed little *abbé*, whose wit and scurrilous humour made him famous altogether apart from the fact that he was the first husband of Madame de Maintenon, was a great user of the c.p. in literature. In *The Whole Comical Works of M. Scarron*, a London translation of 1759, there is a 'Romance of a Company of Stage-Players,' a tedious affair at best. And, every third or fourth chapter, when a humorous interlude is required, he falls back upon the inevitable chamber-pot; I should not like to say how often in the 389 pages, in case I might be disbelieved. But in appreciating humour of this sort all Gaul is not divided into three parts: it laughs as one man.

In present-day folk-lore the c.p. seems to rank the symbol of domestic intimacy and connubial bliss. The ritual of the old Scottish tinkers' wedding was to dig a hole in the ground into which the bridegroom and the bride micturated. Then, grasping hands, they repeated the words, 'Let them that can sinder (separate) that, sinder us,' and the ceremony was complete. An ancient custom, doubtless, with traces still surviving. For miniature chamber-pots frequently adorn the mantel-shelves of quite 'respectable' members of society: even people who—to use the smug expression of the various ecclesiastical courts—'have a church connection.' These things are sold openly in the china shops of the back streets. One pair I saw recently bore the inscriptions, 'For me and my girl,' and 'After you, dear.' On the bottom of the c.p. was painted an eye. This merry jest is, of course, old and English—Devonshire, I understand, was a prominent rejoicer in this artistic effort, and the eye bore around it the legend of 'Oh! I see you!' I came across a specimen, however, in a billet in Champagne in 1918; and judicious enquiries established the fact that they were not uncommon in the district. Recently, too, in a crockery shop in Quimper, famed for its *faïence,*, I saw miniatures freely on sale, the eye being a prominent part of the decorative scheme.

The extracts below were sent me by a well-known official of one of our largest friendly societies. They were new to me, and may be to others, although I think they have appeared in print before:

Extracts from Applications under the National Insurance Acts

1. I cannot get sick pay—I have six children, can you tell me why this is so?
2. This is my eighth child. What are you going to do about it?
3. Mrs. Brown has had no clothing for a year, and has been regularly visited by the clergy.
4. I have been co-habiting with several officers at the headquarters, but so far without result.
5. I am glad to say that my husband, who was reported missing, is now dead.
6. Sir, I am forwarding my marriage certificate and my two children, one of which is a mistake, as you will see.
7. I am writing to tell you that my baby was born two years old. When do I get the money?
8. Unless I get my husband's money I shall be forced to lead an immortal life.
9. I am writing these few lines for Mrs. Jones, who cannot write herself. She expects to be confined next week and can do with it.
10. I am sending my marriage certificate and my six children. I had seven and one died, which was baptised on a half sheet of paper by Rev. Thomas.
11. Please find out for certain if my husband is now dead, as the man I am living with won't eat or do anything until he knows for certain.

12. I was very annoyed to find that you had branded my eldest son as 'illiterate.' It is a dirty lie, because I married his father a week before he was born.

13. My son has been put in charge of a spittoon. Do I get the money?

14. In answer to your letter I have given birth to son weighing ten pounds. I hope this is satisfactory.

15. Please send my money at once. I have fallen in error with the landlord.

16. I have no children. My husband is a bus driver and works day and night.

17. I want my money regularly. I have been in bed with a doctor for a week and he hasn't done me any good. If things don't improve I shall have to send for another doctor.

18. You have changed my little boy into a girl. Will this make any difference?

19. In accordance with your instructions I have given birth to twins in the enclosed envelope.

When you are tired, or when you feel bone-lazy and can give way to the feeling, which, of course only happens when you are on holiday, one of the best occupations to be found is to light a pipe and gaze into the heart of a fire; a real, genuine, coal fire, a companionable and living thing, not gas or electric contraptions which at best are but ghosts. Not that coal is the only possible thing to put light to: wood, and especially birch, can be a charming companion. Yes, upon due consideration, I think I prefer birch wood to coal, only it is not so easily got. Most of us know the good character it bears in the old saying:

> Birk will burn
> Pu'd through the burn,
> But saugh will sing
> Though simmer won.

And this, I hold, is a much better rendering than the tamer variant of

> Birk will burn be it burn drawn,
> Saugh will sab if it were simmer sawn.

That, however, is a slight deviation from my theme: what I was setting out to say was—How is it that trifling things, especially rhymes or fag-ends of songs (the more ridiculous the better) so often contrive to stick in the memory when better things are razed from its tablets? Take an example. The other evening, without any sound reason therefor, I suddenly remembered the following soul-inspiring lines:

> My name is Rhadamanthus Pratt,
> My trade is that of an acrobat,
> I can stand like this and never pant,
> And this is Jumbo, my elephant.

Well, careful consideration of this musty relic of the past—Jumbo, of course, dates it—recalled to me the fact that I had first seen it in an American paper, *The Detroit Free Press*, 'way back in the 'eighties. This periodical, much addicted to humour of the transatlantic variety, circulated widely in Britain for many years. The Pratt verse was, of course, illustrated so as to bring out the points about the panting and Jumbo. Hence the 'like this' and 'this.'

I think it was this paper, too, which (appropriately) celebrated the death of Walt Whitman by inserting a free verse elegy. The last lines ran:

> But John L. Death has tumbled you at last,
> Still, you've got the underhold,
> Sing him square in the face, old boy!
> I bet on you—Goodbye!

And here, again, one is dated: for John L. Sullivan, who supplied the figure of speech required by the elegist, was then in his prime. And that wasn't exactly yesterday, either.

A good many years ago, however, a Scots newspaper very nearly touched the Detroit level with some 'In Memoriam' verse recalling the death of a seaman.

> In 54 deg. 49 sec. N.,
> From life he did depart,
> West long. 1 deg. 51 sec.,
> 'Tis marked upon the chart.
> Whene'er we look upon that place,
> Many a tear we'll shed,
> No more on terra firma
> With him again we'll tread.

The writer was obviously a sailor, but not, perhaps, accustomed to the writing of elegiac verse. And, after all, when it comes to elegies, not everyone can rank with Gray.

I remember another example of sentimental poetry; song in this case, and love song at that. I heard it over forty years ago at a country concert held in a crowded schoolroom, where it was sung and applauded as a sentimental ditty. The owrecome ran:

And aye I saw her sittin' an' knittin',
The time that I was smokin' an' spittin',
And aye my heart went tittin' an' flittin'
 For Nannie wha lived next door!

But those were the hardier days, when a smoke was a smoke, and meant bogie roll in a blackened clay pipe (none of your jackanapes cigarettes); copious expectoration being a recognised and routine part of the pleasure. (And it was the use of the cutty which popularised the connundrum: 'Why did Adam smoke a widden pipe? Because he'd nae claes.') The point I ask you to note, however, is that the song ranked in popular esteem as a *love* song: it is as this that it clings to my memory.

The comic song, the song sung with definite intent to excite laughter, had frequently, forty years ago, a certain mild breadth of its own. When the singer was sure that the parish minister was absent, and that the laird and his lady were not patronising the entertainment, he might treat the audience to 'The Duke of Argyll.' This, while probably non-historical, tended to be somewhat clinical in its detail. Only one verse stays with me, to wit:

 The Duke of Argyll
 He was bathered wi' the bile,
  And the bile it bathered him sairly,
 Sae he took some castor ile
 An' it wrocht him in a while,
  Roon' aboot the Bonny Hoose o' Airlie.

I have said that the song is (so far as I know) without historical foundation, but it has some points of interest to the anthropologist or the student of folk-lore. It may be, of course, that it arose from the desire on the part of some enemies (and there were many) of the Clan Campbell to hold the titular chief up to derision, with the secondary idea of arousing the wrath of the Ogilvys against him by the alleged insult offered to the policies (*Scottice*) of 'The House': many of the squibs written in the seventeenth and eighteenth centuries were of the shrapnel order. But this is sheer surmise, based on the assumption, possibly erroneous, that the song is of some age.

No, strictly speaking, the interest lies more in the song's anthropological associations. The child shares with the more primitive type of mankind a keen interest in the emunctories. An illustrative case, you may remember, occurred not long ago, when a sensitive mother wrote a letter to a school teacher with the plaintive request: 'For

[295]

ony sake dinna tell oor Jessie Ann ony mair aboot her inside: she maks me seeck,' and thus put an end to some tentative teaching of elementary physiology. And the statement, often made, that Scots song is inherently broad and naive applies with equal force to any country with a literature deriving from primitive conditions of life, where the 'inside' and all that it does (or does not) is a matter of table-talk, and 'the facts of life' are learned from observation of the farm-yard.

'Bile,' in the sense of 'a bilious attack,' known usually in Scotland as 'the boil' (a boil, to avoid confusion, being called a 'bile'), figured in another country-concert song, the hero of which, not feeling well at 3 a.m., had risen, gone to a press in the dark, and taken, per the neck of a bottle, a 'guid sook' of what he mistakenly thought was the drug used by the nobleman above mentioned. The owrecome of the song explains what actually happened:

> Paraffin ile, paraffin ile,
> Drink it like me when ye're bad wi' the bile,
> Drink it like tea, and lie doon on the flair,
> An' ye'll niver be bathered wi' bile ony mair!

I am sorry that I cannot remember any of the verses: only the chorus remains with me.

Another song, to the air of 'Wae's me for Prince Charlie,' started off bravely with:

> A black cat sat at oor stair fit,
>   It sang baith lood an' rarely,
> Says I tae masel', 'Gin I was at your side,
>   I'd cheenge your tune entirely!'
> Sae I creepit doon the stair, in ma haun' was hauf a brick,
>   An' I flang't at the cat richt squarely—
> But Losh keep me! I hit a pollisman,
>   An' he took me tae the Bonnie Hoose o' Airlie!

Yes, 'The Bonny Hoose o' Airlie' again, and 'Prince Charlie' on top of that! The parodist, like the Deil, has a liking for all the best tunes, confound him!

Now, that last ditty smacks of Glasgow. So does this final one, which I will recall to the memory of some and introduce to the notice of others. It is a good example of the low-mentality comic song, based for comic effect on gross exaggeration, and it was originally sung by one of the precursors of Harry Lauder, which of them I know not. It was (why, O why?) always a favourite. Here are two sample verses:

There was a lad was born in Ayr,
   Rob Roy MacGreegor, O!
His face was twenty-fowre fit square,
   Rob Roy MacGreegor, O!
The lad was big an' he was braw,
His fechtin' weicht was twal ton twa,
He'd as mony teeth as a j'iner's saw,
   Rob Roy MacGreegor, O!

Ae day he tried to stop a train,
   Rob Roy MacGreegor, O!
The like he'll niver dae again,
   Rob Roy MacGreegor, O!
The sole o' his clug was split in twa,
His nose was levelled wi' his jaw,
That was the last o' him we saw,
   Rob Roy MacGreegor, O!

Yes, comrades, there are several strata of Scottish song, and this effusion cannot claim to go so far back as the more virile effort in exaggeration known in Aberdeenshire as 'Lang Johnny More.' But 'Johnny' was not sung in the country-concert circles I once moved in, for the days of the many-versed ballad were, even then, fading away.

42

The President's Address

[From *Transactions of the Buchan Club* 15 (1934–39), 123–8]

On this occasion it falls to my lot to deliver, as President of The Buchan Club, a Presidential Address. Now, in connection with the appellation of President there are various other associated grades and degrees—ex-president, past president, president elect, vice-president, and so on—and these positions many of us here hold or have held. But there is still another, evolved from the subtle inner consciousness of our energetic secretary—you will pardon the hackneyed phrase in this case on account of its obvious truth—and that is the grade of Postponed President, to which (and to my no little bewilderment) I have now attained.

How exactly all this came to pass I do not know. You may remember that Mrs. Cluppins, when giving evidence in the notorious case of Bardell *versus* Pickwick, saw fit to remark: 'My lord and jury, I will not deceive you,' and that Mr. Justice Stareleigh promptly and acidly replied: 'You had better not, ma'am!' I am bearing the learned judge's dictum in mind as I address you; and while I would be the last person in this hall to attribute my present position to any secretarial sleight of hand, I have nevertheless a vague and uneasy recollection that I was really appointed President of this club some five years ago. Through no fault of my own I was unable to function during my proper year of office; and, that year having gone past, I fondly imagined, until quite recently, that my tenure of the position had lapsed, as so many things kindly and automatically do lapse, if you only keep quiet and give them a little time in which to do it. But no! It was not to be; my lease has been extended, and the cares of office still cluster on my brow—or on my shoulders; I forget what anatomical position cares of office usually take up. (Laughter).

That, then, is for me handicap number one: I have grave doubts as to whether I should be here at all. But there are others. I have just returned from a holiday in the West Highlands, an environment always eminently suitable for indulging in the gentle art of putting off till to-morrow what should quite definitely be tackled to-day: it is a kind of Lotus-land, where it is always afternoon before the native starts his forenoon programme; and to do in Rome as the Romans do is nowadays not only advisable but imperative. And yet, thanks to the Presidential Address, I was enabled to renew my youth, not after the fashion of the eagle of the Psalmist, but by once again experiencing in their fullness the feelings of the schoolboy. Many, if not most, of us can recall that odious imposition 'the holiday task.' It might merely be an essay one had to write on a specified subject; worse still, the subject might, like the spelling of the historic name of Weller, be left to individual taste and fancy; or, yet again, a book might be prescribed which had to be read, and on this book—which, incidentally, was thus black-listed and cordially hated for ever afterwards—one had to face an examination when school reopened. But with whatever diabolical ingenuity that task was devised, one fact was an unalterable as the laws of the Medes and the Persians, namely, that the performance of the task was invariably put off until the last possible moment, and all through the holidays the thought of it hung over our heads like the sword of Damocles. It was—or so we held it to be—a malicious device of our pedagogues to damp down the high-spirited and care-free enjoyment of youth; and, by taking it merely as a malicious device, it was a highly successful one. For those who imposed it were adepts at putting a cloud the size of a man's hand—and a schoolmaster's heavy hand at that—on the horizon of our happiness, a cloud which grew in size and blackness as the precious days of our freedom hurried past. It was in this manner, then, that I renewed my youth: *verbum sat sapienti*. (Applause).

But, as soon as I found that a Presidential Address was an inevitable part of to-day's proceedings, I had the presence of mind to jot down the following note in my engagement book: 'A presidential address should above all things be brief and audible.' I am able at this stage to guarantee the brevity, and when I am finished I hope to be assured of the audibility; with the addendum, perhaps, from my intimate and always frankly critical friends that, on the whole, it was rather to be regretted.

· · · · ·

I have not the time, nor am I expected, to give you any detailed account of the Club's history. Most of us have read the selection made by Dr. Tocher of the titles of contributions to the Transactions of the Club during the past 50 years, and recognise how fully the story of Buchan has been dealt with from every possible point of view. For future generations these Transactions will be treasure trove. . . . There is mental pabulum therein for many tastes. (Applause).

And tastes, of course, vary: to each man his fads and his prejudices. To be quite frank, I think that a man without a few respectable prejudices is like an egg without salt. We hear a great deal about keeping an open mind, but the trouble nowadays is that so many people keep their minds open at both sides so that the wind blows through with a sleepy whistle, and those in the vicinity feel the draught. (Laughter). I would say, then, retain your prejudices, always remembering that there is no necessity to recite a catalogue of them daily from the housetop. And this is really my own rather roundabout *apologia* for choosing the names in the list which specially appeal to me.

One is that of the late Reverend Walter Gregor of Pitsligo, whose book on the Folk-Lore of the North-East of Scotland has long been a classic. He was a model to all collectors of Folk-Lore in the matter of exact recording. He even wrote down phonetically the speech of those among whom he lived. Only the other day I had a letter from the President of the Folk-Lore Society, Mrs. Macleod Banks (who recently brought out her excellent book on *Scottish Calendar Customs*), and in the letter she said of Dr. Gregor that 'he was a remarkable collector and eminently trustworthy. He makes no attempt to dress up his instances and does not go too far for derivations.' (Applause). It is a testimonial from a recognised authority and worth quoting; for two very valuable papers, that on 'Counting out Rhymes of Children,' written in 1889, and the other on 'Kilns, Mills, Millers, and Bread,' written in 1894, were contributed by him to the Club's Transactions, and both of them have stood the test of time.

Another name to be held in high respect is that of Gavin Greig, like Gregor, a collector of proven skill and accuracy. In his researches he was always ready to accept material, but equally capable of rejecting what was spurious. He, too, contributed much valuable matter to the Transactions. And if our Club had nothing else to its credit than the publication, twelve years ago, of *Last Leaves of Traditional Ballads and Ballad Airs*, embodying the work of Gavin Greig and his colleague the late Reverend J.B. Duncan of Lynturk, it would nevertheless have justified its existence. Entrusted to the scholarly and sympathetic editorship of our fellow-member Mr. Alexander Keith, the volume is a joy to possess; to read at any time, to revel in, even, when one is at one's best. (Applause). For the Scot who cannot appreciate a Scottish ballad is but a poor specimen of humanity, and the truth is not yet in him.

References

Allbutt, Sir Clifford. 'Greek Medicine in Rome', *British Medical Journal* (1909), II:1449–55.

Van Andel, M.A. 'Dutch Folk-Medecine', *Janus*, 15 (1910), 452–61, 609–21, 698–711, 730–53, 858–72.

Aubrey, John. *Remaines of Gentilisme and Judaisme.* Ed. James Britten. London, 1881.

Balfour, Marie Clothilde. *County Folklore IV. . . Northumberland.* Publications of the Folklore Society. London, 1904.

Banks, Mary MacLeod. *British Calendar Customs: Scotland.* 3 vols. Publications of the Folklore Society. London, 1937–41.

Black, G.F. *County Folk-Lore III. . . Orkney and Shetland Islands.* Publications of the Folklore Society. London, 1903.

Black, William George. *Folk Medicine.* Publications of the Folklore Society. London, 1883.

Boece, Hector. *Scotorum Historiae.* Paris, 1547.

Boswell, James. *The Journal of a Tour to the Hebrides with Samuel Johnson, LL.D..* London, 1785.

Brand, John. *Observations on Popular Antiquities.* Ed. Henry Ellis. 2 vols. London, 1813.

Brown, John. *Letters.* Eds. John Brown and D.W. Forrest. London, 1907.

Buchan, Peter. *Ancient Ballads and Songs of the North of Scotland.* 2 vols. Edinburgh, 1828.

Bulleyn, William. *Book of Simples.* ? = William Bullein. *Bulleins Bulwarke of defēce against all Sicknes Sornes, and woundes. . . . The booke of Compoundes. . . .* London, 1562.

Burne, Charlotte Sophia. *Shropshire Folk-Lore.* London, 1883.

Cameron, Morag. 'Highland Fisher-Folk and their Superstitions', *Folklore*, 14 (1903), 300–6.

Campbell, John Gregorson. *Witchcraft and Second Sight in the Scottish Highlands.* Glasgow, 1902.

Campbell, John Gregorson. *Superstitions of the Highlands and Islands of Scotland.* Glasgow, 1900.

Carrera y Dellunder, Martin. 'Errores en la higiene de la infancia en nuestro pais', *Gazeta Medica Catalina*, 35 (1910), 81, 161.

Chambers, Robert. *Popular Rhymes of Scotland.* 4th ed. Edinburgh, 1870.

Child, Francis J., ed. *The English and Scottish Popular Ballads.* 5 vols. Boston, 1882–98.

[301]

Cornet, P. 'Les maladies de Luther', *Progrès Medical* (26 Dec. 1908), 3.s., 25 (1909), 125 ff.

Cox, Marian Roalfe. *An Introduction to Folk-Lore.* London, 1895.

Dalyell, John Graham. *The Darker Superstitions of Scotland.* Glasgow, 1835.

Dawson, Warren R. 'The Mouse in Fable and Folklore', *Folklore*, 36 (1925), 227–48.

Dilling, Walter J. 'Girdles: Their Origin and Development Particularly with Regard to their Use as Charms in Medicine, Marriage, and Midwifery', *Caledonian Medical Journal*, 9 (1912–14), 337–57, 403–25.

Dinnie, Robert. *An Account of the Parish of Birse.* Aberdeen, 1865.

Ellis, Havelock. *Psychology of Sex. . . A manual for students.* London, 1933.

Elworthy, Frederic Thomas. *The Evil Eye.* London, 1895.

Fergusson, Robert. *Poetical Works.* Ed. Robert Ford. Paisley, 1905.

Findlay, James A. *On the Edge of the Etheric. Being an investigation of psychic phenomena.* London, 1931.

Folklore 14 (1903): Margaret Eyre, 'Extracts from Signor V. Busutil's "Holiday Customs in Malta"', 79–85.

Folklore 14 (1903): A.R. Wright, 'Some Chinese Folklore', 292–8.

Folklore 18 (1907): W.R. Paton, 'Folk-Medicine, Nursery Lore, etc., from the Aegean Islands', 329–31.

Folklore 20 (1909): S.O. Addy, 'Scraps of English Folklore, III', 342–9.

Folklore 22 (1911): Thos. J. Westropp, 'A Folklore Survey of County Clare', 49–60.

Folklore 29 (1918): J.G. Frazer, 'Women Fertilized by Stones', 254.

Fordun, John of. *Chronica Gentis Scotorum.* Ed. and trans. W.F. Skene. 2 vols. Edinburgh, 1871–72.

Frazer, Sir James. *The Golden Bough.* 12 vols. London, 1914–20.

Geikie, Sir Archibald. *Scottish Reminiscences.* Glasgow, 1904.

Gillies, H. Cameron. 'Gaelic Names of Diseases and Diseased States', *Caledonian Medical Journal*, 3 (1897–99), 94–107, 183–94, 233–45.

Gomme, Alice Bertha. *The Traditional Games of England, Scotland, and Ireland.* 2 vols. London, 1894–98.

Gordon, J.F.S. *The Book of the Chronicles of Keith.* Glasgow, 1880.

Graham, Henry Grey. *Social Life of Scotland in the Eighteenth Century.* 2 vols. Edinburgh, 1899.

Grant, John. *Legends of the Braes o' Mar.* Aberdeen, 1876.

Gregor, Walter. *Kilns, Mills, Millers, Meal, and Bread.* London, 1894.

Gregor, Walter. *Counting-Out Rhymes of Children.* London, 1891.

Gregor, Walter. *Notes on the Folk-Lore of the North-East of Scotland.* Publications of the Folk-Lore Society. London, 1881.

Greig, Gavin. *Last Leaves of Traditional Ballads and Ballad Airs.* Ed. Alexander Keith. Aberdeen, 1925.

Gutch, Eliza, and Mabel Peacock. *County Folklore V. . . Lincolnshire.* Publications of the Folklore Society. London, 1908.

Hartland, E.S. *Folk-Lore: What is it? And What is the Good of it.* Popular Studies in Mythology, Romance and Folklore. London, 1899.

Hartland, E.S. *Primitive Paternity: The Myth of Supernatural Birth in Relation to the History of the Family.* 2 vols. London, 1909.

Hartland, E.S. 'The Romance of Mélusine', *Folklore*, 24 (1913), 187–200.

Helps for Suddain Accidents. London, 1633.

Henderson, John A. *Aberdeenshire Epitaphs and Inscriptions.* Vol I (of 1). Aberdeen, 1907.

Henderson, William. *Folklore of the Northern Counties of England and the Borders.* London, 1866.

Hope, R.C. 'Holy Wells of Scotland: Their Legends and Superstitions', *Antiquary*, 31 (1895), 26–7, 150– 1, 180–1, 214–7.

Jamieson, John. *An Etymological Dictionary of the Scottish Language.* 2 vols. Edinburgh, 1808.

Kelly, James. *A Complete Collection of Scottish Proverbs.* London, 1721.

Kinloch, George Ritchie. *The Ballad Book.* Edinburgh, 1827.

Kirk, Rev. Robert. *The Secret Common-Wealth (ca.* 1691). Ed. Andrew Lang. London, 1893.

Krappe, Alexander Haggerty. *The Science of Folklore.* London, 1930.

Krafft-Ebing, (Baron) Richard von. *Psychopathia Sexualis.* London, 1892.

Lang, Andrew. 'Second Sight', *Caledonian Medical Journal*, 3 (1897–99), 178–83.

Lang, Andrew, trans. *Aucassin and Nicolete.* London, 1887.

Lang, Jean. *North and South of Tweed.* Edinburgh, 1913.

J[ames] F[leming] L[eishman]. 'The Dying Guizard', *The Scotsman*, 31 December 1902, p. 8.

Le Rouzic, Zacharie. *Carnac. Légendes, traditions, coutumes et contes du pays.* 2nd ed. Nantes, 1912.

Lockhart, John Gibson. *Memoirs of the Life of Sir Walter Scott, Bart.* 7 vols. Edinburgh, 1837–38.

Louandre, Charles. *La Sorcellerie.* Paris, 1853.

Lubbock, John. *The Origin of Civilisation and the Primitive Condition of Man.* London, 1870.

MacGregor, Alastair. 'Second Sight', *Caledonian Medical Journal*, 3 (1897–99), 42–56, 141–56; 4 (1899–1901), 258–71, 297–308.

MacKenzie, Daniel. 'Children and Wells', *Folklore*, 18 (1907), 253–82.

McKenzie, Dan. *The Infancy of Medicine. An enquiry into the influence of folk-lore upon the evolution of scientific medicine.* London, 1927.

MacKinlay, James M. *Folklore of Scottish Lochs and Springs.* Glasgow, 1893.

MacPherson, James. *The Poems of Ossian.* 2 vols. Edinburgh, 1805.

McPherson, J.M. *Primitive Beliefs in the North-East of Scotland.* London, 1929.

Markham, Gervase. *Countrey Contentments in two books. . . . The second intituled, The English Huswife.* London, 1615.

Martin, Martin. *A Description of the Western Islands of Scotland.* 1703; Glasgow, 1884.

Michie, John Grant. *Desside Tales.* 1872; rev. ed., ed. Francis C. Diack. Aberdeen, 1908.

Miller, Hugh. *Scenes and Legends of the North of Scotland.* Edinburgh, 1891.

Moncrief, John. *Tippermalluch's Receits. Being a collection of. . . remedies for most distempers.* Edinburgh, 1712.

Moncrief, John. *The Poor Man's Physician or The Receits of the Famous John Moncrief of Tippermalluch*. 3rd ed. Edinburgh, 1731.

Moodie, Mrs. Robert. 'Highland Therapy', *Caledonian Medical Journal*, 5 (1902–04), 320–41.

Moore, A.W. *Folklore of the Isle of Man*. London, 1891.

Munro, Neil Gordon. *Prehistoric Japan*. Yokohama, 1908.

Napier, James. *Folklore in the West of Scotland*. Paisley, 1879.

Neuburger, Max. *History of Medicine*. Trans. E. Playfair. Oxford, 1910.

Ord, John. *The Bothy Songs and Ballads of Aberdeen, Banff and Moray, Angus and the Mearns*. Paisley, 1930.

Park, Mungo. *Travels in the Interior of Africa*. Edinburgh, 1858.

Paul, William. *Past and Present of Aberdeenshire*. Aberdeen, 1881.

Pickin, F.H. 'Ancient Superstitions that still flourish', *Practitioner*, 83 (1909), 848–54.

Proceedings of the Society of Antiquaries of Scotland 16 (1881–82): William Jolly, 'On Cup-Marked Stones in the Neighbourhood of Inverness, VIII: The Basin Stone near Arpafeelie', 385–7.

Ramsay, Allan. *The Works*. 3 vols. London, 1851.

Salmon, William, trans. *Pharmacopoeia Londinensis, or the New London Dispensatory*. London, 1678.

Scot, Reginald. *The discoverie of witchcraft*. London, 1584.

Scott, Walter. *Demonology and Witchcraft*. London, 1868. (Originally published as *Letters on Demonology and Witchcraft*, 1830.)

Seward, Thomas. *The Conformity between Popery and Paganism illustrated*. London, 1746.

Sibbald, Sir Robert. *The History Ancient and Modern of the Sheriffdoms of Fife and Kinross*. Cupar, 1803.

Stewart, Alexander. *Nether Lochaber*. Edinburgh, 1883.

Stewart, Alexander. *Twixt Ben Nevis and Glencoe*. Edinburgh, 1885.

Theophilus Insulanus. *A Treatise on the Second Sight. . . .* Edinburgh, 1753.

A Thousand Notable Things. 1595; London: Printed by Edward Crowch for John Wright at the Globe in Little Britain, 1670.

Tylor, Edward B. *Primitive Culture*. 2 vols. London, 1871.

Tytler, William. 'Dissertation on the Scottish Music', *Archaeologica Scotica: Trans. of the Society of Antiquaries of Scotland* I (1792), 469–98.

Wilkie, Thomas. 'Old Rites, Ceremonies, and Customs of the Inhabitants of the Southern Counties of Scotland Collected by T. Wilkie', ed. John Ferguson, *Proceedings of the Berwickshire Naturalists' Club*, 23 (n.d.), 50–146.

A Bibliography of David Rorie

I. BOOKS

The Auld Doctor, and Other Poems and Songs in Scots. London: Constable, 1920.

A Medico's Luck in the War. Aberdeen: Milne & Hutchison, 1929.

The Lum Hat Wantin' the Croon, and Other Poems. Edinburgh: Moray Press, 1935.

Ed. *The Book of Aberdeen*. Aberdeen: for the BMA, 1939.

Poems and Prose. Ed. William Donaldson. Aberdeen: Aberdeen University Press, 1982.

II. SHORTER PROSE PIECES

'"A Teeth". A Humorous Reading', *The People's Friend*, 7 December 1896, p. 890.

'Tammy Tamson's Cuits. A Humorous Reading', *The People's Friend*, 4 January 1897, p. 9.

'"Olive-Ile". A Humorous Reading', *The People's Friend*, 18 January 1897, p. 50.

'A Complicated Case. A Humorous Reading', *The People's Friend*, 22 February 1897, pp. 139–40.

'On some Scots Words, Proverbs, and Beliefs bearing on Diseased Conditions', *Proceedings of the Royal Philosophical Society of Glasgow*, 31 (1899–1900), 38–45.

'The Scottish Bonesetter', *Caledonian Medical Journal*, 5 (1902–04), 2–5.

'The Obstetric Folk-Lore of Fife', *Caledonian Medical Journal*, 5 (1902–04), 177–85.

'Popular Pathology: Being an Essay on What the Patient Thinks', *Caledonian Medical Journal*, 5 (1902–04), 387–92.

'Some Superstitions of the Fifeshire Fisher-Folk', *Folklore*, 15 (1904), 95–8.

'Some Fifeshire Folk-Medicine', *Edinburgh Medical Journal*, n.s. 15 (1904), 513–9.

'Case of Repeated Anencephalic Birth', *Caledonian Medical Journal*, 6 (1904–06), 100–2.

'Some Survivals of Folk Medicine in Scotland', *British Medical Journal* (1906), I:385.

'Scottish Amulets', *Folklore*, 20 (1909), 231–2.

'New Year's Day in Scotland, 1909', *Folklore*, 20 (1909), 481–2.

'Colliery Accident Stations', *British Medical Journal* (1909), I:753.

'Scraps of Scottish Folklore: Lanarkshire', *Folklore*, 21 (1910), 92.

'The Stone in Scottish Folk-Medicine', *Caledonian Medical Journal*, 8 (1909–11), 410–15.

'Old Poem about Doctor and Patient', *British Medical Journal* (1911), I:1330–1.

'The Folk-Lore of the Umbilical Cord', *British Medical Journal* (1912), I:28.

'Folk-Medicine in the Report of the Highlands and Islands Medical Service Committee', *Folklore*, 24 (1913), 383–4.

'On Second Sight, and the cases of "Theophilus Insulanus"', *Caledonian Medical Journal*, 9 (1912–14), 70–3, 182–6.

'Queries, Notes, and Extracts', *Caledonian Medical Journal*, 9 (1912–14), 46–8, 98–101, 222–3.

Review of J. Scott Riddell, *A Manual of Ambulance* (London: Griffin, n.d.) in *Aberdeen University Review*, I (1913–14), 184–5.

'Stray Notes on the Folk-Lore of Aberdeenshire and the North-East of Scotland', *Folklore*, 25 (1914), 342–63.

'The Romance of Mélusine, and Absence of Men during Childbed', *Folklore*, 25 (1914), 383–5.

'The Mining Folk of Fife', *County Folklore VII . . . Fife, . . . Clackmannan and Kinross*, ed. J.E. Simpkins. London: Folklore Society, 1914, pp. 385–419.

'Folk-Medicine in Scots Ballad and Rhyme: I. Gynaecology and Obstetrics', *Caledonian Medical Journal*, 10 (1914–17), 62–71.

'Folk-Medicine in Scots Ballad and Rhyme: II. Medicine and Surgery', *Caledonian Medical Journal*, 10 (1914–17), 225–34.

'As Locum for Cousin Anatole', *Caledonian Medical Journal*, 10 (1914–17), 242–6.

'Migratory Stones in Banffshire', *Folklore*, 34 (1923), 162–4.

'George Boswell, Chirurgion to King James VI', *Caledonian Medical Journal*, 12 (1923–25), 67–81.

'The "Coamic"', *A Cadger's Creel: The Book of the Robert Louis Stevenson Club Bazaar*, ed. Sir George Douglas. Edinburgh: W. Brown, 1925, pp. 151–6.

'The Lighter Side of Leechcraft', *Scots Magazine*, 8 (1927–28), 211–4.

'On Scottish Folk-Medicine I: Introductory', *Caledonian Medical Journal*, 13 (1926–28), 70–4.

'On Scottish Folk-Medicine II: Menstruation', *Caledonian Medical Journal*, 13 (1926–28), 74–6.

'On Scottish Folk-Medicine III: Conception', *Caledonian Medical Journal*, 13 (1926–28), 85–9.

'On Scottish Folk-Medicine IV: Pregnancy', *Caledonian Medical Journal*, 13 (1926–28), 90–8).

'On Scottish Folk-Medicine V: Labour', *Caledonian Medical Journal*, 13 (1926–28), 98–102.

'On Scottish Folk-Medicine VI: The Child', *Caledonian Medical Journal*, 13 (1926–28), 153–63, 231–3.

'On Scottish Folk-Medicine VII: Vernacular Anatomical and Medical Terms', *Caledonian Medical Journal*, 13 (1926–28), 234–7.

'On Scottish Folk-Medicine VIII: Disease and its Cure', *Caledonian Medical Journal*, 13 (1926–28), 259–68, 375–81.

'On Scottish Folk-Medicine IX: Scottish Proverbs Bearing on Medicine', *Caledonian Medical Journal*, 14 (1929–31), 20–7.

Review of J.M. McPherson, *Primitive Beliefs in the North-East of Scotland* (London: Longman's, 1929) in *Caledonian Medical Journal*, 14 (1929–31), 177–9.

'Folk-Medicine in Scottish Ballad Literature', *Caledonian Medical Journal*, 14 (1929–31), 259–70, 291–9).

'Going, Going—Gone?' *The Aberdeen Book-Lover*, 6 (1928–31), 150–2.

'Crossing the Legs', *Folklore*, 44 (1933), 390–1.

'Hastening the Death of the Aged, Infirm, and Sick', *British Medical Journal* (1933), II:611–2.

'Upper Donside Fairs and Feuds: A Minister's Memoirs', *Scots Magazine*, 20 (1933–34), 429–42.

'The Weighty Eighties', *University of Edinburgh Journal*, 6 (1933–34), 8–15.

'Surgery and Medicine of the Scottish Ballads', *Scots Magazine*, 21 (1934), 104–12, 220–8.

'Chamberpots Filled with Salt as Marriage Gifts', *Folklore*, 45 (1934), 162–3. With add. note by M.E. Durham, 268.

'The Galar Mor', *Scots Magazine*, 22 (1934–35), 118–22.

'Stones that Wander', *Aberdeen University Review*, 22 (1934–35), 212–21.

'Some Old Scottish Rhyming Riddles', *Scots Magazine*, 23 (1935), 148–54.

'Preserving the Scottish Tongue', *Scots Magazine*, 24 (1935–36), 105, 113–4.

Review of Clement Bryce Gunn, *Leaves from the Life of a Country Doctor*, ed. Rutherford Crockett (Edinburgh: Moray Press, 1935) in *Caledonian Medical Journal*, 15 (1932–36), 464–6.

'Urine as a Remedy', *British Medical Journal* (1936), I:142.

'Pregnant Women as Pall-Bearers', *Folklore*, 47 (1936), 230.

'The Healing of the Circle', *Scots Magazine*, 25 (1936), 61–4.

'Forty Odd Years of It', *People's Journal*, 27/2/37, pp. 6–7.

'Doctoring in Days Gone By', *People's Journal*, 6/3/37, pp. 6–7.

'Sailing the Seas as Ship's Surgeon', *People's Journal*, 13/3/37, pp. 6–7.

'Incidents on Indian Voyage', *People's Journal*, 20/3/37, pp. 28, 27.

'My Early Days in the "Kingdom"', *People's Journal*, 27/3/37, pp. 6–7.

'Anecdotes of Tayside Personalities', *People's Journal*, 3/4/37, pp. 6–7.

'My Sojourn over the Border', *People's Journal*, 10/4/37, pp. 6–7.

'My First Independent Brass Plate', *People's Journal*, 17/4/37, pp. 24, 26.

'Happy Years in Auchterderran', *People's Journal*, 24/4/37, p. 24.

'When I Took a Hand in Local Affairs', *People's Journal*, 1/5/37, pp. 24, 26.

'Work with VAD and RAMC', *People's Journal*, 8/5/37, p. 28.

'With the Men in the Trenches', *People's Journal*, 15/5/37, p. 28.

'The President's Address', *Transactions of the Buchan Club*, 15 (1934–39), 123–8.

A Bedfast Prophet. A version in Scots of *A Rogue in Bed* by Ronald Elwy Mitchell. London: Samuel French Acting Edition, 1937.

'Stray Notes on Scottish Folklore', *Folklore*, 49 (1938), 85–91.

'Our Old Spas and Some of their Votaries', *The Book of Aberdeen*, ed. David Rorie. Aberdeen: for the BMA, 1939, pp. 148–60.

'Some Folklore and Legends of Lower Deeside', *The Book of Aberdeen*, ed. David Rorie. Aberdeen: for the BMA, 1939, pp. 206–17.

'At the Sign of the Blue Pill', *Caledonian Medical Journal*, vols. 8–16, *passim*.

III. APPRECIATIONS AND OBITUARIES

'David Rorie', *Transactions of the Buchan Club*, 15 (1934–39), 76–9.

L.F. Newman. 'Obituary', *Folklore*, 57 (1946), 96. With add. note by M.M. Banks, 152.

A. Greig Anderson and Alexander Keith. 'Obituary', *British Medical Journal* (1946), I:415–6.

Evening Express, 18/2/46.

Press and Journal, 19/2/46.

Alexander Keith, 'From a Scottish Study', *Press and Journal*, 22/2/46.

May Thomson, 'Doctor Whose Song Went Round World', *Evening Express*, 26/5/79.

Moreen Simpson, 'Urbane Master of Rural Wit', *Press and Journal*, 26/5/83.

Ian A. Olson, 'David Rorie of Cults (1867–1946): Poet Laureate of the Society', *Aberdeen Medico-Chirurgical Society. A Bicentennial History 1789–1989*, ed. George P. Milne. Aberdeen: Aberdeen University Press, 1989, pp. 203–11.

Glossary

a, all
aboon, abune, above
aboot, about
ae, one
aff, off
afore, before
ahint, behind
ain, own
aince, once
airm, arm
alang, along
amery, cupboard
ane, one
aneath, beneath
anither, another
appleringie, southernwood
'at, that
a' thegither, all together
atween, between
aucht, eight
auchteen, eighteen
auld, old
Auld Clootie, Devil
Auld Nickie Ben, Devil
ava, of all, at all
awa, away
awfu, very, extremely
awyte, assuredly
aye, always
bairn, child
baith, both
bakkit, backit, backed
bane, bone
bannock, girdle-cake
bather, bother
bawbee, halfpenny
beddin, ceremony of putting a
bride to bed

bed stock, the side of a bed farther
from the wall
beel, fester, suppurate
beerial, interment and accompanying
occasion
ben, through the house; in or
towards the inner room, or parlour
benison, blessing
benty, coarse (grass)
be's him, compared with him
bidden, invited
bide, stay
big, build
bile, boil
bile, boil, bilious attack
billie, lad, fellow
binder, strip of cloth put round cheese
birk, birch
birr, whirring sound
birse, bristle
bit, (small portion of) food;
but
blae, bluish
blaw, blow
bleck, black
blethers, foolish talk
blude, blood
bodies, persons
bogie-roll, coarse black tobacco
bool, ball; bowl; marble
bools, bowls
boucht, bocht, bought
boukit, bulky
brae, braeside, hillside
braid, broad
bran, husks of grain separated from
the flour after grinding
braw, handsome

bree, liquid in which something has been steeped or boiled
breed, breid, oatcake; bread
breeks, trousers
breist-bane, breast-bone
brent, burned, branded
brewster, brewer, brewing
bricht, bright
brig, bridge
bring hame, give birth to
brither, brother
brochan, gruel
brocht, brought
brock, badger
broo, eyebrow; brow
broon, brown
broose, race at a country wedding from the church or the bride's home to the bridegroom's home
brose, oatmeal dish, variously prepared
bruck, break in pieces
brucket, streaked with dirt
bude, had to
buke, book
bummin, humming and buzzing
burn, brook, stream
burn-brae, hillside adjacent to a stream
burrows-toon, burgh
burst, injury from over-exertion
but, through the house; towards the outer room, or kitchen
bye wi't, 'done for'; pregnant
by-ordinar, by-or'nar, extraordinary
byre, cattle shed
ca, push; knock; call
ca awa, keep going; work away
cannels, candles
canny, careful, esp. with money; skilful; favourable, lucky
canny man, wifie, folk, person(s) whose knowledge exceeds the natural
canny-wife, midwife
cantrip, spell; trick
cap, caup, (wooden) cup or bowl
carline, old woman
cateran, (Highland) marauder
cauld, cold

causeway, cobbled or paved area on a farm
causey, street; paved area
chacked, chackit, hacked, cracked
chafts, jaws
chappin-stick, stick etc. for striking with
chappit, mashed
chaumer, ploughman's bedding place
checkit, reproved
cheek, side of anything, e.g. a fireplace
chief, friendly, intimate
churching, see kirking
clachan, hamlet
claes, clothes
clapper o a mill, that which shakes the hopper to move the grain down to the millstones
clarty, dirty
clash, tell tales; chatter
cled, clad
clog, log or block of wood; wooden shoe
cloured, struck; with a swelling caused by a blow
cloutie, small piece of cloth
clug, wooden-soled shoe
clype, inform on; tell tales
clyte (play -), fall heavily, suddenly
coalheugh, coal-working or -pit
cockit bonnet, boat-shaped cap of thick cloth, with the points at the front and back
coo, cow
coortit, coorted, courted
cowe, surpass
crack, talk, conversation; story
cracker, talker
cran, measure of herrings
cran, crane
crap, crop; stomach
cratur, creature, (sentimentally) person
craw, crow
creel, basket
crood, crowd
crukit, crooked

cuddy, donkey
cunnin stane (he's ta'en a walk roond the —), used to describe an untrustworthy, undependable person
cutty, short (clay) pipe
dae, do
dag-durk, dagger
dambrod, draught-board
darg, work
daur (pit a – owre), instil a feeling of awe or fear
daw, dawn
dee, do
dee, die
deid, dead; death
Deil, Devil
deil a, not a
denner, dinner
dight, clean, wipe; ordained
dinna, do not
dirl, tingling pain
disna, does not
div, do
divot, turf, sod; (#37, bonnet)
doe, dough
dominie, schoolmaster
doon, down
doon-lyin, confinement
doup, buttocks, bottom
dowe, decay
draff, malt refuse
dram, glass of whisky
drap, drop
dree, drie, suffer; endure
drink oot, drink off
Droggie, the Chemist
drogues, drugs
droon, drown
drooth, drouth, thirst; drought, drying breezy weather; a drunk
drouthy, thirsty
drucken, drunken
dub, pool (metaphorically, ocean)
dule, sorrow, grief
dune, done
dung, struck
dyke, wall of stones, turf, etc.

ee(n), eye(s)
een, one
efter, after
eith, easy
elbuck, elbow
eneuch, enough
fa, fall
fa, who
fair fa, a blessing on
fan, fin, when
fan, found
far, where
far-ben, extensive
farden, farthing
fash, trouble
Faster's-even, Shrove Tuesday
fat, what
faurer, further
fause, false
fau't, fault
feart, scary
feat, fitting
fecht, fight
feckless, weak and ineffective; spiritless
fen, effort
ferlie, marvel, wonder
fidging, excitedly
findy, full of substance and pith
finnan haddy, haddock cured with the smoke of green wood
fit, foot
fitale, celebratory (drink or feast)
fitular, fiddler
flauchter spad, spade for cutting turf
flair, floor
flee, fly
fleg, fright
flicht, the fly of a spinning wheel
flit, remove (to another house e.g.); flutter
fluffy, puffy, chubby
flype, turn inside out
fog, moss, lichen
Foggie loan, Aberchirder
foonder, strike down, render useless
fore, front; front part
fore (to the -), still in existence

forenicht, earlier evening, esp. as time of winter conviviality
fore-runner, harbinger
fore-shot, (in distilling) the whisky that comes over first
forgaither, *foregather*, keep company
foul, dirty, soiled, in bad condition
foular, fowler
foulis, fowls
fowk, folk, persons, people
fowre, four
frae, *fae*, from
frait, *freit*, superstitious belief, observance, act, saying, omen
fraucht, load
fremit, strange, foreign
fricht, fright
frippish, frivolous
fu, *fou*, full; drunk
full, foul
fushionless, lacking vigour and spirit
fustle, whistle
gab, mouth
gae, gave; go
gaed, *gied*, given, gave; went
gane, gone, went
gang, go
gangrel, vagrant
gant, yawn
gar, make
gare, triangular piece of cloth inserted in a garment; gusset
gaun, going
gaun-aboot, vagrant
geary, wealthy
geistis, tales, jests
gey, very, quite; good-sized
ghaistie, ghost (dim.)
gie, give
gied, *gaed*, given, gave; went
gin, *giff*, if
Gin, hoisting apparatus
girth, hoop
glamour, enchantment
gless, glass
gloamin, evening twilight
glour, stare, scowl
gore, stab, pierce

goukit, foolish
gowd, gold
gowf, golf
graivel, gravel
gree, live in harmony
green, yearn
greet; *grat*, cry; cried
gress; *girse*, grass
grewsin, shivering
grow, be favourable to growth
grun, ground
gude-man, *goodman*, head of a household
gudewife, *goodwife*, mistress of a house
guess, riddle
guid, *gude*, *gueed*, good
gully, large knife
haar, cold mist or fog
hae, have
hain, spare
hainch, throw under the leg or thigh by striking the hand against the thigh
hairy, impure
hale, *haill*, sound; whole; robust
hallin, partition inside the outer door
hame, home
hame-ower, homely
han, *haun*, hand
handy-wife, midwife
han'lt, handled
hap, cover
hap, luck
harden, a very coarse cloth
harns, brains
harry, rob birds' nests
haud, hold; keep
haud awa, except for; keep away
hauf, half
haugh, river-meadow land
heich, high
heicht, height
heid, head
heir-skep, inheritance
hereaboots, adj., local
hert, heart
hesp, length of yarn
het, hot; v. heat

heuk, hook
hickery-pickery, purgative of bitter
aloes with other ingredients
hilt, walk with a limp
hinch, haunch
hing, hang
hinna, do not have
ho, high
hoast, cough
hogger, footless stocking worn
as gaiter
holing, the depth of coal displaced at
a blasting
hoo, how
hoor, hour
hoose, house
horse-couper, horse-dealer
howdie, midwife
howe, adj. hollow, sunken; n.
depression, tract of land bounded by
hills
howk, dig; uproot
hunner, hundred
hurly, handcart, trolley
ile, oil
ilka, each, every
ilke (in that -), at that same moment
ill, difficult; bad; inexpert
ill-willer, person who wishes evil
on another
ingle(-neuk), fireside; chimney corner
intil, into
intilt, inside
ir, her
jack, martial jerkin
jeely, jelly
jine, a clubbing together to buy drink
j'iner, joiner, woodworker
jing-bang (the hale —), the whole lot
kail, cabbage, cole
kailyard, vegetable plot
kaim, kame, comb
Kalendars, cold spell which
frequently occurs at the beginning of
Spring months
kebbuck, a whole cheese
keek, peep
kelpie, supernatural water-horse

ken; kent, know; known
keppit, received, caught
kiest, cast
Kilmarnock, broad flat woollen
bonnet
kimmers, female friends; midwives
kindly, congenial, natural
kinker, one suffering from the
kink-hoast
kink-hoast, whooping cough
kirking, ceremonial kirk attendance
for, e.g., the first time after a
wedding, birth, or funeral
kirkyaird, churchyard
kitchen, relish; something taken with
oatcake or bread or potato
kittle, adj. ticklish, dangerous; v.
tickle
knowe, knoll
kye, cattle
kyles, skittles, ninepins
kyte, stomach
laigh, low
laird, lord; heritor
landlouper, adventurer, vagabond
lane (its –), on its own
lang, tall; long
lang syne, langsyne, long ago
lap, leapt
lasher, blow
lauch, laugh
lave, rest, remainder
laverock, lark
lawburrows, legal security that a
person will not injure another
leddy, lady
leear, liar
leen (my –), alone, by myself
len, loan
licht, light
lichter, having given birth
lift, carry out the dead for burial
linn, pool below a waterfall,
river pool
lit-pot, dye-pot
lodomy, laudanum
loe, love
loesna, loves not

lood, loud
loon, boy
looten, allowed
loss, lose
loup, leap
loup for spang, with a leap and a bound
lowe, flame
lowse, undo; end the day's work
lug, ear
lum, chimney
lunt, smoke (a pipe)
lyke-wake, watch kept at night over a dead body
mae, more
mair, more
mairrit, married
maist, most
maist, almost
maisterfu, powerful
mak, make
manna, must not
manse, minister's dwelling-house
masel, myself
mask, brew
maun, must
maut, malt
meal doon, crumble
meat-hale, having a healthy appetite
mebbe, maybe
meen, mune, moon
meer, mare
men, reform
micht, might
mickle, muckle, much; great
mild, meek, gentle, demure
mim-mou'ed, affectedly proper
mind, remember
mirk, dark
misca, speak ill of
mither, mother
mony, many
moo-tash, moustache
More, Moorish
mou, mouth
mowdie-wort, mole
muck, clean dung out of (sty)
muckle, much; great

muckledom, size, bulk
mutch, close-fitting cap worn by married women
nae, no; not
naethin, nothing
nane, none
nappie, foaming, strong
neebor, neighbour
neeps, turnips
neist, next
nepkin, napkin
nervish, nervous, easily agitated
nicher, whinny
nicht, night
niffer, exchange
nirl, shrink, shrivel
noo, now
nowte, cattle
ocht, ought
off-take, deduction from wages
ony, any
oor, our
oot, out
or, before; until
outlier, farm animal which remains outside during the winter
owre, ower, oure, over
owrecome, refrain
oxter, armpit
parrot seam, seam of highly volatile bituminous coal
pawkie, shrewd; roguish
piece, snack
pinch, belly
pine, pain
pish, urinate
pit, put
pleugh, ploo, plough
plooky, pustular
plunk (play –), make a plopping sound
policies, estate park
pollisman, policeman
pooch, pocket
poorin, pouring
poother, powder
pose, hoard
pot, pool

pottinger, apothecary
pow, head
press, large cupboard
prinkling, tingling
puddens, entrails, innards
puir, poor
pyock, sack, bag
quat, rid, quit
quey, heifer
rale, real, really
rantin, roistering, romping, revelling
rashes, rushes
ravel, tangle
redd, disentangle; comb and arrange hair
redd up, clear up
rede, pronouncement
reedie row, a swell in the sea
reekin, emitting vapour
reid, red
reist, arrest (motion or action)
remeid, remedy
richt, right
rickle, heap, pile
rig, raised strip of ploughed land
rin, run
ripe, pick (pockets)
rive, burst; rip
roch, bawdy; rough
roch dram, enough liquor to cause drunkenness
roon, roond, round
rotten, rat
roup, sale or let by public auction
row, rowe, v. wrap; roll; n. roll
rowan, mountain ash
rush, rash (of scarlet fever)
sab, sob
sae, so
sain, bless; shield from evil influences
sair, sore, sorely
sall, shall
sangstar, singer
sark, shift, shirt
sau, saw, salve
saugh, willow
saunt, saint
saut, salt

sax, six
scabbit, scabbed
scale, cast
scholar, school pupil
scouther, shower
scunner, repugnance; nuisance
seeck, sick
seton, skein of cotton etc. used esp. in veterinary practice
shearin, reaping, harvest
shee, shoe
shew, sow
shoe-latch, thong for fastening shoes, shoelace
shooder, shoulder
shoon, shoes
shot, catch of fish
sic, such
siccar, wary
sicht, sight
siller, money; silver
simmer, summer
simple, medicine made from herbs
sin, since
siven, seven
skail, disperse
skeely, skilly, skilled, esp. in the art of healing
skeely-wife, midwife
sliver, slaver, saliva
sma, small; narrow; slender
sma hoors, very early hours of the morning
smiddy, smithy
smit, infect by contagion
Smith (The Auld –), the Devil
snap, ginger biscuit
snaw, snow
socht, asked for; sought
sodger, soldier
sonsy, comely
soo, sow
sook, suck
soom, swim
soon, soun, sound
soor, sour
sorit, of a sorrel colour; ? hence sorie: (skin of) a sorrel colour

souter, shoemaker
sowens, dish made from oats
speerit, spirit
speir, ask
spile, spill, spoil
spill, pour forth
splent, hard coarse splintering coal
spole, shoulder
spull, spill
spune, spoon
spurtle, stirring-rod
sta, stall
stan, stand
stane, stone
Stanehiven, Stonehaven
stane-raw, the lichen Parmelia saxatilis
stap, step
stark, strong
staved, sprained, wrenched
stickit, killed
stirk, young bullock or heifer
stood, participated in market as herd
stoop, pillar of coal left to support the roof of the working
stoot, stout, corpulent; robust
stot, bullock
stoup, wooden pail
stoved potatoes, stovies, dish of stewed potatoes, onions etc.
stovin, steaming
strack, struck
strae, straw
strait, straighten, stretch
strath, valley of river that flows to the sea
straucht, straight
stuffy, sturdy, full of vigour
succar, sugar
sune, soon
supple Tam, jointed wooden toy figure
swall, swell
swine's seam, pig's fat, lard
syne, then
tacketty, studded with tackets, hobnailed
tae, toe, to
taen, taken

tak, take
talis, tales
tap, top
Tarans, souls of unbaptized children
Taubroner, drummer
taul, tauld, told
teind, tithe
tent (tak – o), pay heed to; beware
teuch, tough
thae, pl. of that
theek, thatch
the-gither, together
thirl (play –), have a tingling sensation
thirled, bound by law
thocht, thought; worry
thoom, thumb
thrang, busy
thrapple, throat
thrasher, thresher
thrift, success, prosperity
throw, through
till, to
tine, tyne, lose
tinkler, itinerant tinsmith and pedlar
tit, twitch
tod, fox
toom, empty
toun, toon, farmstead; hamlet; town
traivel, travail
tribble, sickness, disease, ailment
troot, trout
trump, Jew's harp
tryst, n. assignation; market, esp. for livestock; v. make an appointment
tuilzie, brawl
turn (o the nicht), midnight; dead of night
twa, two
twal, twelve
tyke, rough person
umman, woman
uncanny, dangerous from supernatural causes
unco, remarkable
verra, very
wa, wall
waal, well

wad, would
wadna, would not
wae, woe
wae mat worth ye, may woe come to you
walletie, beggar's bag, pedlar's pack
wallop, make convulsive movements
waly, exclamation of sorrow
wan, won
wan, wane, colourless, pale
wapinschaw, rifle-shooting competition
wark, work
warl, world
warrant (I'se –), I'll be bound
wasie, way
wast, west
wauchie, , weak, smelly
waur, worse
weary fa, expression of exasperation
weel, well; healthy
weel-daein, (*in the wey o – *), prosperous; pregnant
weel-faured, handsome, well-favoured
weicht, weight
weim, wame, belly
weird, destiny
wey, wye, way
wha, who
whalp, whelp
whaur, where
wheen, number, amount
whiles, at times

whirligiggie, child's toy that spins in the wind
wi, with
wice, knowing, prudent
widden, wooden
widow, widower
wife, woman
wight, person, fellow
wight, strong, lively
wimple, rippling sound
win, proceed; win; gain by labour
wincey, cloth with a woollen weft and a linen or cotton warp
windlestrae, tall thin withered stalk of grass
winna, will not
winnerfu, wonderful
wise woman, person whose knowledge exceeds the natural
wiss, know
wran, wren
wrocht, purged
wull (hae your – o), do what you like with
wut, wit, common sense
wylicoat, woman's sleeved nightdress
yark, ache, gnaw; tug, pull
yird-fast, fixed firmly in the earth
yoke till, set to
yon, that, those (with a certain distance in time or space)
yowe, ewe